Teaching Elementary School Mathematics

Teaching
Elementary School
Mathematics

Michael L. Mahaffey
and
Alex F. Perrodin
THE UNIVERSITY OF GEORGIA

F. E. PEACOCK PUBLISHERS, INC.
ITASCA, ILLINOIS

CONTENTS

PREFACE

Teaching Elementary School Mathematics is written for college students who are preparing to teach in elementary schools. In-service teachers will also find it useful in updating their information on mathematical content, materials, and procedures.

The authors have attempted to provide the prospective elementary school teacher with:

1. A reasonably brief mathematical background for the major topics included in the typical elementary school mathematics curriculum.
2. An understanding of curriculum, methods, and procedures appropriate for achieving goals of elementary school mathematics.
3. A guide to making, purchasing, collecting, and using mathematics teaching aids.

Although the text is organized into three parts, Part I does not necessarily have to be read before Part II, and, in some situations, it may be advisable to begin reading at Chapter 6. For some the text may be more useful as a reference to be consulted as particular questions or needs arise.

The text assumes that the reader has had some course work or experience in the content of mathematics for the elementary school. In Part I recommended mathematical content areas for the elementary school are presented from the point of view of the teaching procedures to be used. Part II investigates the teacher's role in developing these concepts, and Part III is a comprehensive study of available teaching-learning aids.

Because the authors believe it to be unlikely that a teacher will be assigned to a classroom where all the learners will be at the same level in their understanding of mathematical concepts, Chapters 1–5 are organized to show the development of a concept or skill from the readiness stage through the algorism stage, without concern for specific grade levels.   For example, teachers who work with sixth graders will find that some pupils need help in understanding whole numbers before they can handle decimal notation.   The authors encourage prospective teachers to become well acquainted with all of Chapters 1–5, even though they anticipate teaching at a particular grade level.   Teachers in nongraded situations or schools organized like the English primary schools will find the text suggests numerous ideas for providing individualized or small-group instruction.

It has been the aim of the authors to use the research on mathematics education in the elementary schools as a guiding hand.   Extensive quotations from research, however, have been kept at a minimum so the presentation of ideas could proceed without interruption.

Throughout, the text attempts to provide usable ideas, many of which are illustrated.   Suggestions as to making and using teacher aids are presented not as cookbook recipes but as starting points, with the hope that creative teachers will be stimulated to adapt and improve the items and discover uses not listed.

The authors wish to express their appreciation to Dr. Joseph Hooten, who participated in the early planning of the textbook content and provided ideas for certain chapters; to Dr. Randall Hicks, whose research study is frequently cited in Chapter 8; and to the mathematics educators who reviewed the manuscript at each stage of its preparation.   Thanks are also due the prospective teachers in Dr. Mahaffey's EMT 337 classes at the University of Georgia, with whom much of the content has been tested, and the many experienced teachers in whose classrooms the senior author has observed the values of wise choice and use of arithmetic aids.

MICHAEL L. MAHAFFEY

ALEX F. PERRODIN

PART I

Basic Mathematical Concepts

Chapter 1

TEACHING WHOLE NUMBERS

Fundamental to a child's ability to succeed in mathematics is his understanding of the basic concepts of number and numeration. Yet teachers have inadvertently neglected or underestimated the importance of these concepts. It has been taken for granted that if a child could verbalize or mechanically reproduce a set of symbols (1, 2, 3, 4, . . .) that were mistakenly called numbers, there was no further need to pursue the matter. One need only pick up any contemporary elementary mathematics text to see that this gross misconception is no longer tolerated. An attempt should be made to see that a child understands the underlying concepts of number before he is asked to verbalize or write the symbols to represent specific numbers. It is far easier to teach number from this point of view than to reteach certain aspects of these concepts at a later date.

Sets

The basic vehicle for developing the concept of number is the notion of a set and its operations. The language of sets provides a simple and precise vocabulary for the teaching of mathematics at all levels and, because of its social usage, is easily adapted to the children's vocabulary. However, a basic difference between the normal and mathematical connotation of the term "set" must be kept in mind. In mathematics the term "set" refers to a well-defined collection of objects, symbols, or ideas. Each of these is referred to as an element of the set.

3

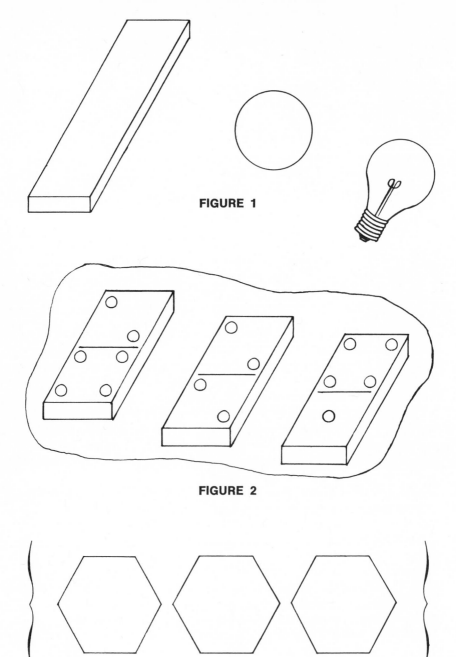

FIGURE 1

FIGURE 2

FIGURE 3

These elements need not have anything in common, other than being placed in given groups, to be considered part of a particular set. Figure 1 represents a set of objects illustrating this idea. However, while this concept is mathematically true, it can cause considerable confusion if it is the first concept of set the child encounters. For this reason, in the early work with sets it is best to keep the elements alike. Then in later stages of learning we can progress through sets whose elements are not all the same but do have commonality, to the totally mathematical concept of a set where the elements need have nothing in common.

In the primary grades most work with sets is usually conducted on the concrete or pictorial level. There is no doubt as to what is a member of a given set. Therefore, there is little need for set notation; a simple closed curve (string or yarn) around the objects will suffice as a set indicator (Figure 2). An attempt at this time to require the use of the standard set notation is superfluous. The children will have enough difficulty without having to perform the almost physically impossible task of making the set brackets (Figure 3).

Set Comparison

The concept of set is basic to the concept of number and order. It is through the matching of sets that the pupil encounters his first experience with comparative mathematical statements. This initial contact seems better served if the materials used are manipulative in nature. For example, the use of blocks, checkers, toy horses, and so forth proves quite beneficial. Also, as research bears out, the use of physical materials keeps the learning at the concrete level and thus more desirable.

Initially the use of sets does not involve any counting. At this point, the child should not be asked to find the number of a set. The function of sets is far more critical than mere rote counting. The use of numerous set-comparison activities should serve to develop the child's understanding of number. It is through the one-to-one matching comparisons of the members of one set with the members of another that the child determines whether there are as many elements in one as in another. (For example, there are as many balloons as diamonds in Figure 4.) Care must be taken so that an incorrect idea is not conveyed to the child when discussing the concept "as many as." To avoid any possible erroneous notion, the teacher should show or have the child show that there are many ways to match the balloons and stars in order to demonstrate they are equivalent sets or have the same number (Figure 5).

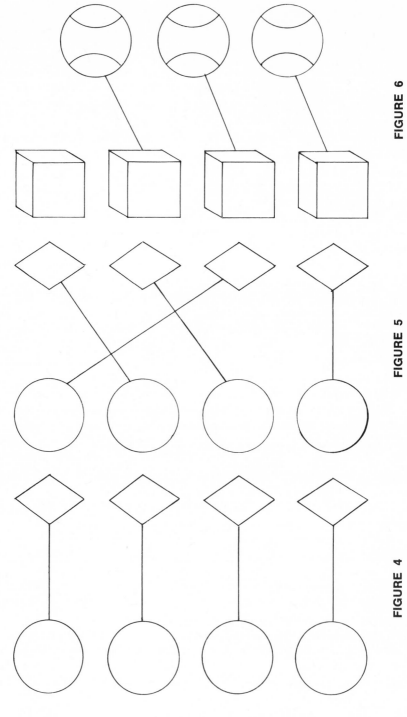

FIGURE 6

FIGURE 5

FIGURE 4

Another concept is that when two sets are matched one to one and there are one or more members left over in either of the sets, the set with the leftovers has more members than the other one. In Figure 6 there are more boxes than balls. When the one set has more members than another, we say it has the "greater number" of elements.

After the child has experienced the matching of physical sets, he should be moved on to pictures of sets. Pictorial representations of physical objects are considered to be *semiconcrete* in nature. Matching of semiconcrete examples will be similar to that used with physical objects, but the use of pictures will take us one step in the direction of abstraction.

The teacher will find it helpful to have a good number of physical sets ready for immediate use. Quite helpful also are a large feltboard and accessories. (See Chapter 9 for suggestions on the use of flannel boards.) As far as pictorial sets are concerned, most textbooks provide an ample supply.

Cardinal Numbers

Once a student has experienced numerous activities similar to those above, he is ready to encounter the number names. Some students, of course, will already be familiar with some of these number names. This familiarity has usually been acquired through rote counting methods. It is therefore advisable to see that all students proceed through activities similar to those in the following section. It is extremely important that a pupil is able to count rationally; this portion of development of the number system is critical to all students.

The numbers 0, 1, 2, 3, . . . constitute the set of cardinal numbers or the set of whole numbers, as they are sometimes called. These symbols, which are so easily recognized by the reader, pose one of the most difficult teaching tasks that will confront an elementary teacher. It is not that the task is insurmountable, but the complexity of the number concept is usually underestimated. Pupils must acquire an intuitive feel for what a number is. A child need not be able to verbalize or symbolize his knowledge of number to understand its meaning. It is possible and desirable that he understand what is meant by the number six before we expect him to produce a symbol (6) to represent it. There is no reason that a child should not know that 3 + 3 = 6 before he ever sees it in print.

One of the most successful ways to teach cardinality of sets is to discuss several numbers, one at a time. To avoid the possibility of rote memoriza-

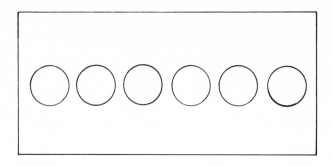

FIGURE 7

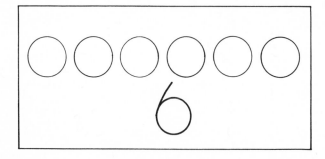

FIGURE 8

FIGURE 9

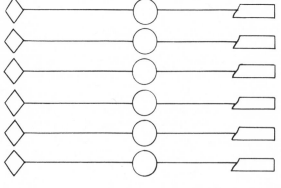

FIGURE 10

tion of order the teachers should randomly select numbers for presentation. Once the number to be taught has been established, the teaching process is the same for all other counting numbers, with the exception of zero. This will be discussed later.

For the sake of discussing this developmental process, let six be the number name we are trying to teach.

1. We begin by establishing visual recognition or matching of the number of the set to a given set, before we attempt to make any further progress. We accomplish this by asking the child to place the same number of objects on his desk as we are holding. The number name is not mentioned. When the child can satisfactorily perform this task, we may continue.

2. The child is presented with a card or feltboard containing six objects (Figure 7). As the set is displayed he is asked to place six counters on his desk. We have now extended the child's awareness of six through both the visual and verbal stimulus.

3. We now make one addition to our presentation by including the numerical symbol for six along with all the preceding stimuli. For instance, the child is presented with a card containing six objects and a symbol "6" and told to place six counters on his desk (Figure 8).

4. Once this can be completed with minimal error we can present the student with the symbol only, as illustrated in Figure 9, and instruct him to place as many counters on his desk as is indicated. At this point, he not only knows the symbol for six but realizes that any set that can be matched one to one with the "six set" has six elements (Figure 10).

To establish zero as the name for the number of elements in a set can provide considerable difficulty if care is not taken from the beginning. It is hard for a child to conceive of a set having no elements, and it is necessary to establish the fact that such sets do exist. This can be accomplished by describing meaningful sets that have no members: the set of toys in the classroom, the set of boats on the playground, and so on. In each case we ask, "How many elements are there in the set?" The usual answer is none and we say, "That many is called zero." It will be discovered that in this case, as in many others, far greater success is achieved if the students provide the examples.

When the number names from zero to nine have been learned, the next and final step is the writing of the symbol for each number. This, like any other writing task, is a mechanical skill and should be taught as such.

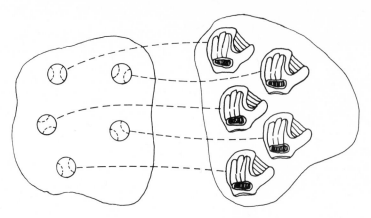

There are 5 balls in the one set. Can you tell, without counting, how many gloves are in the other set?

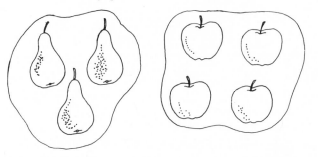

Draw a set of dots so your set has the most members in it. Draw a set of dots so your set has the fewest members.

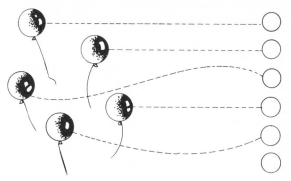

There are 5 balloons in the set above. Draw a set of dots so your set has more members.

FIGURE 11

Most texts will proceed as follows:

(1) Trace the numeral 6 as it appears in the box.

(2) Draw a numeral 6 as shown by the arrows.

(3) Draw a numeral 6 in the box.

It is important to reemphasize the use of sets throughout the development of the number concept. This incorporation of sets can be both developmental and readiness oriented. Consider the examples in Figure 11. Examples similar to the first function as a tool for learning the actual number concept. The number property of five is being transferred to a second set. Through the use of one-to-one matching and the pupil's knowledge of equivalent sets, he can establish the fact that the second sets also have five members. The latter two illustrations, while dealing with the number concept, also perform the function of readiness activities. The terms more, most, and fewer will lead the way to the expressions "greater than" and "less than" when work is begun on the ordering of the natural members.

Ordering Numbers

Most every child upon entering school is able to rote count. That is, he may be conditioned to saying the words "one," "two," or "three," with little regard to what he is saying. The establishment of number names for sets of objects allows exploration of certain relationships between numbers. This is, in fact, the true nature of mathematics, be it elementary or not.

The pupils may examine two sets and tell which has the greatest number or least number of objects (Figure 12). By this time the child will have made considerable study of the comparisons of sets. This study has, however, been in terms of the set themselves. A careful teacher can capitalize

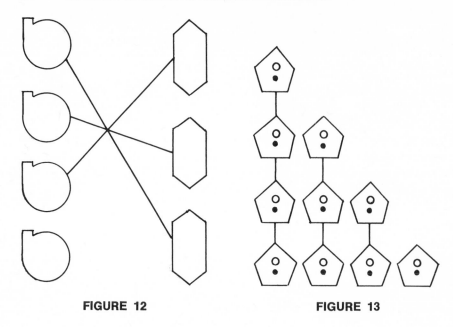

FIGURE 12   **FIGURE 13**

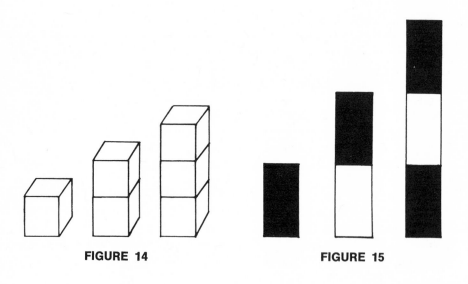

FIGURE 14   **FIGURE 15**

on these experiences and make a smooth transition from the *comparison of sets* to the *comparisons of the numbers of sets.* This is not a game of semantics, but a move into the abstraction of numbers.

The concept of "one more than" is essential to the ordering process. In Figure 13 the matching shows that each set is one more than the set that precedes it. Activities like stacking blocks or ordering children according to height are quite useful (Figure 14). Number sticks and commercial materials such as Cuisenaire rods, however, can have far more useful applications (Figure 15).

To help the teacher determine the child's extent of understanding, he can provide a work sheet with simple completion exercises (Figure 16).

Write the correct numeral in the blank.

FIGURE 16

In this way pupils can progress from work with sets to work with the numbers of a given set. The questions, of course, can be presented with a variety of activities, such as follows:

(1) Which of the two numerals names the largest number?

6   7

(2) Which of the three numerals represents the smallest number?

4   6   8

These activities will, at a later time, lead to the use of the symbols $<$ and $>$. The children will be presented with sentences such as the following and asked to provide the correct symbol for the relationship.

5_____6.   8_____3.

However, once addition has been introduced, the considerations of inequality may be of a more complicated form. For example:

4 + 3_____2 + 4.

Ordinal Numbers

Numbers play a dual role in our system of mathematics. The discussion thus far has been concerned with the teaching of the concept of cardinal numbers, or numerousness of a set. A second function of number is that of naming a position or place in a given set. An ordinal number answers the question, Which one? or What position is it in? The order of the cardinal numbers should be established prior to making an attempt to teach the ordinal property of numbers.

The teacher should take every opportunity to use the experiences of the normal school day to provide awareness of this property. Such questions as, "Who is first in line?" or "Whose row will go first?" or directions such as "Turn to page 6" will provide an excellent lesson on "position numbers." If the teacher is conscious of this property, little organized time will need to be spent on its development. It lends itself quite well to informal presentations.

The teacher's primary concern should be that of the children's verbal usage of all the words, such as "first," "second," "third," and so forth. This can be greatly facilitated by showing the similarity between words, and it is advisable to make some form of written check on this idea. A child's inability to verbalize or visually recognize a word like "fifth" does not necessarily mean he does not understand the concept of "ordinal numbers." Activities to accompany Figure 17 will help make this distinction apparent. Instructions should be as follows:

1. Direct the children to tell how many rows are in the picture. Ask them to tell what is in the first row, second row, etc.

FIGURE 17

2. Call attention to the line of boys and girls in the picture in the first row. Have them put an asterisk above the fifth, and so forth.

Such verbal instructions should be given for each row and pupils should be encouraged to discuss their choices. A child may know what is meant by the term "fifth" and be able to succeed at a task similar to those above, whereas he may not yet be able to say, "The tiger is in the fifth position." This is the reason care must be taken to check all aspects of the concept you are attempting to relate to the child.

Another subtle concept is also inherent in this lesson—the ordinal position is dependent upon the viewpoint the observer takes. For example, the elephant is first in the second row, whereas the engine is first in the third row. Thus position does not always depend on a "left-to-right" orientation.

System of Numeration

Thus far we have been concerned with the exploration of the meaning of natural numbers. The major concentration has been directed toward counting and ordering of the whole numbers 0 to 9. The concept of sets and the concept of "one more than" have been developed. It is upon this latter notion that the rest of the development of the concept of whole numbers is based. There is, however, one more ingredient necessary for this task, and that is some form of numeration system. By this we mean a collection of symbols and a systematic way in which these symbols are used to express numbers.

To illuminate our own decimal system of numeration, we will consider some of the characteristics of the Egyptian and Roman systems. This discussion is meant to give an intuitive feeling for the arbitrary nature of a number system. Therefore, it will be brief, and the reader interested in learning more about these systems should consult one of the references listed in Chapter 10.

Possibly one of the earliest written number systems that was developed might be called a simple grouping system. In this system some number was selected for a base (b) and then symbols were assigned to 1, b, bxb, bxbxb, and so forth. To express a number, one need only use these symbols additively. Each symbol would be repeated as many times as necessary to represent the number.

One of the best examples of a simple grouping system is the Egyptian numeration system. The Egyptian hieroglyphic numeration system is based on the scale of 10. The hieroglyphic symbols illustrated below are those commonly used to name the first few powers of 10.

$$1 = 10^0$$

$$10 = 10^1$$

$$100 = 10^2$$

$$1000 = 10^3$$

$$10000 = 10^4$$

$$100,000 = 10^5$$

Any number may now be expressed by using these symbols additively. For example, 4256 would be expressed as follows:

$$4256 = 4 (1000) + 2 (100) + 5 (10) + 6$$
$$= 4 (10^3) + 2 (10^2) + 5 \, 1(10) + 6 (10)$$

We are considering here an additive system in which the symbols that appear will not affect the value of the number. For example, the above numeral could be written as follows:

The value of the number would still be the same. That is:

$$= 100 + 100 = 200$$
$$= 1000 + 1000 + 1000 + 1000 = 4000$$
$$= 1 + 1 + 1 + 1 + 1 + 1 = 6$$
$$= 10 + 10 + 10 + 10 + 10 = 50 \qquad \text{or}$$
$$200 + 4000 + 6 + 50 = 4256$$

Historically speaking, this system is thought to have been used as far back as 3400 B.C. The symbol for 1 was called a vertical staff; the symbol for 10 was called a heel bone; the symbol for 100 was called a scroll; the symbol for 1000 was called a lotus flower. Thus it is not unreasonable to assume that both verbal and written communication of number ideas could have taken place with this particular numeration system.

One of the more prevalent numeration systems other than the Hindu-Arabic that is taught today is the Roman system. This system still has some practical use in modern times.

The Roman numeration system also used certain symbols to represent particular groups of numbers. However, unlike the Egyptian system, where the groupings were always powers of 10, the Roman system varied the base groupings, as can be seen in the following table:

$$1 = I \qquad 100 = C$$
$$5 = V \qquad 500 = D$$
$$10 = X \qquad 1000 = M$$
$$50 = L$$

Although there is some disagreement, we basically think of the Roman numeration system as an additive-subtractive system. For example, the Roman numeral for 67 is LXVII or $50 + 10 + 5 + 2$. However, if we wish to write the Roman numeral for 97, we write XCVII of $(100 - 10) + 5 + 2$.

The property illustrated above does not make the Roman numeral system a place-value system; it only demonstrates a relationship between two adjacent numerals. As you may recall, the strategy for designating numbers with Roman numerals was based on two simple facts. First, if the symbol representing greater value is preceded by a symbol of lesser value, then the lesser is subtracted from that of the larger.

(a) $IV = 5 - 1 = 4$

(b) $XC = 100 - 10 = 90$

Second, if the symbol representing the greater value is to the left of the symbol representing the lesser value, then the numbers represented by the two symbols are combined.

(a) $XV = 10 + 5 = 15$

(b) $CL = 100 + 50 = 150$

Both of the numeration systems mentioned above provide a means by which arithmetic operations could be performed. For example, we can complete the computation, $316 + 754 = 1070$, by using either system thus far discussed.

1. Egyptian notation.

$$\text{𝓈𝓈𝓈}∩|\,|\,| \;+\; \text{𝓈𝓈𝓈𝓈𝓈𝓈𝓈}∩∩∩|\,|$$

$$\text{𝓈𝓈𝓈𝓈𝓈𝓈𝓈𝓈𝓈}∩∩∩|\,|\,|\,|\,|\,|$$

$$\text{𝒸}∩∩∩∩∩$$

2. Roman numeration.

CCCXVI + DCCLIV
$$= \text{DCCCCCLXX}$$
$$= \text{DDLXX}$$
$$= \text{MLXX}$$

As is quite apparent, neither of these systems is the picture of simplicity. It becomes very obvious why man would look for a more efficient method by which to represent and compute with numbers.

Decimal Numeration System

The Egyptian and Roman numeration systems did not answer man's need for such a system. Not only were they unwieldy to compute with, but they did not lend themselves well to recording very large numbers. For example, to record a date (June 6, 1942) could become a time-consuming task (VI June, MDCCCCXLII). The need for a simple way to denote large numbers was instrumental in bringing about the derivation that we employ today.

The Hindu-Arabic numeration system is often called a decimal system; that is, it is based on groupings of 10. In this respect it is similar to the Egyptian numeration system of being based on powers of 10. However, rather than employing a symbol to represent 10, 100, 1000, etc., the Hindu-Arabic system assigns value of 1, 10, 100, 1000, etc., to positions in a given numeral. This is often referred to as a place-value system. The following table illustrates a partial place-value chart for the decimal system.

10^4	10^3	10^2	10	Units
10,000	1000	100	10	One

If we continued to the left with the chart, the column value would be increased by a multiple of 10. The Hindu-Arabic numeration system uses ten digits (0, 1, 2, 3, 4, 5, 6, 7, 8, 9); each digit used in a numeral is a factor by which its column or place value is multiplied. The numeral 475 indicates that 100 is multiplied by 4, the 7 shows that 10 is multiplied by 7, and the 5 shows that 1 is multiplied by 5. The use of the place-value system thus affords a precise and convenient means to symbolize numbers. It is possible to express any number in the expanded form to demonstrate the value each digit represents. The real meaning of 4768 is clearly shown below.

$$4768 = 4000 + 700 + 60 + 8$$

It is, of course, possible to rewrite this numeral so it even more closely represents our definition of place value. For example:

(a) $4768 = 4 \times 1000 + 7 \times 100 + 6 \times 10 + 8 \times 1$

(b) $4768 = 4 \times 10^3 + 7 \times 10^2 + 6 \times 10^1 + 8 \times 10^0$

Both (a) and (b) are called the polynomial form of the numeral 4768. Whether you use the exponential form or not will not matter. It is, however, somewhat more convenient to use exponents in cases where the place value may be extremely large.

One more important fact about the Hindu-Arabic system of numeration should be reviewed. This is the use made of the digit 0. Now all digits in a place-value system perform two tasks: that of place holder and to indicate the number of times the value of the place is used. Zero is even more important; it is the key to indicating a move in column value without increasing the value of the number. Thus in the numeral 407 the 0 tells us there are no tens, but it also makes it possible to indicate that 4 is the number of hundreds we are to use. Leaving the 0 out (47) would be somewhat confusing.

This brief discussion of the base-ten numeration system is not meant to teach that system. It is only to provide an outline of what a child needs to know in order to function with our numeration system. In turn this should alert the teacher to the need of a systematic development of the system in the classroom.

Teaching the Decimal Numeration System

Before a child encounters the decimal numeration system in its entirety, the teacher must be aware of the child's capabilities. Certain minimal competencies are needed prior to introducing the next stage. This competence is more commonly referred to as "readiness." The more experience a child has had, the more readily he will comprehend our numeration system. Therefore, it is imperative that a child is able to (1) read and write the digits 0–9, (2) understand the meaning of numerousness and to order the numbers 0–10, and (3) rationally count the members of sets containing no more than ten numbers.

An activity of great value as a readiness experience is counting sets of more than ten by never using a number greater than 5. Since the child is able to identify sets of five, this is not an extremely difficult task. In Figure 18, we have 1 set of five fives, 2 sets of fives, and 3 more ones. The number by which you group, as long as it is less than 10, does not matter. It is the act of grouping that is important.

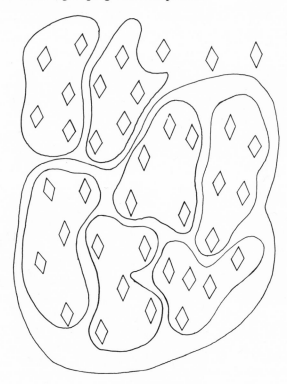

FIGURE 18

If a child has grasped the concepts enumerated above, he can count any set of elements up through 100 without any additional new vocabulary. He can do this by grouping sets of ten elements. A good way to start is by counting familiar objects in the room. Direct a student to count a group of his classmates. When he counts to 10, tell him to stop. Have that group of ten go stand by the wall. He then continues with his counting. When he again gets to ten, say "stop." This group of ten is asked to stand in another part of the room. This continues until all members of the class have been counted. The number of students will be reported to be so many sets of ten, and so on. For example, if you had selected 30 students from the class the pupil would answer the question "How many classmates were there?" by saying "3 sets of ten."

This form of counting process should continue with as many examples as the teacher feels are necessary to establish the concept of grouping by ten. The type of counting objects should be as varied as possible so the pupil is allowed to broaden his concept of numerousness. Sheets of paper, pencils, straws, or popsicles, make excellent aids for grouping by ten, since they all lend themselves to physical groupings or bundling.

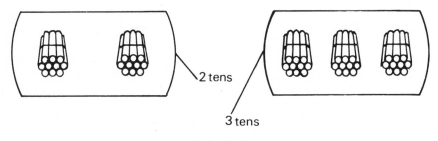

FIGURE 19

At first the answers to "how many" are given in terms of "sets of tens." In Figure 19, the answer is, "There are 2 sets of ten in the first picture," or "There are 3 sets of ten in the second picture." It is the responsibility of the teacher to help the child reduce this response to "2 tens" or "3 tens." Not only physical activities but also semiconcrete exercises like the examples in Figure 20 should be provided to help accomplish this.

When the child demonstrates the ability to perform this type of exercise, the next step is the development of the appropriate symbol to represent the number of "ten sets." For example, 2 tens would be written as 20. This, of course, is a writing skill, and the teacher should not try to introduce such names as "twenty" or "thirty." At this time it will suffice to have the child refer to 50, for example, as 5 tens.

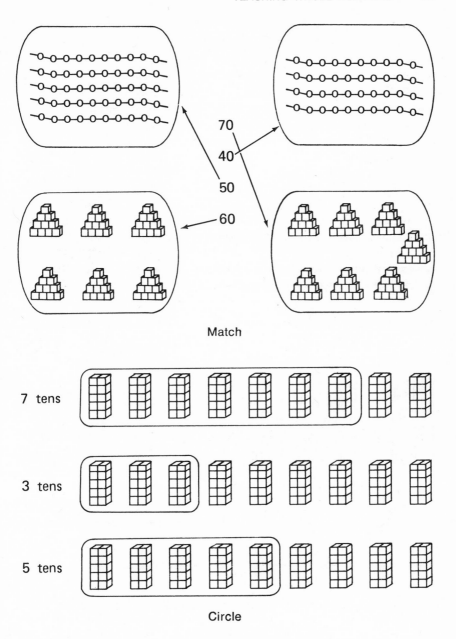

Match

7 tens

3 tens

5 tens

Circle

FIGURE 20

The next step is the development of the "ten ones" notation. This may be introduced just as the tens notation, with one minor change. The sets will now have extra elements after the groups of ten have been removed. In counting these sets, the answers could be "2 tens and 2 extras" or "2 tens and 2 more." We want the child to finally think, "2 tens 2."

In developing this system of numeration (decimal) we are primarily concerned with creating a means of recording representation for numbers using the digits 0, 1, 2, 3, 4, 5, 6, 7, 8, and 9. An excellent method used by many teachers to teach the writing of numerals is the pocket chart shown in Figure 21. We can count strips of cardboard, placing each strip in the ones pocket. When we reach a count of 10, they are bundled together and placed in the tens pocket. This process is repeated until all the objects are counted. We then count the numbers of elements in each pocket and have a pupil record this under the appropriate pocket. The child then tells how many objects are represented: 4 tens, 6 ones. We finally write 46 as we say "four tens and six ones."

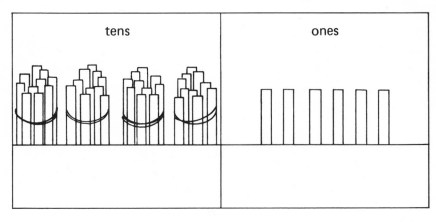

4 tens   6 ones

FIGURE 21

The pupils should write numerals from the teacher's verbal instruction and discuss numerals such as 67 and 76 to emphasize the positional nature of our system. Through this we establish that the numerals are always written from left to right in descending value. That is, the tens are listed first in the numeral 67 and the ones are listed second.

At this stage of the development of the numeration system, the child should be able to recognize any two-digit numeral as to its number of tens and ones and its total value. Most pupils already comprehend the concept of order of the two-digit number because they recognize the fact that we must have one set of tens before we can have two sets of ten, and so on. Thus he need only combine what he knows about the order of the numbers 1 to 9 to come up with the table in Figure 22. He will be thinking:

one, two, three . . . . one ten
one ten-one, one ten-two . . . . . two tens
two tens-one, two tens-two . . . . three tens

. . . . . .
. . . nine tens-nine

1	2	3	4	5	6	7	8	9	10
11	12	13	14	15	16	17	18	19	20
21	22	23	24	25	26	27	28	29	30
31	32	33	34	35	36	37	38	39	40
								99	

FIGURE 22

Once the order concept has been established, there is one final step in developing the first 99 numerals. All that remains is to attach a name to each of the symbols developed, such as "twenty" or "thirty."

The extensions of the decimal numeration system could follow a pattern identical to that used for developing two-digit numerals. However, the structure of the Hindu-Arabic system would be better served by using a different approach. If the numeral 99 means 9 tens 9, the next logical numeral must represent 10 tens. We should review the meaning of grouping by tens and try to lead the pupil to reexpress 10 tens as 100 or one hundred. This will allow us to write all three digit numerals, or up to 999. At this point we introduce the thousand as meaning 10 hundreds.

The teaching of place value and the decimal numeration system, through a thousand, may be made far more meaningful by employing Dienes Multibase Blocks (Figure 23) as a teaching aid. Squared paper can be substituted for this commercial aid.

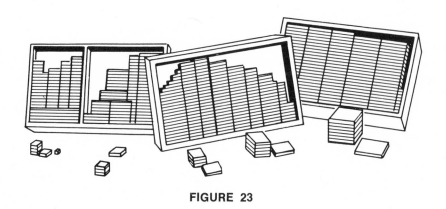

FIGURE 23

Once we have developed numeration through a thousand by the above method, we normally will use a more abstract strategy to extend our system. We begin the process in the first three grades, while in grades four, five, and six we concentrate on developing within the pupil an "adult" level of proficiency with respect to his understanding of the numeration system. It is at grades four, five, and six that the expanded or polynomial is introduced.

In the primary grades the introduction of new ideas is minimal, with the exception of some different notation. By the end of the third grade a pupil should have progressed from expressing 3798 as: 3 thousands, 7 hundreds, 9 tens, 8 ones, to 3000 + 700 + 90 + 8. By the end of the fourth grade the expansion would be: $3798 = 3 \times 1000 + 7 \times 100 + 9 \times 10 + 8 \times 1$. Finally the child has both an understanding and working competence with $3798 = 3 \times 10^3 + 7 \times 10^2 + 9 \times 10^1 + 8 \times 10^0$. With this level of proficiency the student is prepared for the development of the standard algorisms for the operations as they become relevant.

Chapter 2

TEACHING ADDITION AND SUBTRACTION OF WHOLE NUMBERS

Addition

As addition is merely another form of counting, preparation for it can begin very early—in most cases, before a child enters school. After the number concept has been presented by use of sets, pupils should be introduced to the idea of partitioning sets. Partitioning is best understood if the child is allowed to manipulate real objects. While there are innumerable commercial aids available specifically for this purpose, child-made or teacher-made materials are of equal, if not better, value (Figure 1).

With such devices the child can see that a set of 6 can be interpreted as a set of 4 and a set of 2, a set of 3 and a set of 3, or a set of 5 and a set of 1. The child can be led informally to realize that "5 and 1" and "6" are names for the same number. While this is not a formal introduction to addition, it does provide excellent readiness activities. Figure 2 illustrates a semiconcrete or abstract activity along this same line. Such experiences in partitioning are used to strengthen and provide depth to the child's knowledge acquired in a concrete experience, such as is illustrated in Figure 1.

After considerable experience with this idea the pupils should work with the joining of two sets that have no elements in common (Figure 2). The feltboard and cutouts can serve as an excellent method of presenting this

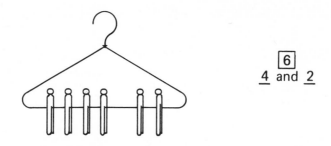

A. Clothes hanger and multicolored clothespins.

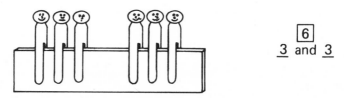

B. Strip of wood and clothespins on which children have placed different pictures.

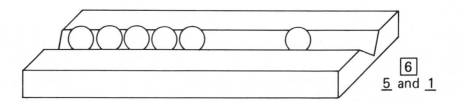

C. Piece of board with groove in which marbles have been placed.

FIGURE 1

idea through a number story that offers a visualization of the union of two disjoint sets. The teacher and the class can make up stories to dramatize this concept. For example, the story for Figure 4 could be: "Two red birds are eating at the feeder and three yellow birds come down to eat. How many birds are at the feeder?" The pupils are led to abstract "2 and 3" as the description of the number of birds at the feeder. Then they are asked if one number could be used to name the number of birds. They are expected to respond "5." The pupils have now completed the sentence "2 and 3 is 5," and they are, of course, adding.

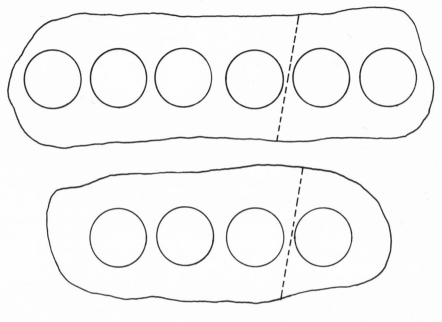

FIGURE 2

Implicit in the number-story approach to addition is the fact that addition is a binary operation. It presents addition as the union of *two* disjoint sets or as the combining of pairs of numbers. The exact number of activities can by no means be predicted. The focus should be on the idea of finding a simpler name or another name for pairs of numbers, such as "7 and 2" and "6 and 3," rather than on how rapidly the exercises can be completed. Here, of course, the single number that names each pair is "9." This idea is used throughout the work with computation. For example, the expression "4 and 36" is just asking for a more convenient way of naming the pair of numbers.

Sentences like "3 and 4 is 7" will be replaced at a later stage of the pupils' development with $3 + 4 = 7$. We have substituted a plus ($+$) for the "and," and an equal sign ($=$) will replace the word "is." This is the most abstract level at which we expect a child to work.

The pupil now has a slim grasp of the meaning of addition. We must make every effort to see that a relatively high degree of proficiency is obtained and maintained throughout the grades. There are a number of visual aids that adapt themselves quite well to this stage of learning.

The *number line* (Figure 5) is probably the best known and yet the least understood of these aids. The fault does not necessarily lie in its usage, but in its introduction. A few words of caution should suffice. When intro-

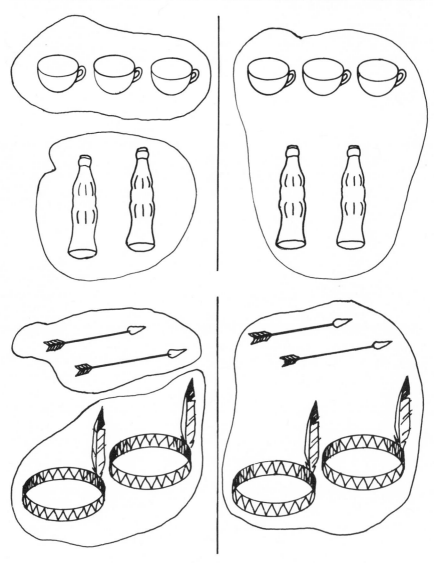

FIGURE 3

ducing the number line the pupils must be given some insight into what is meant by a "standard unit length." Without this understanding the number line is meaningless. A common pupil error is illustrated in Figure 6. This is very prevalent among students just beginning work with the number line.

FIGURE 4

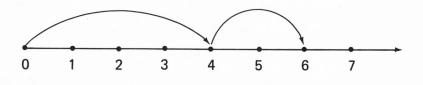

4 + 2 = 6

FIGURE 5

Errors of this nature stem from the child's erroneously counting the dots instead of the unit lengths.

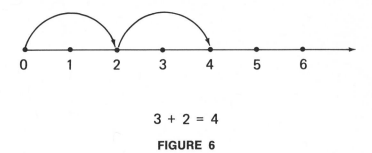

3 + 2 = 4

FIGURE 6

The actual construction of the number line is based on the one-to-one matching of the natural numbers and the unit lengths (Figure 7). For convenience the numeral is placed at the end of the space or unit to which it has been matched. Since zero refers to the absence of (or no) unit length, it comes at the beginning of the number line. This aid presents an excellent opportunity to review the order property of the natural numbers by using it in the extension of the number line. (Other uses of the number line are described in Chapter 9.)

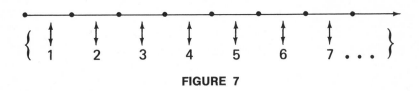

FIGURE 7

Properties of Addition

The number properties are in evidence throughout the entire elementary mathematics program. The advantage gained from these properties depends upon the alertness of the classroom teacher. The entire spectrum of abstraction can be used to present and utilize them.

Elementary pupils are introduced to the associative property and commutative properties of addition. The role of zero in addition (additive identity) is also explored.

The presentation of these properties goes through the following developmental stages: (1) concrete, (2) semiconcrete, (3) abstract—specific examples, and (4) abstract—general case. For example, in developing an understanding of the commutative property in addition of whole numbers, the teacher could proceed as follows:

1. Using checkers or similar objects, the teachers can ask the children to:

   (a) Place 4 checkers on your desk. Place 2 more checkers on your desk. How many checkers do you have all together?
   (b) Place 2 checkers on your desk. Place 4 checkers on your desk. How many checkers do you have all together?

2. After discussing the number story, the children are instructed to complete number sentences suggested by pictures (Figure 8).

_____ and _____ is _____   _____ and _____ is _____

FIGURE 8

3. Once the mathematical sentences have become part of the child's experience, expressions such as $4 + 3 = 3 + 4$ may be used to establish additional number facts.
4. In the later stages of the elementary mathematics program, the generalized statement of the property may appear:

$$a + b = b + a.$$

Although extensive use is made of these properties, the teacher must be extremely careful. There is a tendency to be overly eager to use their names. This is entirely unnecessary and possibly detrimental. The pupil is fully capable of acquiring an understanding of these properties without the introduction of vocabulary.

Once a child has discovered that when he adds, any order of two numbers will give the same sum, we can begin to write addition problems in the vertical form, as shown below.

$$
\begin{array}{r} 5 \\ + 4 \\ \hline 9 \end{array}
\qquad
\begin{array}{r} 4 \\ + 5 \\ \hline 9 \end{array}
$$

Now the interpretation depends on whether you read up or down (commutative). For example, we could read the above example "5 plus 4 equals 9" or "4 plus 5 equals 9."

Generally speaking, the learning of addition should first involve sums to 5, then sums to 10, and finally sums of up to 18. Once proficiency is acquired with these, the child is ready to develop an adult-level algorithm.

After the sums have been discovered to each of the above levels, a table similar to that shown in Figure 9 can be used to organize them. The pri-

+	1	2	3	4	5	6	7	8	9	
1	2	3	4	5	6	7	8	9	10	
2	3	4	5	6	7	8	9	10		
3	4	5	6	7	8	9	10			
4	5	6	7	8	9	10				
5	6	7	8	9	10					
6	7	8	9	10						
7	8	9	10							
8	9	10								
9	10									

FIGURE 9

mary purpose of this table is to provide a cumulative view of the discovered sums from which some of the following generalizations can be observed. All lower left to upper right diagonals have the same sum; the rows and columns sums increase by 1; the sums on the diagonals (lower left to upper right) are either all odd or all even; the upper left to lower right diagonals are always consecutive odd or even numbers, and so on. The empty cells should be used to stimulate discussion about new sums yet to be discovered.

The table also provides another means by which we can observe the pupil through his verbalization of number sentences from the table.

Little emphasis has been placed up to this point upon drill, not because it is not needed but because it was not, until now, an appropriate or necessary strategy. There is a time when the discovered sums (through 18) must be committed to memory or automatic recall. The practice needed can take on many forms. Drills should, however, be short in duration and appropriate to the child's needs and interests. A few suggestions are listed below.

1. A game can be played with dice and toy cars. The six on each die is taped over and a zero substituted. The children make a racetrack on which to place cars. A child rolls the dice and is required to find the sum of the numbers represented by the dots that appear. If he is correct he moves his car that many spaces. This game also is useful in developing the number line and unit length ideas.
2. Many number card games can be invented. Make up two sets of 3 × 5 unlined cards, one containing just the numerals 0–9 and the other containing number expressions. Each child is dealt five cards on which different number expressions appear. A card is drawn from the numeral deck and placed on the table. Then, in turn, each child "plays" the card whose expression represents the same number.
3. Traditional flash cards are not outdated. They can still be used in the customary way by holding up the card and listening to the children's response. However, the child responds more readily if a game can be devised in which the cards are used—for example, flash-card bingo. Each child is provided with a card on which is printed a random set of numerals such as 0 to 18. A student displays one of the flash cards; if the sum is on the child's card, he covers it.

The teacher will find that the makeup of the class should dictate the type of approach used with drill. She should, however, keep in mind that the drill is not synonymous with good mathematics; rather, it is just one of many procedures used to achieve objectives.

Subtraction

The development of subtraction can be based upon the development of addition. As a consequence many teachers attempt to teach subtraction as soon as the pupil begins work with the combining of sets. This practice can prove to be quite detrimental, however, so educators suggest that the addition process be understood before subtraction is encountered. The rationale for this is that when two similar processes are presented before

FIGURE 10

FIGURE 11

one is well established, the learning of one interferes with that of the other. For this reason the teacher should attempt to introduce the relationship between addition and subtraction as subtly as possible, but she should make sure that these similarities are implicit throughout the development stages. For example, when a child sees that a set of 5 and a set of 2 is 7, he should also perceive that 7 less 2 is 5.

Subtraction is far from being a simple concept. It can be the answer to many questions: How many less? How many more are needed? How much larger is it? Because answers must be found for this multiplicity of questions, the pupil should have a thorough understanding of the idea that subtraction is a process of removing subsets from a given set.

The same type of number-story development can be used for subtraction as was used for addition. For example, real situations lend themselves well to number stories such as:

Six pupils are seated at the reading table; then two go back to their desks. How many are left at the table?

A name is then given for "6 less 2." We try to lead the pupil to the response of 6 less 2 is 4. Such concrete and pictorial work leads to the concept of subtraction. The number sentence "6 less 2 is 4" is later replaced by "6 − 2 = 4."

It must be realized that the work with subtraction requires many activities similar to those mentioned above. These experiences make use of concrete and semiconcrete material, as was true for addition. The culmination of the development of the subtraction concept is, of course, with subtraction sentences without pictures.

$$9 - 5 =$$

A few sample subtraction developmental exercises are illustrated in Figures 10 and 11. Examples in Figure 10 would be used immediately after the concrete stage of development. Those in Figure 11 would come just before the abstract mathematical sentence stage.

Relating Addition and Subtraction

Once the concepts of addition and subtraction have been acquired by the children, we can be more explicit about the relationship between the two operations. As indicated previously, some groundwork has been laid in this respect by the nature of the set development of both addition and subtraction. By exhibiting the relationships between addition and subtraction, we can reinforce the learning by demonstrating that adding a number has an inverse operation—namely, subtracting the same number. Again you should be cautious in the vocabulary used, remembering that the child's use of the word "inverse" does not necessarily mean he understands the concept.

If you recall, when you were learning to add and subtract a method was provided to check your addition. For example:

$$\text{If } 5 + 9 = 14, \text{ then } 14 - 9 = 5.$$
$$\text{Also if } 9 + 5 = 14, \text{ then } 14 - 5 = 9.$$

By considering all four of these related facts together, we have what is sometimes called a "family of facts." Actually, given any pair of numbers you can write down the associated facts or family of facts.

An excellent method of providing for the presentation of such associated facts is through the use of open number sentences, or what is more commonly referred to as frame arithmetic. Each child will no doubt use his own strategy for obtaining the answer to an associated number sentence. He should by all means be encouraged to do so, as well as to verbalize such methods. The following examples of frame arithmetic of open sentences should reveal some of the subtle complexity of the two operations.

(1) $5 + 9 = \square$
(2) $\square + 9 = 14$
(3) $5 + \square = 14$
(4) $9 + \square = 14$
(5) $9 + 5 = \square$
(6) $\square + 5 = 14$

These problems, while appearing to be simple addition, present the child with a far deeper problem. He must recognize that subtraction is also involved in many of them.

(1) $14 - 9 = \square$
(2) $14 - 5 = \square$
(3) $14 - \square = 9$
(4) $14 - \square = 5$
(5) $\square - 9 = 5$
(6) $\square - 5 = 9$

As was true for addition, the child can use varying methods to fill the frames. For example, he may remember that $14 - 9 = 5$, or he may recall that $9 + 5 = 14$ is related to the subtraction problem.

A great number of children will acquire their own strategies for finding solutions to such problems as $3 + 6 = \square$, $6 + \square = 9$, or $9 - 6 = \square$. However, in the early stages the child may depend on some form of counting objects. The use of counters, even fingers, is by no means bad; it is merely a step in the child's process of learning. This stage of development usually leads to the following approach by a child. When confronted with a problem such as $4 + 3 = \square$, he will think or say "one, two, three, four — five, six, seven, — four plus three equals seven."

Strategies similar to this are very common and are necessary if the child is to understand addition and subtraction rather than merely memorizing an "addition table." However, this approach becomes obsolete as soon as larger addends are introduced. For instance, when a child is asked to find the replacement for "$\square$" in $9 + 8 = \square$, his initial attempts will most likely be by the "counting" method. It will not be long before he finds this strategy much too inefficient. To do such a problem on the fingers will also prove to be somewhat difficult. It is the teacher's responsibility to foresee that a change in strategy will be necessary and to provide experiences aimed at a smooth transition.

Two strategies for solving $9 + 8 = \square$ might be as follows:

1. Reliance on basic counting makes this strategy somewhat easier than most and therefore more desirable as far as teaching is concerned. When confronted with a problem like $9 + 7 = \square$, $8 + 6 = \square$, or $4 + 6 = \square$, the child is expected to perform with as little wasted effort as possible. For example, when asked to solve $9 + 4 = \square$, he merely says "nine — ten, eleven, twelve, thirteen, — $9 + 4 = 13$." Thus, rather than count both sets in their entirety, he realizes he can start with one of the sets he already knows. The number line provides an excellent tool for developing this strategy. Figure 12 shows $8 + 4 = 12$ using the number line. Instructions would be:

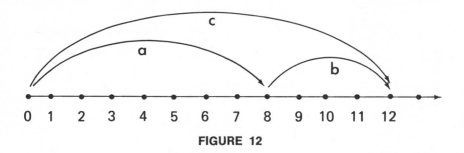

FIGURE 12

    (1) Draw an arrow from 0 to 8.
    (2) Count four more units and draw a related arrow.
    (3) Draw curve (c) and read answer as $8 + 4 = 12$.

Soon the child will merely move his fingers along the number line, where he once drew the arrows. Finally, he no longer traces or draws the path to the first addend; he just knows he will be at a given point. For example, to solve $9 + 4 = \square$, he may imagine the line from 0 to 9, but he still starts at the 9 (Figure 13).

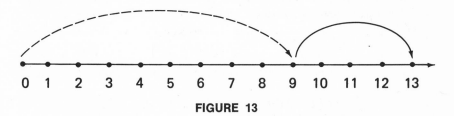

FIGURE 13

2. Most children find it easier, comparatively speaking, to remember the sums of equal addends like $8 + 8$, $3 + 3$, $4 + 4$, and so on. Thus, a child might reason that "since $8 + 8 = 16$ and 9 is $8 + 1$ or one more than 8, then $9 + 8$ must be one more than $8 + 8$ or $9 + 8 = 17$." This appears to be a rather complicated form of solution. However, you must recall that the development of number and order was through the use of set comparison and the "so many more than" concept. An extension of this method can also be made to problems like $7 + 9 = \square$. A child merely thinks in terms of "two more than." A strategy of this nature is more likely to materialize if the teacher is cognizant of its existence when he is developing the order of the natural numbers.

If confronted with $3 + 8 = \square$, the child would likely say "three, four, five, six, seven, eight, nine, ten, eleven, — $3 + 8 = 11$." Of course, this gets the correct solution, but not necessarily in the easiest way. However, if the teacher has made a concerted effort to give the children an intuitive understanding of the commutative property of addition for natural number, this situation may be overcome. The child can be led to think of $3 + 8 = \square$ as being equivalent to $8 + 3 = \square$.

Addition and Subtraction Algorisms

An algorism is a set of rules for a procedure for solving a mathematical problem that frequently involves the repetition of a certain step or steps. For example, the act of finding the greatest common divisor can be considered an algorism. Prior to this step of learning it was only a matter of developing single-digit addition or the basic facts of arithmetic. It is obvious that it is not sufficient just to know and understand what addition and subtraction are. A faster, more accurate, method of computation is needed.

An algorism is much like an iceberg, inasmuch as the bulk of its substance is hidden beneath the surface. The part we observe of an algorism is quite deceiving and can lead the unsuspecting teacher to utter failure. It is of the utmost importance that a critical evaluation be made of a child's understanding and command of certain necessary concepts and skills before undertaking this new enterprise.

A suggested list of needed skills and associated concepts is as follows:

1. The child has learned the sums to 18. He may or may not have instant recall of these sums, but he should know how to reproduce his original findings.
2. The child must be able to find the value of number expressions like "4 + 5 + 7," "7 + 8 + 9 + 6," "3 + 2 + 5 + 1."
3. He needs a thorough understanding of place value for the first two digits. By this it is meant that he is capable of:

   a) Grouping by sets of tens and sets of ones.
   b) Responding either in writing or verbally, "46" to the question, "What number is represented by 4 sets of ten and 6 ones?"
   c) Expressing "56" as "5 sets of ten and 6 ones."
   d) Understanding that "37" is "3 tens, 7 ones," or "37 ones."

If these are not understood, the child will undoubtedly encounter difficulties with the regrouping process necessary to the algorism.

Addition Algorism

Upon the determination of the above qualifications, we are now prepared to develop the addition algorism. This development is a matter of the child acquiring computation processes that are increasingly closer approximations of the final algorism we wish to teach. We will describe an overall picture of this development without too much regard for grade level. The primary purpose is to provide the beginning teacher with some notion of the continuity involved in teaching mathematics. The specifics of each grade level can be obtained with little effort from any elementary pupil textbook.

First, renaming a number is essential to the algorism we normally teach in our schools. A child must be able to think of a number in many different ways; more specifically he needs to understand that $47 = 40 + 7$, or $47 = 30 + 17$. A pocket chart, abacus, number line, bead frame, or other similar aid may be employed to establish this concept (Figure 14).

Second, using the parallel that can be drawn between the numbers 1, 2, 3, . . . 9 and the numbers 10, 20, 30, . . . 90, we can form a foundation upon which to build an addition algorism with two place numerals. Patterns can be developed with the number facts, such as if $3 + 2 = 5$, then 3 tens + 2 tens = 5 tens $(30 + 20 = 50)$.

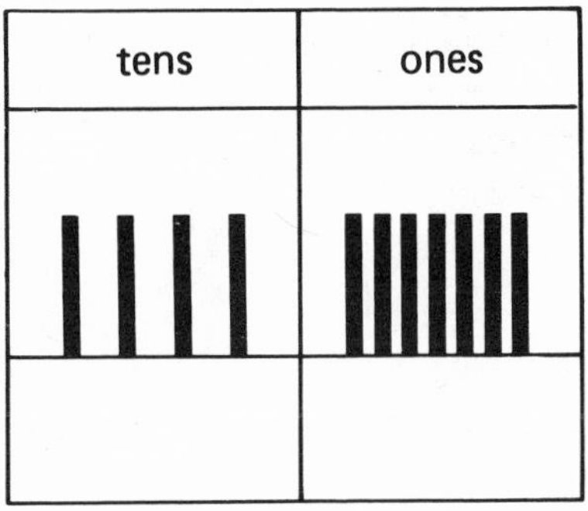

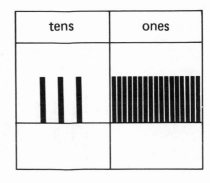

47 shown as 4 tens and 7 ones   47 shown as 3 tens and 17 ones
        in pocket chart   in pocket chart

FIGURE 14

The pocket chart can again be employed to help clarify this type of problem. To complete addition of $30 + 20$, we should use two charts, as shown in Figure 15. A pupil is asked to represent 30 in the first chart and

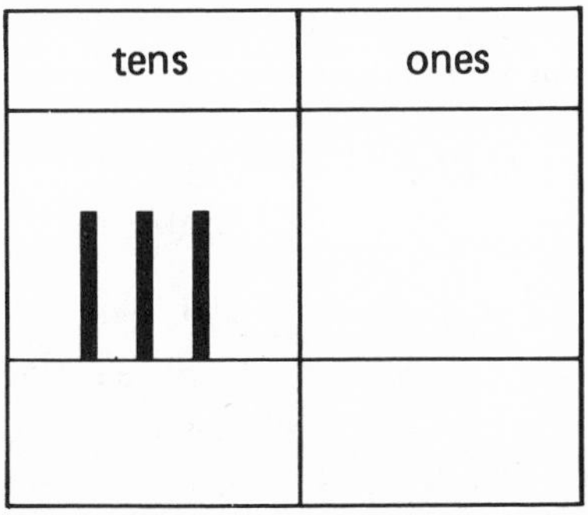

tens	ones
‖‖	

tens	ones
‖	

    30 shown as 3 tens 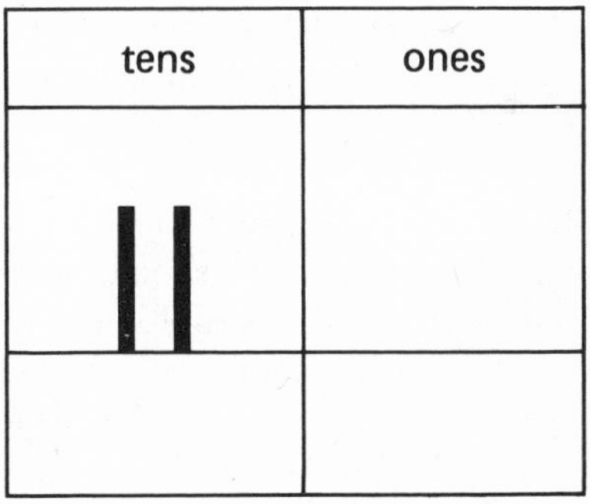   20 shown as 2 tens

FIGURE 15

20 in the second by placing a slip of paper in the pocket for each set of ten to be represented. The reason for the empty ones pocket should be discussed at this time. Now that both numbers have been displayed in the

charts, a pupil is asked to combine all the strips that represent tens in a single chart and to place all the strips that represent ones in another chart. This would appear as shown in Figure 16. The teacher should ask, "How

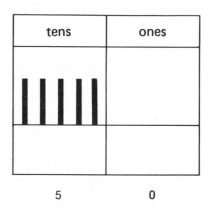

FIGURE 16

many sets of tens are there all together?" The pupil should answer, "There are 5 sets of tens." Then the teacher should ask, "What single number means the same thing as 5 sets of tens?" Of course the answer should be "50."

A bead frame can be used in a similar manner. With this aid it is necessary to write the problems out, however, since both numbers cannot be illustrated on a single bead frame.

After considerable experience with such visual aids, it is advisable to follow up with a semiconcrete activity. Some activity comparable to the exercise in Figure 17 should be sufficient.

As the final presentation at this second stage of the algorism's development, the child would be presented with a totally abstract example such as $60 + 20 = \square$. The number of tens should not exceed a total of 9; that is, a sum of 90 should be the largest encountered at this time.

The third stage is to briefly review numerals such as 45 and 78 by discussing them in class and representing them with bundles of tens and ones in a pocket chart or similar device. After the review the pupils should be presented with problems similar to $45 + 32 = \square$. Neither the sum of the tens nor that of the ones should be larger than 9. The physical aids mentioned above should be used in the initial encounter with these problems. After this primary thrust, additional pencil-and-paper study should be used.

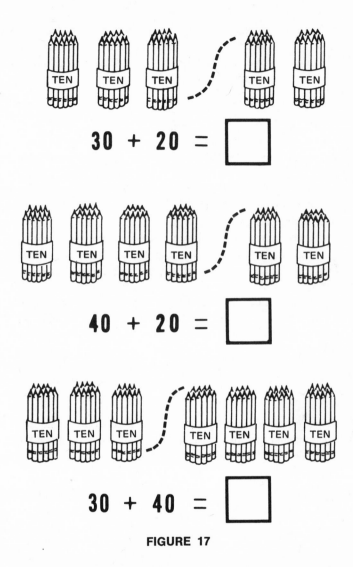

FIGURE 17

It should be noted at this time that both the vertical and horizontal forms of addition have been used. They have not been used, however, without some pictorial or physical aid.

$$\begin{array}{r} 32 \\ + 41 \\ \hline 73 \end{array}$$ $32 + 41 = 73$

When the child has acquired an understanding of the concept of two-place addition, the accompanying aids may be eliminated. At this time, the child should be capable of computing any "free-standing" addition problem in which the sum is not greater than 99, in either this vertical form:

$$\begin{array}{r} 78 \\ + 21 \\ \hline 99 \end{array}$$

or in the horizontal form, $78 + 21 = 99$, using just the single-digit addition facts.

As a fourth step, expanded notation can now be brought in to bridge the gap between two-place addition without regrouping and those sums that require some form of regrouping, as in $76 + 14 = 90$.

It is worth noting that the children have had experience with expanded notations. That is, they have had exercises like "49 means 4 tens and 9 ones." They have also worked with the expanded notation $49 = 40 + 9$.

The purpose at this stage is the all-important introduction of expanded notation into the addition process. Begin with the sums of two-place numbers where no regrouping is necessary. For instance, to find the sum of $47 + 22$, the pupil may write:

$$\begin{array}{r} 47 \\ + 22 \\ \hline 69 \end{array} \quad \text{or} \quad \begin{array}{r} 4 \text{ tens} + 7 \text{ ones} \\ 2 \text{ tens} + 2 \text{ ones} \\ \hline 6 \text{ tens} + 9 \text{ ones} = 69 \end{array}$$

Fifth, we are now at the stage where we can encounter the need for regrouping or exchanging. It is wise to begin with an example that requires that we exchange "1 set of ten" for "10 ones." The following example describes the steps necessary for teaching this process.

1.

$$\begin{array}{r} 48 \\ + 34 \\ \hline \end{array} \quad \text{or} \quad \begin{array}{l} 4 \text{ tens} + 8 \text{ ones} \\ 3 \text{ tens} + 4 \text{ ones} \\ \hline 7 \text{ tens} + 12 \text{ ones} = 7 \text{ tens} + 1 \text{ ten} + 2 \text{ ones} = \\ 8 \text{ tens} + 2 \text{ ones or} \quad 82 \end{array}$$

This, of course, utilizes the expanded notation discussed above.

2. The 12 has to be "renamed" as $10 + 2$ and the problem becomes $70 + 10 + 2$. We obtain $80 + 2$, or 82.

This may be more easily understood if it is illustrated by using sets of objects: First, represent 48 by 4 bundles of 10 straws and 8 single straws and 34 by 3 bundles of 10 straws and 4 single straws (Figure 18). Since we are adding we combine all the straws in one chart. Once this is com-

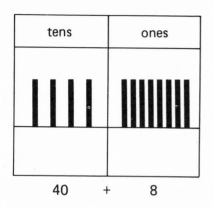

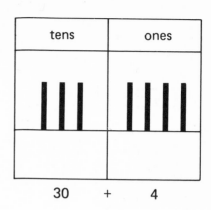

40   +   8

30   +   4

FIGURE 18

plete, we bundle 10 of the single straws together and move them to the tens pocket of the chart. Finally, we can count the number of tens and ones to arrive at the correct answer (Figure 19).

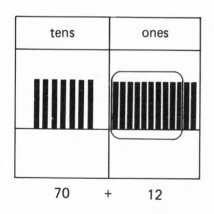

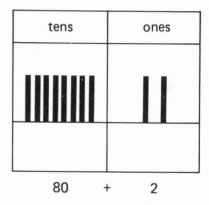

70   +   12

80   +   2

FIGURE 19

Multibase blocks can be used very effectively to demonstrate the above solution (Figure 20). In adding 48 and 34 we add the ones first and find 12. This is 1 ten and 2 ones. The number of units in the sum is 2. Then the number of tens is 4 tens + 3 tens + 1 ten, which is 8 tens, or 80. The

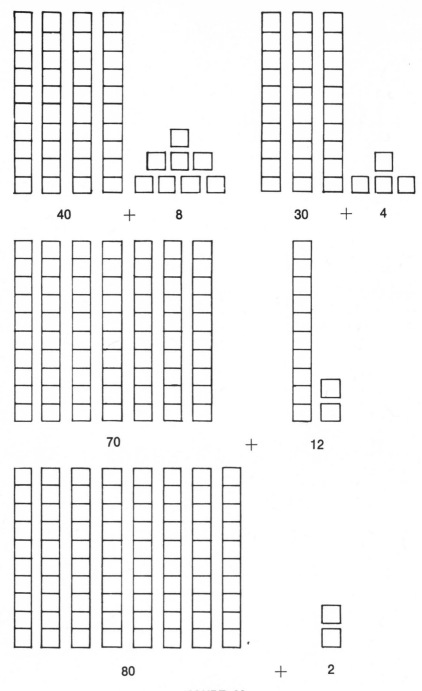

40   +   8   30   +   4

70   +   12

80   +   2

FIGURE 20

sum is 82.   As a bridge between the use of the expanded notation with concrete aids and the desired algorism we can use the following procedure:

tens	ones
1	
4	8
3	4
8	2

This should be an oral discussion by the pupil, with the teacher doing the only writing.   In the discussion, the pupil might say:

"There are 4 tens and 8 ones in 48 and there are 3 tens and 4 ones in 34.   The sum of 8 ones and 4 ones is 12 ones.   However, 12 ones can be written as 1 ten and 2 ones.   I'll keep track of this ten in the tens column. Now I have 1 ten + 4 tens + 3 tens, which is 8 tens.   This gives a sum of 82."

In its final form the algorism would appear as:

$$\begin{array}{r} 1 \\ 48 \\ + 34 \\ \hline 82 \end{array}$$

We have merely removed the place-value aid to arrive at this step.

Once the child has worked with regrouping and has practiced with problems similar to the one above, he should be asked to compute a sum where regrouping is not necessary, for instance, 24 + 35.   If he understands the algorism, this exercise will pose no problem.   However, a child who has attempted to memorize the process or was unable to comprehend might perform as follows:

$$\begin{array}{r} 1 \\ 24 \\ + 35 \\ \hline 69 \end{array}$$

It is clear this child has merely memorized a rule.   He should be given more work with the models and aids mentioned above.   After a pupil has had considerable work with the algorism, he should be confronted with exercises in which both types of problems appear.

The algorism must be extended to finding the sum of any two numbers, regardless of the number of digits or places. We will naturally want to work with three-digit numbers next. This extension can be established by drawing upon the child's knowledge of the expanded notation. At this stage of his development he is capable of understanding that $479 = 4$ hundreds $+ 7$ tens $+ 9$ ones or, even more abstractly, that $400 = 400 + 70 + 9$. Thus we could introduce the addition as follows:

$$
\begin{array}{r}
473 = 400 + 70 + 3 \\
224 = 200 + 20 + 4 \\
\hline
600 + 90 + 4, \text{ or } 694
\end{array}
$$

As before, the initial developmental stage of the algorism requires that we work only with problems that do not need regrouping. Thus the child learns to extend his ability to work and compute with three-digit numbers. In addition he is given an opportunity to make this transfer prior to being introduced to three-digit addition in conjunction with the regrouping process. The child should be given full opportunity to establish a parallel between two-digit and three-digit addition. This can be accomplished if the teacher makes a concerted effort to illustrate the continuing role that place value will play in the operations.

Now we can introduce a problem such as $347 + 485$, in which it becomes necessary to regroup. The steps in teaching this concept are the same as those used for the two-digit additions. The developmental stages might be as follows:

1. The pupil is asked to represent the numbers to be added in expanded form. It will be of great value to discuss this task in terms of sets of hundreds, sets of tens, and sets of ones.

   Step 1: $347 = 3$ hundreds $+ 4$ tens $+ 7$ ones
              $485 = 4$ hundreds $+ 8$ tens $+ 5$ ones

   Step 2: $347 = 300 + 40 + 7$
              $485 = 400 + 80 + 5$

2. Finding the sums of the two numbers follows the same pattern.

   Step 1: $347 = 3$ hundreds $+ 4$ tens $+ 7$ ones
              $485 = 4$ hundreds $+ 8$ tens $+ 5$ ones
              _____
              7 hundreds $+ 12$ tens $+ 12$ ones

Step 2: $347 = 300 + 40 + 7$
             $485 = 400 + 80 + 5$
             $\overline{700 + 120 + 12}$
             or $700 + (100 + 20) + (10 + 2)$

3. We now regroup the hundreds and tens to arrive at the answer of $800 + 30 + 2$ or 832.

4. In the final analysis the process of adding becomes:

$$
\begin{array}{ccccc}
1 & & 1\ 1 & & 1\ 1 \\
347 & = & 347 & = & 347 \\
485 & & 485 & & 485 \\
\hline
2 & & 32 & & 832
\end{array}
$$

In point 4 above, we used a numeral above the appropriate column to indicate the number of sets we have regrouped. This aid, contrary to some beliefs, is not necessarily bad. It is far better for a student to know what he is doing so that he obtains a correct sum than to be concerned with removing some extraneous factor. It has been observed that most of the students will eliminate the use of this crutch by themselves, given the time to do so. We may still find it advantageous to use sensory aids in the extension of the algorism. Although our goal is to use an abstract mode of study we should not, at this stage, continue to consider concrete or visual aids as necessary.

The extension of the algorism to find the sum of four-digit, five-digit numbers and so forth should not present any new problems. The concept of multiple-digit addition should be understood by this time.

Subtraction Algorism

The subtraction algorism is usually developed concurrently with the algorism for addition, since its basic aspects are similar to those required for addition. In fact, the readiness activities used for addition may also be used as groundwork for the subtraction algorism. The basic subtraction facts and a keen understanding for the renaming of numbers through the use of place value are essential.

Since the similarity is so great we can begin our discussion with a problem that requires regrouping (borrowing). For the purpose of discussion we will use:

$$
\begin{array}{r}
54 \\
-\ 39 \\
\hline
\end{array}
$$

We should let the children experiment in an attempt to arrive at a solution. There are, of course, several ways by which it can be solved. The child could count out 54 checkers and then remove 39 of them. He obtains the difference by counting the remaining checkers. A pupil might suggest, for example:

$$54 - 40 = 14 \text{ and}$$
$$14 + 1 = 15 \text{ or}$$
$$54 - 39 = 15$$

The primary purpose of this discussion is to motivate the children to rely on what they have already learned. With skillful guidance the teacher can then lead them to the algorism. It is not always possible, of course, to use a sequence of steps identical to the one that follows:

Step 1:   (a) $54 = 50 + 4 = 40 + 10 + 4$
$\underline{- 39 = 30 + 9 = 30 + 9}$

(b) $54 = 40 + 14$
$\underline{- 39 = 30 + 9}$

(c) $10 + 5 \text{ or } 15$

Step 2:

(a)
Tens	Ones
5	4
− 3	9

(b)
Tens	Ones
4	14
$\cancel{5}$	$\cancel{4}$
− 3	9

(c)
Tens	Ones
4	14
− 3	9
1	5

We are bringing the child closer to the adult form of the algorism. Eventually he would write:

$$\begin{array}{cc} 4 & 14 \\ \cancel{5} & \cancel{4} \\ -3 & 9 \\ \hline 1 & 5 \end{array}$$

This in turn should lead to the mental transfer to the set of ten so he would now need only write:

$$
\begin{array}{r}
54 \\
- 39 \\
\hline
15
\end{array}
$$

The extension of the subtraction algorism to three-place or three-digit numbers can cause considerable difficulty. For this reason, the authors strongly suggest the use of some form of concrete aid. It is true that we could proceed as follows:

$$
\begin{array}{r}
943 \\
- 785 \\
\hline
\end{array}
\qquad
\begin{array}{r}
900 + 40 + 3 \\
700 + 80 + 5 \\
\hline
\end{array}
$$

We conclude that it is not possible to remove 5 ones from 3 ones; therefore we must regroup. Thus:

$$
\begin{array}{r}
943 \\
- 785 \\
\hline
\end{array}
=
\begin{array}{r}
900 + 30 + 13 \\
700 + 80 + \ 5 \\
\hline
8
\end{array}
$$

Similarly, we are at an impasse because we cannot remove 8 sets of tens from 3 sets of tens. Thus:

$$
\begin{array}{r}
943 \\
=
\end{array}
\begin{array}{r}
800 + 130 + 13 \ \text{or} \\
700 + \ 80 + \ 5 \\
\hline
100 + \ 50 + \ 8
\end{array}
$$

$$
\begin{array}{r}
943 \\
- 785 \\
\hline
158
\end{array}
$$

Ultimately we would expect the pupils to perform this subtraction as follows:

$$
\begin{array}{r}
8 \quad 13 \quad 13 \\
\cancel{9} \ \cancel{4} \ \cancel{3} \\
- 7 \ 8 \ 5 \\
\hline
1 \ 5 \ 8
\end{array}
$$

As implied previously, this is a rather abstract concept for pupils to comprehend. Therefore we have illustrated a means by which the same problem could be presented in a far more concrete manner (Figure 21).

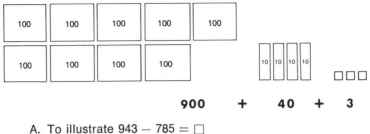

900   +   40   +   3

A. To illustrate 943 − 785 = ☐

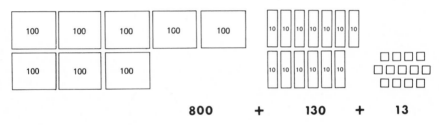

800   +   130   +   13

B. Regroup as:

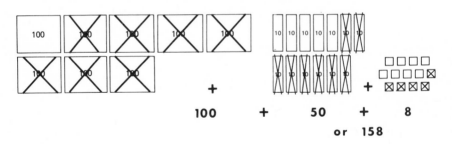

100   +   50   +   8

or   158

C. Subtract 785

FIGURE 21

Subtraction poses one other point of difficulty that is not present in the addition algorism. This difficulty arises when zero is used as a place holder in a number. For instance, 304 − 126 will present this problem. This requires a "series" of regroupings, as shown by the following steps.

Step 1: $\dfrac{304}{-126} = \dfrac{300 + 0 + 4}{100 + 20 + 6}$

Step 2: $\dfrac{304}{-126} = \dfrac{200 + 100 + 4}{100 + 20 + 6}$

Step 3: $\dfrac{304}{-126} = \dfrac{200 + 90 + 14}{100 + 20 + 6}$

$100 + 70 + 8$ or 178

After progressing through each of the above steps, another recommended approach is to rely more fully on the child's understanding of place value. From previous work he should know that the number 304 can be written as 30 tens + 4 ones. This will allow us to proceed as indicated in the following steps and illustrations:

1. We can regroup 1 set of ten as 10 ones, which leaves 29 tens and 14 ones. By removing 6 ones from 14 ones, we obtain a difference of 8.
2. By removing 2 tens from 9 tens, we obtain a difference of 7 tens.
3. By removing 1 hundred from 2 hundreds, we obtain a difference of 1 hundred and thus the total difference of 178.

H	T	O		H	T	O		H	T	O
2	9			2	9			2	9	
̷3	̷0	14		̷3	̷0	14		̷3	̷0	14
− 1	2	6		− 1	2	6		− 1	2	6
		8			7	8		1	7	8

Step 1   Step 2   Step 3

From this we can follow with the mental form of the algorism, with which we are familiar:

$$\begin{array}{r} 2\ \ 9\ \ 14 \\ \cancel{3}\ \ \cancel{0}\ \ 4 \\ -\ 1\ \ 2\ \ 6 \\ \hline 1\ \ 7\ \ 8 \end{array}$$

The child may or may not need to use the "crutch" shown above each column.

There are other algorisms for addition and subtraction. However, we are usually familiar only with the two discussed thus far. One such algorism is the Austrian method, which is dependent upon the property of equal addition. That is, quite simply, that if two numbers differ, they will differ by the same amount if equal amounts are added to each number. More precisely:

$$a - b = (a + k) - (b + k)$$

If we wish to solve a subtraction problem by this method we proceed as follows:

$$
\begin{array}{r}
456 \\
-\ 279 \\
\hline
\end{array}
\qquad
\begin{array}{ccc}
 & & 16 \\
4 & 5 & \not{6} \\
 & 8 & \\
\hline
2 & \not{7} & 9
\end{array}
\qquad
\begin{array}{ccc}
 & 15 & 16 \\
4 & \not{5} & \not{6} \\
3 & 8 & \\
\hline
\not{2} & \not{7} & \not{9}
\end{array}
$$

When we wrote 456 as $45\not{6}^{16}$ we were merely adding 10 to 456. Thus, to keep the difference the same we added 10 to 279 by writing it as 2 $\not{8}$ 9. The other step was handled in a similar manner.

This algorism was at one time referred to as the "moral" method. It was erroneously stated that we were borrowing 10 to give aid to the 6; therefore, we must pay it back to the seven. The phrase "moral method" was coined from this notion of borrowing and paying back. There was, however, no borrowing or paying back, but merely adding the same amount to each number.

Summary

Our goal thus far has been to chart a course of development for teaching, with understanding, the addition and subtraction of whole numbers for the first six grades. The broad development of these concepts is intended to remove the notion of rigid grade placement of specific ideas. In order for a teacher to perform at the highest level in teaching these operations, she must be cognizant of the entire sequence of conceptual development.

To discuss addition and subtraction as being separated from development of the concept of number is misleading. What was discussed in Chapter 1 is closely related to the development of addition and subtraction described in this chapter. Thus far the stages in mathematical development have been presented in which the child:

1. Obtains a concept of number (as discussed in Chapter 1).
2. Begins having experience in combining sets into a single set of objects and assigning a number name to the new set.
3. Has practice in verbalizing mathematical sentences, such as, "Two balls and three balls is five balls."
4. Writes and solves simple sentences like $2 + 4 = \square$.

5. Is introduced to subtraction through the use of sets and the removal of subsets.
6. Has practice writing and solving both addition and subtraction problems.
7. Studies, for immediate recall, the basic addition and subtraction facts through the use of tables, flash cards, etc.
8. Practices problem solving, using addition and subtraction, using both teacher- and student-developed stories.
9. Is introduced to and develops algorisms for both addition and subtraction.

Chapter 3

TEACHING MULTIPLICATION
AND DIVISION OF
WHOLE NUMBERS

Readiness

Before multiplication is formally introduced, elementary school pupils should experience readiness activities as early as the first grade. Probably the first foundation activity is combining equivalent sets. Other activities that help prepare the pupil for multiplication include the following:

1. Displaying and discussing arrays of objects, such as checkers, jacks, or blocks.
2. Adding equal numbers, such as $4 + 4 = 8$.
3. Counting by twos, threes, and so on.

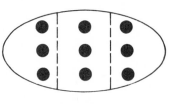

FIGURE 1

4. Partitioning sets into equivalent subsets (Figure 1).
5. Naming a set in terms of equal subsets (Figure 2).

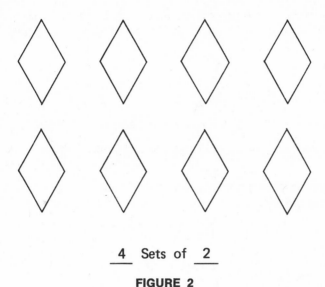

<u>4</u> Sets of <u>2</u>

FIGURE 2

Multiplication

Multiplication can be interpreted in several different ways, each of which relies on the use of set notations and set language. The most familiar and perhaps the clearest of these is joining equivalent disjoint sets. In so doing we obtain a third set, which we can name by a single number. The sets must, of course, be disjoint in order for the correct numerical value to be arrived at. For instance, let's look at the following examples:

1. If we join the sets of blocks,

    □ □ □ □   □ □ □ □

    we obtain a new set that contains 8 blocks. We may write $2 \times 4 = 8$.
2. ⟦a, b, c, d⟧   ⟦a, m, n, o.⟧ However, if we join these two sets of letters we obtain ⟦a, b, c, d, m, n, o.⟧ This new set contains 7 letters (elements). Thus, we could write $2 \times 4 = 7$.

The latter case is obviously not true—it points out the need for considering only disjoint sets (sets with no elements in common). Through teacher awareness this fact need not pose a problem in the introductory phase of multiplication. It is mentioned to emphasize the necessity for employing sets of objects, or pictures of sets, in such a manner as to make it obvious that the sets have no members in common.

A key factor in the introduction of multiplication, regardless of method, is to make certain the process is meaningful to the child. By using activities such as those shown in Figure 3, the child can acquire an intuitive notion

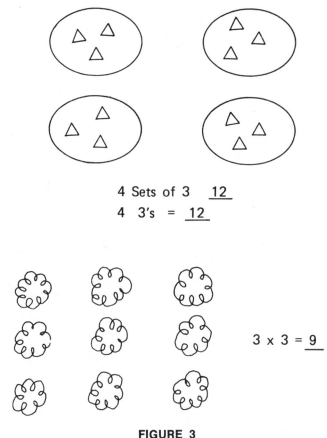

FIGURE 3

of multiplication. The experience with the physical and pictorial set introduction will lead him to make the interpretation shown in Figure 4 when confronted with the set. At this time, when presented with $3 \times 4 = \square$, the child can use a drawing or concrete objects to proceed as shown in Figure 4. Eventually, we should expect him to see that $3 \times 4 = \square$ can be interpreted

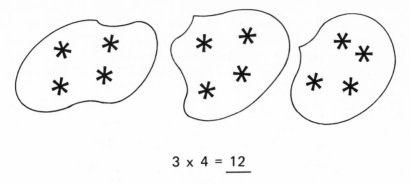

3 x 4 = 12

FIGURE 4

as $4 + 4 + 4 = 12$. Thus, $3 \times 4 = 12$ can be discovered by use of serial addition, rather than counting of the elements of sets.

The number line provides an excellent tool for illustrating multiplication, once the repeated or serial addition concept is understood by the child. We can, for example, find the answer to $4 \times 5 = \square$, as shown in Figure 5. We begin at 0 and make four moves of 5 to the right. By

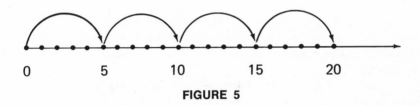

FIGURE 5

recognizing that four moves of 5 are equivalent to one move of 20, we can conclude that $4 \times 5 = 20$. The pupil can also be led to see that 5 moves of 4 will give the same result. Thus an excellent opportunity is provided to introduce the commutativity of multiplication.

After a meaningful development of multiplication as repeated addition, the teacher should confront the children with "stories" that can be interpreted or answered by using multiplication. For example, the questions "How many nickels are there in 3 quarters?" can be answered by completing the open sentence $3 \times 5 = \square$. The teacher should allow the pupils to employ whatever strategy seems necessary to arrive at a solution. Some may merely add $5 + 5 + 5$, while others will depend on counting concrete objects, such as the money itself. The answer in this case is not the ultimate goal, but a means to reinforce the fact that multiplication can be *interpreted* as repeated addition. Using this idea, in the sentence $3 \times 5 = 15$ the 3 tells the number of sets that are to be joined, and the 5 tells the number of members that are in each set.

Another means of arriving at number facts would be to think of multiplication in terms of arrays. The arrangement of dots in Figure 6 rep-

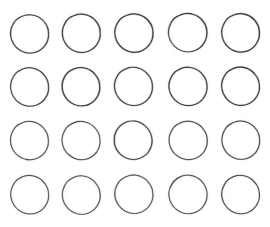

FIGURE 6

resents an array which shows 4 sets of 5's in the horizonal form or 5 sets of 4's in the vertical form. Thus we can discover, from the horizontal view, the multiplication sentence $4 \times 5 = 20$. However, if we use the vertical vantage point, we can also conclude that $5 \times 4 = 20$. It is obvious that we can derive two multiplication facts from each array. At closer inspection we may conclude that $5 \times 4 = 4 \times 5$. Such facts, obtained through the use of arrays, can prove to be quite useful in illustrating the commutative property of multiplication.

A relationship between multiplication and Cartesian products can be demonstrated by means of physical situations. This interpretation is not

FIGURE 7

to be used with those who are just beginning the study of multiplication, but as further justification for older pupils. Suppose you have three different hats and four dresses from which you can choose an outfit (Figure 7). The idea of Cartesian product can be used to determine the different ways in which an outfit can be assembled by matching or pairing the hats and dresses. The pairings can be listed systematically as follows:

Hat a—dress A	Hat b—dress C
Hat a—dress B	Hat b—dress D
Hat a—dress C	Hat c—dress A
Hat a—dress D	Hat c—dress B
Hat b—dress A	Hat c—dress C
Hat b—dress B	Hat c—dress D

Thus there are 3 × 4 or 12 ways of matching a hat with a dress. It follows that if we match the dresses with the hats, we will obtain 4 × 3, or 12 ways of matching the dresses with the hats. It should be clear that we will obtain different ordered pairs when we match the dresses with the hats than we did when we matched the hats with the dresses. However, we will have the same number of pairs.

An interesting analogy can be drawn between the Cartesian product and crossed lines. If you draw 3 parallel lines and then draw 4 parallels perpendicular to the original three, you get the following:

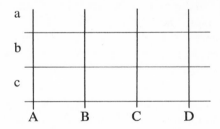

By counting the number of intersections formed by the lines we find it is 12. Again we can illustrate that 3 × 4 = 12. If we name the intersection with the letters assigned to the lines, we get (a,A), (a,B), (a,C), (a,D), (b,A), . . . , which is just another way of finding the Cartesian product (cross product).

The teacher should be aware of the fact that the interpretations discussed above are not synonymous with multiplication. For example, the joining of equivalent sets involves a repeated operation on a given number of sets. Multiplication, on the other hand, is an operation on numbers.

Therefore, the emphasis in developing multiplication should be on the numbers involved. Just as addition is a mapping of an ordered pair of natural numbers onto its sum, multiplication is a mapping of an ordered pair of natural numbers onto its product. For example:

$$(6,3) \xrightarrow{\times} 18$$

We use the symbol $\times$ to indicate we are referring to multiplication, of course. It should also be noted that we have provided another experience in which the child can observe, pictorially, that multiplication is a commutative operation. The multiplicity of such examples (through arrays, number lines, sets, and so forth) makes the attainment of this concept a gradual process rather than something that can be taught in a single lesson.

In the process of discovering the basic facts, pupils begin to make use of the commutative property of multiplication. We are not overly concerned with vocabulary at the developmental state; rather we are interested in the child's understanding of what he observes. The use of the crossed lines or an array will help him inductively arrive at the conclusion that the order in which two numbers are multiplied will not affect the product. Thus a point will be reached where it will be necessary to discover only one fact for two ordered pairs. For instance $3 \times 4 = 12$; therefore we know that $4 \times 3 = 12$.

A meaningful development of multiplication can use one or all of the strategies presented. However, if multiplication is going to be of value we must have all the basic facts available for instant recall. The children should be led to realize it would consume far too much time if they rely on repeated addition, the number line, a picture, or any array of dots to arrive at a solution to a number question.

The discovery of "basic facts" is ordinarily a random process, but there are a few exceptions. We should, for example, systematically develop the multiples of ten (counting by 10), multiples of five (counting by 5), and so forth, and multiplication by 1. The child must also have a systematic way to study, observe, and draw conclusions from the facts he has discovered. It is for this reason that a multiplication table is made. The child should discover the facts himself, and he should construct the table he will use, as shown in Figure 8. If pupils are confronted with a completed table from which all the basic multiplication facts are to be memorized, the teacher will not save time, nor will teaching be served. In fact, by doing so the teacher will in all probability destroy what success he has had to that point.

After the pupils have completed their tables, it is time for drill and practice. Written exercises, flash cards, games, or oral responses to boardwork can be used. Regardless of the means, the end should be near-automatic recall. In addition to the facts, pupils are expected to discover

X	1	2	3	4	5	6	7	8	9	10
1	1	2	3	4	5	6	7	8	9	10
2	2	4	6	8	10	12	14	16	18	20
3	3	6	9	12	15	18	21	24	27	30
4	4	8	12	16	20	24	28	32	36	40
5	5	10	15	20	25	30	35	40	45	50
6	6	12	18	24	30	36	42	48	54	60
7	7	14	21	28	35	42	49	56	63	70
8	8	16	24	32	40	48	56	64	72	80
9	9	18	27	36	45	54	63	72	81	90
10	10	20	30	40	50	60	70	80	90	100

FIGURE 8

patterns (relations) from the table, such as that the product of an odd natural number and an even natural number is an even natural number, or that, because of the commutative property of multiplication, the table is symmetric about the main diagonal. These and many other relationships can be discovered and understood by the children with the aid of the table and the guidance of a teacher willing to allow them to explore.

Properties of Multiplication

We have discussed the commutative property and its possible application to the operation of multiplication and have suggested ways in which the development of the concept might be approached. Once the child has a sound intuitive understanding of the property, we can introduce the algebraic symbolism, as follows:

If a and b are natural numbers, then $a \times b = b \times a$.

It has been stressed throughout this discussion that multiplication is an operation on two numbers. That is to say, it is a binary operation defined upon the set of natural numbers. Therefore it is necessary to provide a means by which three numbers can be assigned a product. When the key basic facts have been established, we are prepared to proceed with sentences with three or more factors.

$$4 \times 3 \times 2 = \quad .$$

When this or a similar problem is presented, pupils can be expected to all but automatically arrive at a solution:

$$4 \times 3 \times 2 = 24.$$

After several such exercises have been worked and illustrated, we might ask how the pupils arrive at a solution. The answers will vary with respect to the way they group in order to find the product. For instance one child might say, "I multiply 4×3 first, then times 2." As this child explains, the teacher should record the following on the board:

$$(4 \times 3) \times 2 = 24$$

Another may say, "I multiplied 3×2 first, then times 4." This too should be recorded as he explains:

$$4 \times (3 \times 2) = 24$$

The use of the parentheses as a means of recording groupings as the pupil explains his method should be introduced without any unnecessary elaboration. The authors have found that using them without explanation works far better than introducing something new for the child to memorize. By not emphasizing the parentheses, we allow the child more opportunity to realize that different groupings of the factors do not change the product. Also, by using the parentheses, we are merely telling how we proceeded in obtaining an answer. Once this is established it can be reinforced by work-ing examples similar to the following:

$$(3 \times 2) \times 4 = \square \qquad 3 \times (2 \times 4) = \square$$

Eventually we write:

$$(3 \times 2) \times 4 = 3 \times (2 \times 4)$$

The associative property will be used extensively at later stages of the development of multiplication.

Through close inspection of the multiplication table and many other experiences with finding products, a child gradually realizes that the product of any two natural numbers will be a natural number. In other words, the set of natural numbers is closed with respect to the binary operation of multiplication.

In a similar manner a child will eventually discover that the product

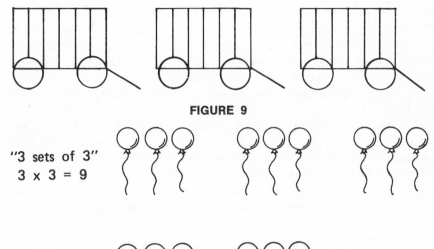

FIGURE 9

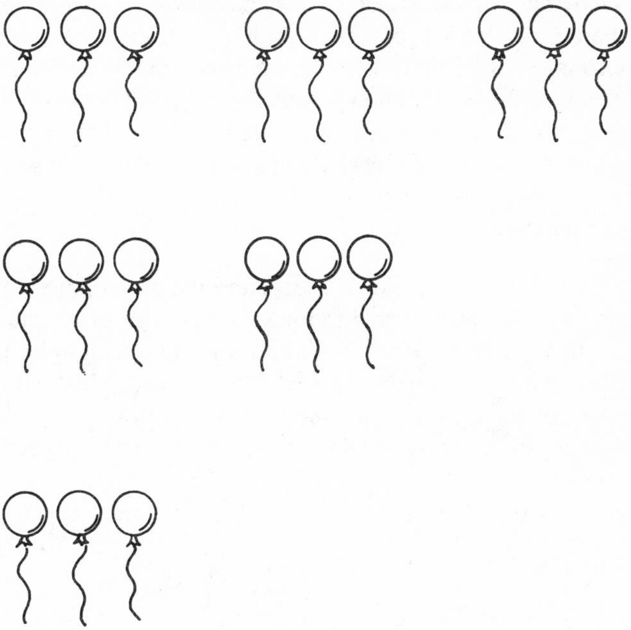

"3 sets of 3"
3 x 3 = 9

"2 sets of 3"
2 x 3 = 6

"1 set of 3"
1 x 3 = 3

"0 sets of 3"
0 x 3 = 0

FIGURE 10

of any number and 1 is that number. He is also capable of recognizing the generalization $N \times 1 = N$ or that 1 is the identity element for multiplication.

While an operation with zero is not a property, it does play a rather special role in multiplication. As we know, the product of zero and any number is zero.

$$0 \times b = b \times 0 = 0$$

This idea appears to be quite trivial, but it can be difficult if care is not taken to present it in a meaningful way. It is far easier to comprehend seven sets of 0 than it is to visualize zero sets of 7. Therefore, examples like the one in Figure 9 should come first in the development. We would ask, "How many circus wagons are there?" The answer of "three" would be followed by the question, "How many lions are there in each wagon?" The response would, of course, be "zero." Then, "How many lions are there in all the wagons put together?" "Zero." By extensive use of such examples, we would soon be able to write that "3 sets of 0" is "0" or $3 \times 0 = 0$. We can now establish the fact that not only is $3 \times 0 = 0$, but $0 \times 3 = 0$. The pupils can be led to this conclusion by use of the commutative property or by study activities similar to those shown in Figure 10.

Multiplication Algorism

In order for a child to understand the development of the multiplication algorism, he must have a thorough knowledge of one additional property— the distributive property. Without this, no meaningful presentation is possible. Shown in Figure 11 is a 6×7 array, which should be drawn on a piece of paper. To find the number of X's in the array we need only multiply 6×7 and obtain 42. However, if the paper were torn, it might appear as the illustration in Figure 12. Now to find the number of X's we could say there are 6×4 or 24 on one piece of paper and 6×3 or 18

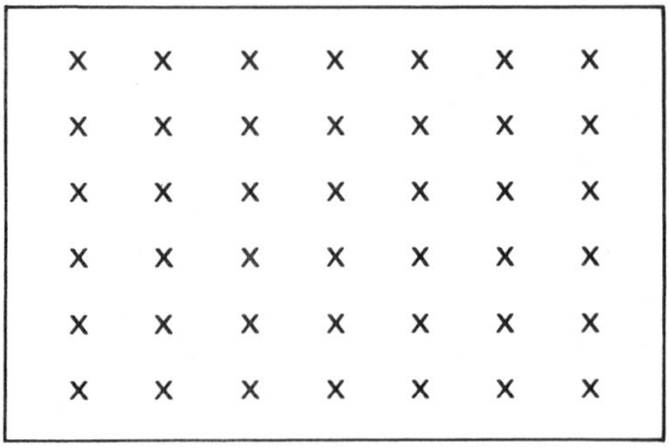

FIGURE 11

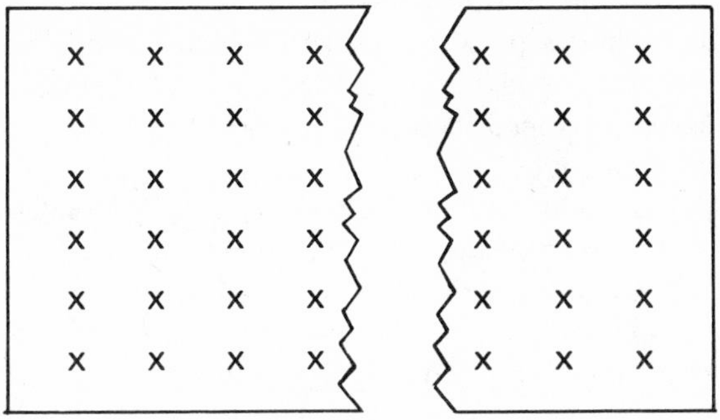

FIGURE 12

on the other. Thus, there are 24 + 18 or 42 X's in all. This could be interpreted as $6 \times 7 = 6 \times (4 + 3) = 6 \times 4 + 6 \times 3$. This illustrates a specific instance of the distributive property.

To this point, the following properties of multiplication have been discussed:

1. The sum or product of any two natural numbers is a natural number (closure).
2. Commutative property: If a and b are natural numbers, then

$$a + b = b + a \qquad \text{and}$$
$$a \times b = b \times a.$$

3. Associative property: If a, b and c are natural numbers, then

$$(a + b) + c = a + (b + c) \qquad \text{and}$$
$$(a \times b) \times c = a \times (b \times c).$$

4. The number 0 is the identity element for addition. That is, if a is the natural number, then

$$a + 0 = 0 + a = a.$$

5. The identity element for multiplication is 1. That is, if "a" is a natural number, then

$$a \times 1 = 1 \times a = a.$$

6. Multiplication is distributive over addition. If a, b, and c are natural numbers, then

$$a \times (b + c) = a \times b + a \times c.$$

The products obtained from all of the ordered pairs composed of the numbers 0 through 9 are called basic facts of multiplication. These facts are committed to memory and are, hopefully, available for instant recall. When we want to find a product that is not included in these basic facts, we must have at our command some computational strategy to do so. At this time, we have developed the necessary tools to develop such a strategy. This strategy is algorism.

The teaching of a multiplication algorism should proceed systematically. Care should be taken to insure that the steps being used to arrive at the desired algorism are sufficiently clear and that they are not based on unwarranted assumptions. The following steps are suggested as levels of competence that should be acquired by pupils to facilitate a relatively smooth development of a multiplication algorism.

First, we have already discussed the teaching of some important foundation work. These activities are comparable to the readiness activities for addition. Included in the child's background should be: (1) understanding of basic facts and capability to recall them, (2) the ability to multiply by 10, (3) experience with finding products of three or more single-digit numbers, and (4) a good understanding of the properties listed above. Second, when these concepts have been mastered, it should be easy for the child to multiply any one-digit number by some multiple of 10. To find the product of 6×30, we need only change the problem to multiplication by 10. Thus, it becomes:

$$
\begin{aligned}
6 \times 30 &= 6 \times (3 \times 10) && \text{renaming} \\
&= (6 \times 3) \times 10 && \text{associative property} \\
&= 18 \times 10 && \text{basic multiplication fact} \\
&= 180 && \text{multiplication by 10} \\
6 \times 30 &= 180 && \text{transitive property} \\
9 \times 70 &= 9 \times (7 \times 10) && \text{renaming} \\
&= (9 \times 7) \times 10 && \text{associative} \\
&= 63 \times 10 && \text{basic multiplication fact} \\
&= 630 && \text{multiplication by 10} \\
9 \times 70 &= 630 && \text{transitive property}
\end{aligned}
$$

This is the basis for a form of mental multiplication that you have most likely used at one time or another. The 6×30 becomes 6×3 multiplied by 10. With experience the children will master this type of operation and be able to perform the multiplication mentally.

Third, a logical extension is the consideration of the product of a two-digit number and a single-digit number:

$$7 \times 63 = \square$$

Most children, when confronted with this problem, will revert to repeated addition:

$$7 \times 63 = 63 + 63 + 63 + 63 + 63 + 63 + 63$$

Barring all arithmetic errors, they will find the correct solution to the problem. We do not want to discourage this kind of thinking but merely to try to lead the children to use properties and skill previously learned. With the proper coaxing and patience they should be able to translate the problem into the following:

$$
\begin{aligned}
7 \times 63 &= 7 \times (60 + 3) & &\text{renaming} \\
&= (7 \times 60) + (7 + 3) & &\text{distributive property} \\
&= 420 + 21 & &\text{multiplication} \\
&= 441 & &\text{addition} \\
7 \times 63 &= 441 & &\text{transitive property}
\end{aligned}
$$

For the purpose of preparing the pupils for vertical multiplication, we should follow up examples like the above with the following interpretation:

$$
\begin{array}{r}
63 = 60 + 3 \\
\times\, 7 = \times 7 \\
\hline
420 + 21 = 441 \qquad \text{then}
\end{array}
$$

$$
\begin{array}{cccc}
63 & & 3 & 60 \\
\underline{7} & & \underline{\times 7} & \underline{\times 7} \\
21 & & 21 & 420 \\
\underline{420} & & & \\
441 & & &
\end{array}
$$

Discussion of such problems should be in terms of place value and the properties of addition and multiplication. The use of the properties can be made rather clear if a sequence similar to that above is followed. The role of place value, on the other hand, can be very obscure at times and will require some additional attention.

If necessary we can use such aids as the pocket chart to illustrate how place value is employed to arrive at a preliminary algorism. Hopefully, we will be able to proceed in the following manner:

Hundreds	Tens	Ones
	6	3 = 6 tens, 3 ones
	×	7 = × 7
	2	1
4	2	0
4	4	1

The child should think "7 × 3 ones is 21 ones or 2 tens, 1 one; therefore, we write 2 in the tens place and 1 in the ones place. Then, 7 × 6 tens would be 42 tens, or 420; therefore, we record 4 in the hundred column, 2 in the tens column, and 0 in the ones column and add."

The zero in the ones column is not needed but will serve as a bridge to the mental form of the algorism presented here:

H	T	O
	2	
	6	3
×		7
4	4	1

The child thinks "7 × 3 ones is 21 or 2 tens and 1 one." He is encouraged to record it as shown above. Then "7 × 60 is 42 tens plus 2 tens is 44 tens." Of course 42 tens are 4 hundreds and 2 tens, and he records it as such. Eventually we would expect the child to write:

$$\begin{array}{r} 2 \\ 63 \\ \times 7 \\ \hline 441 \end{array}$$

As was true in addition the use of the "crutch" above the column is not a matter for serious concern.

Fourth, the number of activities and multiplication exercises used at the preceding learning stage has made the extension of multiplication to a multiple-digit number by a single-digit number comparatively easy. If the pupil is asked how to multiply 435 × 7 we can, with some confidence, expect him to make an interpretation dependent on place value:

$$\begin{aligned} 435 \times 7 &= (400 + 30 + 5) \times 7 \\ &= (400 \times 7) + (30 \times 7) + (5 \times 7) \\ &= 2800 + 210 + 35 \\ &= 3045 \end{aligned}$$

followed by

$$\begin{array}{r} 435 \\ 7 \\ \hline 35 \\ 210 \\ 2800 \\ \hline 3045 \end{array} \qquad \begin{array}{l} 5 \times 7 \\ 30 \times 7 \\ 400 \times 7 \end{array}$$

Finally, we would want the child to perform at the same mental level as the one mentioned above for two-digit multiplication. In the illustration above, the 35, 210, and 2800 are called partial products, the sum of which is the desired product. Because of the commutative property of addition, the order of the partial products can be changed and the same product obtained.

For example:

$$
\begin{array}{r}
435 \\
7 \\
\hline
210 \\
2800 \\
35 \\
\hline
3045
\end{array}
\qquad
\begin{array}{l}
30 \times 7 \\
400 \times 7 \\
5 \times 7
\end{array}
$$

There are, of course, several other ways in which the correct solution can be derived. However, our primary goal is to arrive at a standard algorism. Therefore, once exploration has taken place, it will be necessary to guide the child to the correct order of multiplication, that is, beginning with the ones, tens, hundreds, and so on.

As a fifth step, we will consider multiplication of two two-digit numbers. We again begin with the horizontal form and progress to the vertical notation.

Step 1: $46 \times 78 = (40 + 6) \times 78$ renaming

$\qquad\qquad = (40 \times 78) + (6 \times 78)$ distributive property

$\qquad\qquad = 40 \times (70 + 8) + 6 \times (70 + 8)$ renaming

$\qquad\qquad = (40 \times 70) + (40 \times 8) + (6 \times 70) +$

$\qquad\qquad\qquad\qquad\qquad\qquad\qquad (6 \times 8)$ distributive

$\qquad\qquad = 2800 + 320 + 420 + 48$ multiplication

$\qquad\qquad = 3588$

$\qquad 46 \times 78 = 3588$

Step 2:

$$
\begin{array}{r}
78 \\
\times 46 \\
\hline
48 \\
420 \\
320 \\
2800 \\
\hline
\end{array}
\qquad
\begin{array}{l}
6 \times 8 \text{ ones} \\
6 \times 7 \text{ tens} \\
40 \times 8 \text{ ones} \\
40 \times 7 \text{ tens}
\end{array}
$$

Step 3: After considerable practice with the above method, some refinements should take place. The number of partial products may
now be reduced. Rather than using four to multiply by a 2-digit
number, we can now use just 2.

Pupils at this stage also usually find the partial products by the vertical
form and then record the results:

$$
\begin{array}{c}
78 \\
46 \\
\hline
468 \\
3120 \\
\hline
3588
\end{array}
\qquad
\begin{array}{c}
78 \\
\times\,6 \\
\hline
48 \\
420 \\
\hline
468
\end{array}
\qquad
\begin{array}{c}
78 \\
40 \\
\hline
3120
\end{array}
$$
[The pupil will usually
think $(4 \times 78) \times 10$]

The final step preceding mental calculation is to eliminate the zero
from the partial product 3120. If we have emphasized the numeration
system sufficiently, this can be very easy. We merely have the children
think of "3120" as 312 tens and record it accordingly.

$$
\begin{array}{c}
78 \\
\times\,46 \\
\hline
468 \\
312 \\
\hline
3588
\end{array}
\qquad
\begin{array}{l}
6 \times 78 \\
40 \times 78
\end{array}
$$

Sixth, ultimately the partial products and their addition will become a
mental process. The pupil thinks 6×8 is 48; writes down the 8 ones and
remembers the 4 tens (he may use a crutch). 6×70 is 42 tens, plus the
4 tens remembered, is 46 tens; he records 6 tens and 4 hundreds. 40×8 is
32 tens; record 2 tens and remember 3 hundreds. 40×70 is 28 hundreds,
plus the 3 remembered, is 31 hundreds; he writes down 1 in the hundreds
column and 3 in the thousands place. The final step is to add.

Seventh, we now need to extend this standard algorism to a number
with three or more digits. The presentation and explanation of this development would be the same as the preceding example. The child advances from the cumbersome use of the horizontal method to the adult
level of the algorism.

Step 1: $546 \times 325 = (500 + 40 + 6) \times 325$ renaming
$= (500 \times 325) + (40 \times 325) +$ distributive
(6×325) property
$= (162500 + 13000 + 1950)$ multiplication
$= 177450$ addition
$546 \times 325 = 177450$ transitive property

Step 2:
$$
\begin{array}{r}
325 \\
\times\, 546 \\
\hline
1950 \\
13000 \\
162500 \\
\hline
177450
\end{array}
$$
6×325
40×325
500×325

Step 3: Finally we arrive at the algorism commonly used in multiplication:

$$
\begin{array}{r}
325 \\
\times\, 546 \\
\hline
1950 \\
1300 \\
1625 \\
\hline
177450
\end{array}
$$

We must contend with one more troublesome aspect of this algorism. Children often have considerable difficulty in multiplying by a number that has a zero in it. For example, we can illustrate this problem with 309 × 473. If the pupils continue as they have in the previous problems, they are likely to write:

$$
\begin{array}{r}
473 \\
\times\, 309 \\
\hline
4257 \\
0000 \\
1419 \\
\hline
146157
\end{array}
$$
9×473
0×473
3×473

While this is not incorrect, the writing of a partial product consisting of 0's is not necessary. It is more efficient to write the problems as follows:

$$
\begin{array}{r}
473 \\
\times\, 309 \\
\hline
4257 \\
1419 \\
\hline
146157
\end{array}
$$
9×473
3×473

The algorism just discussed is probably one of the most commonly used methods for finding a product. It is not, however, the only algorism available. Others, while not necessarily being more efficient, are very interesting to study. In addition to novelty, these algorisms provide a new vantage point from which to view the decimal numeration system and reinforce the notion that an algorism is any mathematically sound method for arriving at an answer.

The Egyptian multiplication method (or Russian-peasant method, as it is sometimes called) relies on a successive doubling operation and the fact that all numbers can be represented by the sum of powers of 10. As an example of this method, we will multiply 45 by 25.

*1	45	45
2	90	
4	180	
*8	360	360
*16	720	720
		1125

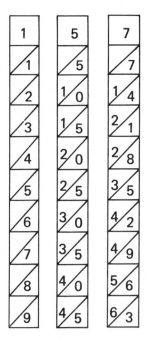

FIGURE 13

Since $25 = 16 + 8 + 1$, we need only add these multiples of 45. By adding those multiples indicated by the asterisk, we get 1125. Mathematically speaking, we are saying:

$$25 \times 45 = 45 + 360 + 720$$
$$= (1 \times 45) + (8 \times 45) + (16 \times 45) \quad \text{renaming}$$
$$= (1 + 8 + 16) \times 45 \quad \text{distributive property}$$
$$= 25 \times 45 \quad \text{addition}$$

Another means of finding products employs the aid of a system of rods devised by the Scotch mathematician John Napier (1550–1617). Originally, strips of metal, bone, or some such material were used. For each of the ten digits there is a strip containing the digit and its multiples, as shown for 1, 5, and 7 in Figure 13.

Once the strips are prepared one need only lay the appropriate ones side by side and, with a minimum amount of diagonal addition, he can

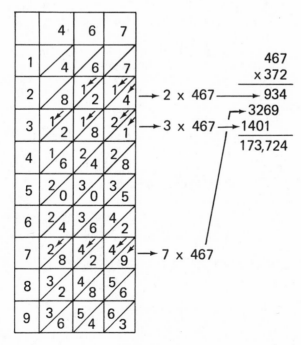

FIGURE 14

read off the needed partial product. We will illustrate by finding the product of 372×467. Place the strips headed 4, 6, and 7 side by side, as shown in Figure 14. The index at the right of the four strips was not originally used by Napier but has been added for convenience. The partial products are then read from the table, and then, by finding their sum, we can arrive at the desired product. We can interpret this as:

$$
\begin{aligned}
372 \times 467 &= (300 + 70 + 2) \times 467 \\
&= (300 \times 467) + (70 \times 467) + (2 \times 467) \\
&= (3 \times 467) \times 100 + (7 \times 467) \times 10 + (2 \times 467)
\end{aligned}
$$

Division

Before discussing the division process it is essential that we understand what division does. In visualizing division it is customary to think of a group of symbols, like $36 \div 4 = 9$. This phrase is useless unless it answers or is capable of answering some kind of question. Division can answer two types of questions: the number of sets needed and the number needed for each set. For instance, consider the following questions:

(1) There are 8 cookies to be given to 4 boys. How many cookies may each have? (Partitioning division)
(2) There are 8 cookies to be given away. If we give 2 cookies to each person, how many people can have cookies? (Measurement division)

Both of these questions can be answered by a division problem. The teacher should be cognizant of these two types of division, but it is not necessary to stress the distinction between them with the children.

As was true for multiplication, our major concern with division in the primary grades is a meaningful development of the concept. At this level a division sentence such as $16 \div 4 = \square$ is of very little, if any, value. Therefore, in the beginning, it follows that far more can be gained if the children are presented with "real" problems that they can solve without resorting to abstract sentences. Through this approach we can introduce all the basic division facts.

Suppose we pose the following problem:

John, Peter and Frank were paid 15¢ for helping their mother. How many pennies should each boy receive?

A very direct and simple way to begin is with a set of 15 pennies. We let the children actually divide the money among three boys and arrive at the answer of five pennies. Such role playing and manipulation of objects not only helps present the division concept but also illustrates a need for the operation.

The children should have considerable experience in solving both types of division problems through some form of physical endeavor. After such experience they should be guided into using pictorial rather than physical means of solution. For example, consider the problem:

12 marbles are to be equally divided among 4 boys. How many marbles does each boy get?

Instead of the number sentence 12 ÷ 4 = □, it is much clearer to ask the question, "How many sets of four are there in 12?" We begin with 12 elements and partition this set into subsets containing 4 members each. The children can arrive at a solution in a manner similar to that illustrated in Figure 15. Thus, he finds he can partition (divide) a set of 12 members into 3 subsets of 4 each, or there are 3 4's in 12. (12 ÷ 4 = 3.)

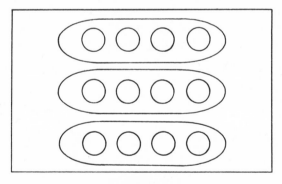

FIGURE 15

Another means for introducing division is by removing equivalent subsets. We should still use the story approach at this stage and allow for some pictorial or concrete method of solution. We could, for example, pose the following problem:

There are 10 pencils in a box. How many students may have pencils, if we give each student 2?

The children can "act out" this problem and remove sets of two pencils until all of the original set is gone. Obviously they can remove five such sets, with nothing remaining.

As the child progresses he can use a more abstract form of the above solution. He may answer the question, "How many 2's in 10?" by actual subtraction.

$$10 - 2 = 8 \quad \text{(1 time)}$$
$$8 - 2 = 6 \quad \text{(2 times)}$$
$$6 - 2 = 4 \quad \text{(3 times)}$$
$$4 - 2 = 2 \quad \text{(4 times)}$$
$$2 - 2 = 0 \quad \text{(5 times)}$$

The repeated subtraction interpretation lends itself well to work on the number line. We can first indicate the number of pencils by drawing a line from 0 to 10. Then from the 10 we make as many moves of 2 as possible. In this case we make 5 moves of 2, as indicated (Figure 16).

Because arrays are extensively used in multiplication, they are a natural way to deepen a child's understanding of division. For example, to solve the pencil problem the pupil could be guided to the following method. We interpret the problem as a 2 × 5 array (Figure 17). Not only can the original problem be answered, but the pupil can be led to see that:

If 2 × 5 = 10, then there are 2 sets of five in 10.
Also if 5 × 2 = 10, then there are 5 sets of two in 10.

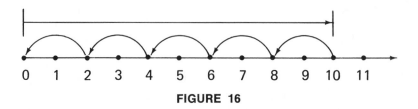

FIGURE 16

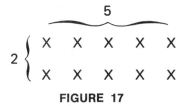

FIGURE 17

Thus the child is provided with an intuitive notion of the relationship between division and multiplication. Hopefully, he will realize, at a later date, that if he knows the multiplication facts, he also knows the division facts.

The activities we have discussed thus far can be classified as readiness activities. Their sole purpose is to provide a child with meaningful experiences that are analogous to division. Therefore, in the early stages of development (first and second grade) there is no need to introduce abstract symbolism like the sentence 12 ÷ 3 = □. Once a basic understanding of the division process has been acquired through activities similar to those above, the division symbolism can be introduced.

We can now concentrate on the establishment of the basic division facts and the relationship between multiplication and division. When a child first encounters a sentence like 16 ÷ 4 = □, he should be asked to give a verbal interpretation of it. For instance, the pupil may say "If 16 sheets of paper are to be divided among 4 boys, how many sheets should each get?" Also, it may be necessary for him to rely on such aids as concrete objects, or a number line for a solution. For example 16 ÷ 4 = □ could be solved as shown in Figure 18. The 16 is represented by the line from 0 to 16, and the repeated subtraction of 4 is indicated with four moves, thus, 16 ÷ 4 = 4.

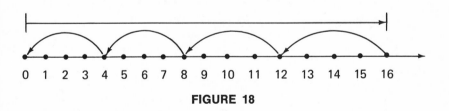

FIGURE 18

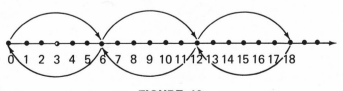

FIGURE 19

After developmental experience such as that given above, the teacher should begin to compare multiplication and division in terms of inverse operations. This can be an outgrowth of the use of the number line (Figure 19). The upper part of the number line illustrates that $3 \times 6 = 18$, and the lower portion shows that $18 \div 6 = 3$. This also shows that multiplying by 6 can be "undone" by dividing by 6.

This introduction should be followed by practicing simultaneously with multiplication and division. The following exercises can provide this needed practice:

(1) Since $2 \times 4 = 8$, we know that $8 \div 4 = \square$.
(2) $\square \times 4 = 12$ and $12 \div 4 = \square$.
(3) We know that $24 \div 6 = \square$ because $4 \times 6 = 24$.
(4) If $6 \times 7 = 42$, we know that $42 \div 6 = 7$ and $42 \div 7 = 6$.

It should be stressed again that it is not unusual for a child to use set partitioning or the number line as an aid to a solution. In fact, this should be encouraged over the alternative of sheer rote learning.

There is a span of time between the development of basic facts and the learning of a standard algorism for division. This stage of a child's learning must be devoted to acquiring the ability to give instant answers to basic division questions. As was indicated previously for the other arithmetic operations, understanding is necessary for learning, but it is not sufficient. There are many techniques for arriving at this level of mastery, limited only by the teacher's ingenuity. We have discussed several of these methods in previous sections.

Properties of Division

We have found the operations of multiplication and addition to be closed over the set of natural numbers. (If we operate on any two natural numbers, we obtain a natural number.) Division and subtraction, on the other hand, do not have this property. It is possible to find many pairs of natural numbers that when divided will derive a natural number—for example, $4 \div 2 = 2$, $15 \div 5 = 3$, and so on. However, if we should choose $7 \div 3$, the answer is $2\frac{1}{2}$, which is not a natural number. It stands to reason, then, that division is possible within the entire set; it just is not closed with respect to the natural numbers.

Neither the commutative nor the associative property applies to the division of natural numbers. We need only exhibit a counter example to illustrate this.

1. Since $14 \div 7 \neq 7 \div 14$, it follows that division is not commutative.
2. It also follows, from the fact that $(48 \div 6) \div 2 \neq 48 \div (6 \div 2)$, that the associative property does not hold.

Again, as in the other operations, 1 and 0 have special characteristics. We can find by experimentation that any natural number divided by 1 is that natural number: $N \div 1 = N$. Since $1 \div N \neq N$, we cannot label 1 the identity element for division.

Zero poses two different problems, depending upon whether or not it is the divisor or the dividend. If we consider examples like $0 \div 4$, we soon discover the answer is 0. Furthermore, if N does not equal zero, $0 \div N = 0$, since $0 \times N = 0$.

Now we look at $0 \div 0 = \square$. We must find one natural N, such that $0 \times N = 0$. But no matter what number we substitute for N the product is 0. Thus, we cannot find a unique solution for $0 \div 0$.

Finally we investigate $6 \div 0 = \square$. That is, we must find a natural number such that $0 \times \square = 6$. This, of course, is impossible, since any number multiplied by zero is 0. Hence, we cannot divide by zero.

Division Algorism

Once the basic division facts have been established, we can develop an algorism that will enable us to find any other quotients. Our first concern should be the review of place value and multiplication by 10, 20, 30, 40, 50 and so on. Then we can proceed with problems that involve single-digit divisors and multiple-digit dividends.

Division problems should be presented as answers to arithmetic questions, or the pupil should interpret arithmetic sentences into questions. This will help him keep in mind the real meaning of division while he is learning an algorism. Consider the problem:

There are 65 boxes of apples to be loaded on a truck by 5 boys. If each boy is to load the same number of boxes, how many should each carry to the truck?

The answer to the question can be found by solving the division sentence:

$$65 \div 5 = \square.$$

We could, of course, rely on repeated subtraction:

$$
\begin{array}{ll}
65 & 30 \\
-5 \quad (1) & -5 \quad (1) \\
\hline
60 & 25 \\
-5 \quad (1) & -5 \quad (1) \\
\hline
55 & 20 \\
-5 \quad (1) & -5 \quad (1) \\
\hline
50 & 15 \\
-5 \quad (1) & -5 \quad (1) \\
\hline
45 & 10 \\
-5 \quad (1) & -5 \quad (1) \\
\hline
40 & 5 \\
-5 \quad (1) & -5 \quad (1) \\
\hline
35 & 0 \\
-5 \quad (1) & \\
\hline
30 &
\end{array}
$$

Here we are merely making each boy responsible for only one box at a time. However, at this stage of the child's development, he is able to recognize that we can immediately say each boy must carry at least 10 boxes of apples.

$$
\begin{array}{r}
5\overline{)65} \\
50 \qquad 10 \times 5 \\
\hline
15
\end{array}
$$

There are 15 boxes left to carry. If we give each boy 3 more each, the task is complete.

$$
\begin{array}{r}
5\overline{)65} \\
-50 \qquad 10 \times 5 \\
\hline
15 \\
-15 \qquad 3 \times 5 \\
\hline
0 \qquad 13 \times 5 = 65
\end{array}
$$

Through such interpretations we are leading the child to the realization that we are still using the "removal of equivalent sets" as a basis for division. Only now we remove more than one set at a time and record the number removed (the quotient).

To facilitate the acquisition of the standard division algorism it is suggested that the estimated quotients be written above the dividend. This notation also makes use of the child's ability to multiply by multiples of 10 and his knowledge of the decimal numeration system. For example a pupil may use the following process for solving a problem: $168 \div 8 = \square$. He knows that $8 \times 10 = 80$, which is less than 168. This leaves 88 members of the original set to be partitioned. He may realize another set of 10 can be removed. The conclusion will be obvious:

$$
\begin{array}{r}
1 \\
10 \\
10 \\
\hline
8)\overline{168} \\
80 \\
\hline
88 \\
80 \\
\hline
8
\end{array}
\quad
\begin{array}{l}
\\
10 + 10 + 10 = 21 \\
\text{or 21 sets of 8 is 168} \\
\\
8 \times 10 \\
\\
8 \times 10 \\
8 \times 1
\end{array}
$$

It should be emphasized that the division problem must be presented in story form at the early stages, and the answer should be related to the story.

By considering the following problem and its solution, it can be easily seen that the child has grasped the concept behind the algorism and only needs to be pushed in the direction of a more efficient method of solving the problem.

$$
\begin{array}{r}
5 \\
10 \\
10 \\
10 \\
10 \\
10 \\
\hline
7)\overline{385} \\
-70 \\
\hline
315 \\
-70 \\
\hline
245 \\
-70 \\
\hline
175 \\
-70 \\
\hline
105 \\
-70 \\
\hline
35 \\
-35 \\
\hline
0
\end{array}
\quad
\begin{array}{l}
\\
\\
10 + 10 + 10 + 10 + 10 + 5 = 55 \\
\\
\\
\\
\\
7 \times 10 \\
\\
7 \times 10 \\
\\
7 \times 10 \\
\\
7 \times 10 \\
\\
7 \times 10 \\
\\
7 \times 5
\end{array}
$$

The problem should be solved and discussed in terms of the number of tens used. The child will see that 7 tens and 7 tens is the same as (7 times 2) tens; 7 tens, 7 tens, and 7 tens is the same as (7 times 3) tens, and so forth. Eventually we arrive at:

$$
\begin{array}{r}
5 \\
50 \\
\hline
7)\overline{385} \\
-\ 350 \\
\hline
35 \\
-\ 35 \\
\hline
\end{array}
\qquad
\begin{array}{l}
\\
50 + 5 \\
\\
7 \times 50 \\
\\
7 \times 5
\end{array}
$$

Mastery of this process will be evident when the children's mental "guesses" become more accurate. At this time we may advance to four-, five-, and six-digit dividends and a more systematic form of estimating the partial quotients. This process will probably have been employed by a number of pupils already. For example, when presented with $6)\overline{3534}$ we want the pupils to work as follows:

Step 1:

$6 \times 10\ \ \ = 60$, but since 60 is less than 3534 we try again.
$6 \times 100\ = 600$. This is also less than 3534.
$6 \times 1000 = 6000$. This is greater than 3534. We conclude that the answer is in hundreds.

Step 2:

Continuing on this basis, the first estimates would be in hundreds:

$$
\begin{array}{ll}
6 \times 400 = 2400 & 2400 < 3534 \\
6 \times 500 = 3000 & 3000 < 3534 \\
6 \times 600 = 3600 & 3600 > 3534
\end{array}
$$

Thus, the child may conclude that 500 is the first partial quotient.

$$
\begin{array}{r}
500 \\
\hline
6)\overline{3534} \\
3000 \\
\hline
534
\end{array}
\qquad 6 \times 500
$$

Step 3:

$$6 \times 10 \ = 60 \qquad 60 < 534$$
$$6 \times 100 = 600 \qquad 600 > 534$$

Thus, the next partial quotient is in the tens.

Step 4:

$$6 \times 10 = 60 \qquad 60 < 534$$
$$6 \times 20 = 120 \qquad 120 < 534$$
$$6 \times 30 = 180 \qquad 180 < 534$$
$$6 \times 40 = 240 \qquad 240 < 534$$
$$6 \times 80 = 480 \qquad 480 < 534$$
$$6 \times 90 = 540 \qquad 540 > 534$$

Hence, the next partial quotient is 80.

$$
\begin{array}{r}
80 \\
500 \\
\hline
6)\overline{3534} \\
3000 \\
\hline
534 \\
480 \qquad 6 \times 80 \\
\hline
54
\end{array}
$$

Step 5:

The child would continue as he had in the previous steps to arrive at:

$$
\begin{array}{r}
9 \\
80 \qquad 500 + 80 + 9 = 589 \\
500 \\
\hline
6)\overline{3534} \\
-\ 3000 \qquad 6 \times 500 \\
\hline
534 \\
-\ 480 \qquad 6 \times 80 \\
\hline
54 \\
-\ 54 \qquad 6 \times 9 \\
\hline
\end{array}
$$

The most difficult aspect of learning the division algorism arises when we first encounter two-digit divisors. It is for this reason that introduction to division should be made with divisors and dividends that are multiples of 10. Since the child has a good understanding of multiplying by 10, this is an easier transition. It is also recommended that the work be begun with problems that result in a single-digit quotient, such as:

$$\begin{array}{r} 6 \\ 30\overline{)180} \\ -\,180 \end{array}$$

Pupils should relate this to multiplication problems they have already solved:

$$(3 \times 6\,) \times 10 = 18 \times 10$$
$$= 180$$

Once the above process is mastered, problems in which two-, three-, and four-digit quotients appear should be presented, as in the following:

(a)

$$\begin{array}{r} 1 \\ 10 \\ 50\overline{)550} \\ -\,500 \\ \hline 50 \\ -\,50 \\ \hline 0 \end{array} \qquad \begin{array}{l} 10 + 1 \\ \\ 50 \times 10 \\ \\ 50 \times 1 \end{array}$$

(b)

$$\begin{array}{r} 4 \\ 20 \\ 60\overline{)1440} \\ 1200 \\ \hline 240 \\ -\,240 \end{array} \qquad \begin{array}{l} 20 + 4 \\ \\ (60 \times 2) \times 10 \\ \\ 60 \times 4 \end{array}$$

These division exercises and their associated multiplication interpretations are a means by which estimating a quotient can be introduced.

When the pupils have mastered single-digit divisors and two-digit divisors that are multiples of 10, we can confront them with the following type of example:

$$37\overline{)286}$$

In such a problem the pupil would be expected to estimate the quotient. Obviously there are possibilities of under- and over-estimating this quotient. Thus the pupil should be reminded, if necessary, of the method first used to arrive at partial quotients. The solution to the above may appear as:

1. If we round 37 to 40, we may think $40 \times 7 = 280$. Therefore, the partial quotient is 7. (The remainder is indicated by "REM.")

$$
\begin{array}{r}
7 \\
37\overline{)286} \\
259 \\
\hline
27
\end{array}
\qquad
\begin{array}{l}
\\
\\
37 \times 7 \\
\textbf{REM}
\end{array}
$$

2. If the pupil had desired to round 37 to 30, he may have estimated the partial quotient to be 9, since $30 \times 9 = 270$. However, this proves to be too large, and a new partial quotient must be tried.
3. If the estimate proves to be too small, there is no reason to rework the entire problem. The remedy is merely to continue working the problems. Estimations will eventually get better.

$$
\begin{array}{r}
4 \\
37\overline{)286} \\
148 \\
\hline
138 \\
-\ 74 \\
\hline
64 \\
-\ 37 \\
\hline
27
\end{array}
\qquad
\begin{array}{l}
\\
\\
4 \times 37 \\
\\
2 \times 37 \\
\\
1 \times 37 \\
\textbf{REM}
\end{array}
$$

Once we have established a relatively solid grasp of the estimation idea, we can proceed to problems that not only have two-digit divisors but also produce multiple-digit quotients. We should use a procedure that parallels the one just described for single-digit divisors.

(a)

$$
\begin{array}{r}
5 \\
20 \\
100 \\
38\overline{)4764} \\
-\ 3800 \\
\hline
964 \\
760 \\
\hline
204 \\
190 \\
\hline
-\ 14
\end{array}
\qquad
\begin{array}{l}
\\
\\
\\
\\
38 \times 100 \\
\\
38 \times 20 \\
\\
38 \times 5 \\
14\ \text{REM}
\end{array}
$$

(*b*)

```
          5
         30
        500
       7000
   46)346745
    - 322000        (46 × 7) × 1000
      24745
      23000        (46 × 5) × 100
       1745
       1380        (46 × 3) × 10
        365
```

The extension of this division algorism should be a repeated use of the development thus far. This extension poses only one new problem worthy of mention, and that is a quotient that contains a zero. However, it is possible to handle the problem before the concept is developed if some caution is exercised.

```
          5
        600
   24)14520
    - 14400
        120        24 × 600
      - 120        24 ×   5
          0
```

Our ultimate goal, of course, is to have the child use the adult form of the algorism, such as:

```
        117
   36)4234
       36
       63
       36
      274
      252
       22 REM
```

Basically we have only a few necessary refinements to make on the algorism we are presently using. We need only make the multiplication, which appears at the right of all the examples used thus far, a mental process.

With all the exercises used to develop the present algorism, it is likely that this has already been done by most of the children. We must also concentrate the quotient on a single line. This can be accomplished by using a place-value chart in working a number of exercises, as follows:

(a)

	T	H	T	O	
			9	7	
48)4	6	7	9	
4	3	2	0	
	3	5	9	
	3	3	6	
		2	3	REM

(b)

TT	T	H	T	O	
		2	8	4	
98)2	7	8	8	3	
1	9	6	0	0	
	8	2	8	3	
	7	8	4	0	
	4	4	3	
	3	9	2	
		5	1	REM

The elimination of the zeros (see arrows) is usually required by most teachers. Such a refinement may be explained to the better students, but there is no reason to confuse those who will not benefit from it.

Chapter 4

TEACHING POSITIVE RATIONAL NUMBERS AND DECIMAL NOTATION

Rational Numbers

As we have noted, whole numbers are not closed with respect to division; that is, there is no whole number that can be used to replace the box in $4 \div 3 = \square$ and make it a true statement. Some new type of number is needed to correct this deficiency. Such needs give rise to numbers like 3/4, 2/3, 1 1/2, or the rational numbers. Mathematically we define a rational number as any number that can be put in the form of a/b, where a and b are whole numbers and $b \neq 0$. In the following discussion we will use the terms "rational number" and "fraction" interchangeably.

In developing fractions, the teacher must keep in mind the fact that they can represent any of four different situations. As is the case with many topics in mathematics, we must make the child aware of the interpretation with which we are working. A fraction is most commonly thought of as indicating a certain part of the whole, for example, 1/2 cup sugar, 3/4 of the pie, and so on. In this interpretation the bottom number indicates the parts into which the whole has been divided, and the top number indicates the number of these parts being referred to (Figure 1).

We can also think of a fraction as one of the equal parts of a set or group. This interpretation is necessary to answer such questions as:

If three children divide two candy bars equally among themselves, what part of a candy bar will each get?

As shown in Figure 2, each girl would, of course, receive 2/3 of the candy.

The third way to think of a fraction is as an indicator of division. For

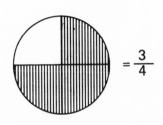

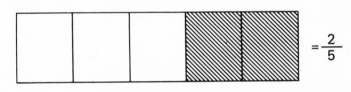

FIGURE 1

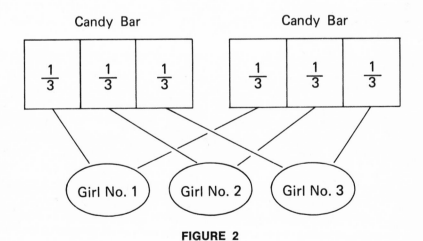

FIGURE 2

example, we can rewrite 7/8 as 7 ÷ 8.   We can also use fractions to express ratios, the fourth way they can be used.   For example, if James receives $5 for a job and Hank receives $10, we say Hank got twice as much money as James.   We could also say that James got 1/2 as much as Hank.   In ratio form we would say Hank has $2 for every $1 James has. This is expressed in fractional form as 2/1 or as 2:1 in ratio form.   Again we could take this situation from James's point of view and say "James has $1 for every $2 Hank has."   We would write 1/2 and 1:2 as the fractional and ratio representations, respectively.

Notation

A fraction such as 3/8 is made up of two terms: the 3 is the numerator and the 8 is the denominator.   The denominator is the name of the fraction and indicates the number of equivalent units into which the original set or unit has been divided.   The numerator is the number of the fraction and designates the number of the equivalent units to be considered. Thus the fraction 3/8 represents three parts of eight equivalent pieces (Figure 3).

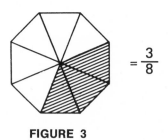

FIGURE 3

An *improper fraction* is a fraction that is equal to or greater than 1 (4/3, 6/6, 27/4).

A *proper fraction* is less than 1.

A *unit fraction* is any fraction whose numerator is 1.

Like fractions are fractions with the same denominator.

Unlike fractions have different denominators.

As long as we think of a fraction as being a rational number, we must clarify the term *mixed number*.   In the mixed number 5 3/8, for example, we do not use this term because we believe 5 and 3/8 are not rational. Obviously, 3/8 is a rational number, and, after inspection, we see that 5 can be written as 5/1.   Thus it too is a rational number.   (In fact all whole numbers are rationals.) The real reason for the term "mixed number" is the mode in which the numbers are written. That is, we have written one in rational form and the other in whole-number form.

Properties of Fractions

The rational numbers of arithmetic are closed with respect to addition, division (except by 0), and multiplication. However, as was true for the whole numbers, the positive rational numbers of arithmetic are not closed with respect to the operation of subtraction, as illustrated in the following example:

$$\frac{3}{5} - \frac{6}{5} = -\frac{3}{5}.$$

The commutative and associative properties are valid for both addition and multiplication. We can readily conclude from the example,

$$\frac{3}{4} - \frac{2}{4} = \frac{1}{4} \quad \text{and} \quad \frac{2}{4} - \frac{3}{4} = -\frac{1}{4}, \quad \text{thus} \quad \frac{3}{4} - \frac{2}{4} \neq \frac{2}{4} - \frac{3}{4},$$

that subtraction of rational numbers is not commutative. The following example demonstrates that with rational numbers, division, too, is not commutative:

$$\frac{5}{7} \div \frac{3}{5} = \frac{25}{21} \quad \text{and} \quad \frac{3}{5} \div \frac{5}{7} = \frac{21}{25}, \quad \text{thus} \quad \frac{5}{7} \div \frac{3}{5} \neq \frac{3}{5} \div \frac{5}{7}.$$

We can conclude that multiplication with fractions is distributive over addition and that division is not distributive over addition.

The additive identity for the rational numbers is $0/1$; it is customary to write it as 0, which is, of course, a rational number. The multiplicative identity is 1. However, it may appear as $1/1$, $2/2$, $3/3$, and so on.

There is one additional property of the rational numbers of arithmetic —the multiplicative inverse property, or reciprocal property. This simply refers to the situation where the product of two numbers is 1. For example: $3/4 \times 4/3 = 1$. In the example we say that $3/4$ is the inverse of $4/3$ or that $3/4$ is the reciprocal of $4/3$. In general, if $a/b \times b/a = 1$, then we say that a/b and b/a are inverses of each other. It is true that every rational number except 0 has an inverse. Does every whole number have an inverse? Does any whole number have an inverse?

Obviously these properties, excluding the latter, are identical with those discussed in relation to the set of whole numbers. Therefore, the method of presentation is not repeated here. One need only be conscious of the strategies used in their original presentation and the fact that we have merely enlarged the set of elements being encompassed by the properties.

Concept Formation

No child comes to school "concept free," so to speak, with reference to fractions. He has been exposed to such expressions as "half a candy bar," "half a dollar," and "half a glass." But it is sometimes the case that the child has a misconception of half. It may mean "part of" as far as he is concerned. This is apparent when a child says, "My half of the cookie is smaller than his." Thus the teacher needs to provide a rich environment in which erroneous ideas may be dispelled and correct concepts strengthened. It is also necessary, at this time, to build the vocabulary and symbols that will be used in the future development of the operations with fractions.

In the primary grades teachers should concentrate on a concrete development of the concept of a fraction. This development will normally begin in kindergarten or first grade with the fractions 1/2, 1/4, 1/3, and so on. After considerable work with the unit fractions as one part of a whole, other fractions like 2/3, 3/7, and so on are introduced. As mentioned above, the child's notion of half sometimes allows for different-sized halves of the same item. Therefore, we must be very careful, in our introduction of fractional parts, to correct this idea. To accomplish this, we must select our examples so the child is always working with congruent elements or segments. For the child this would mean the elements were the "same," or exactly alike.

Thus in developing the concept of fractions it may be unwise to use items like an apple to demonstrate fractional parts. Since an apple cannot be cut into congruent pieces, its use to teach halves most likely will be quite misleading. Not only must selection of concrete objects be scrutinized,

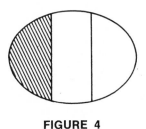

FIGURE 4

but the pictorial aids selected must also convey the correct idea. For example, the Figure 4 line drawing would be a poor choice to illustrate thirds.

The foundation activities should initially be concerned with dividing a whole into parts. The child must be presented with models of halves, thirds, and so on. He must understand that the fraction gets its name (halves, fourth, and so forth) from the number of congruent segments or equivalent subsets. The child may model these numbers by folding or cutting paper into parts, as shown in Figure 5, to illustrate the partitioning

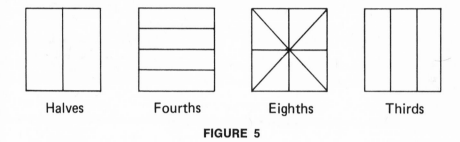

Halves   Fourths   Eighths   Thirds

FIGURE 5

of a whole or a unit. He must also be familiar with dividing a given set of objects into equivalent subsets, such as dividing a set of six checkers into 2 equivalent subsets in order to model halves. In Figure 6 the dotted line indicates a physical move.

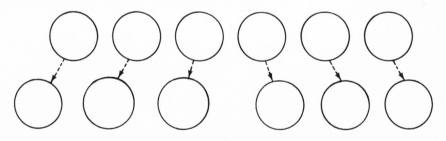

FIGURE 6

Another model that can be used very effectively in developing fractional numbers is the set of Cuisenaire rods. The child begins by selecting one rod as a unit. He is then asked to place rods of equal lengths end to end so that they cover the "unit" rod. As with the other models, he relates the number of parts with a fractional name (Figure 7).

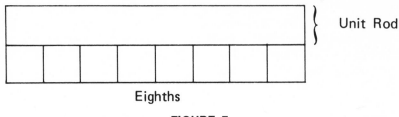

Eighths

FIGURE 7

It should be noted here that a child can inadvertently be allowed to draw a false conclusion about fractional parts. He may be falsely led to believe that halves, thirds, and so forth must always be the same size. For example, he may think that if, in the figure on the left in Figure 8, the shaded portion represents a half, then the shaded portion in the figure on the right must also be a half, since they are of the same size.

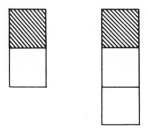

FIGURE 8

To correct or avoid this idea, pupils could be presented with pieces of paper of varying sizes and instructed to cut them in half. Once completed, they can compare their halves with one another. Of course, the sizes will be different. Through discussion, it should be agreed that they are all halves and that the reason they differ in size (possibly shape too) is that they are from different units. This type of activity should be repeated with the introduction of all fractions, halves, thirds, fourths, and so on.

Once a child becomes familiar with how fractions are named, the teacher should endeavor to strengthen these ideas through more challenging activities. Pupils could be presented with rectangular- and square-shaped paper and asked to demonstrate as many different models for a given fraction as they can. For example, they might discover the means of folding paper to illustrate fourths that is shown in Figure 9.

When it comes to reinforcement of the concept, fractions pose no exception to the need for practice. The development of the fraction concept should be accompanied by activities designed to be instructive as well as diagnostic. For example, the exercise shown in Figure 10 could be pre-

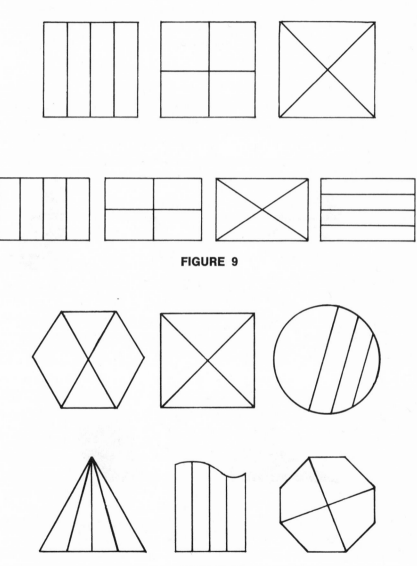

FIGURE 9

FIGURE 10

sented to the child with these instructions: "Place a check by those pictures that show fourths." From activities of this nature and the accompanying discussion, we can discover if the child has the true concept of fractions. That is, does he merely check any figure with four pieces, or does he look for equivalent segments?

After developing an understanding of fractional parts such as halves and fourths, the child should be ready to identify fractional parts of a whole. The following are some possible activities and a suggested order in which they might be presented.

(1) Circle the picture that illustrates one half (1/2) in Figure 11. (Both the word form and the fractional numeral should accompany the instruction.)

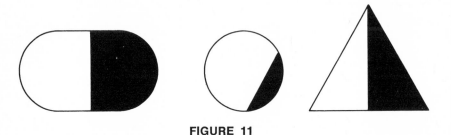

FIGURE 11

(2) Circle the fractional numeral that is represented by the shaded area.

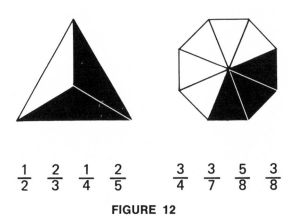

$$\frac{1}{2} \quad \frac{2}{3} \quad \frac{1}{4} \quad \frac{2}{5} \qquad \frac{3}{4} \quad \frac{3}{7} \quad \frac{5}{8} \quad \frac{3}{8}$$

FIGURE 12

It should be noted that in none of the learning aids previously employed (paper folding, cutting paper, counters) does the child make use of any fractional numbers. Until now we have been primarily concerned with developing relationships that will hold for fractional numbers as well as for the concrete situations he has observed.

(3) Write the fractional numeral that will name the fraction represented by the shaded portion of the figure.

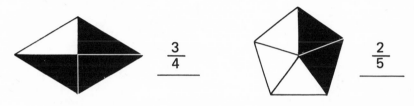

FIGURE 13

After the three exercises above, the child should be able to represent the basic fraction through the use of physical aids or geometric figures when presented with a fractional numeral. Using Figure 14, he should be asked to illustrate the fraction 3/5 by shading in the appropriate portion.

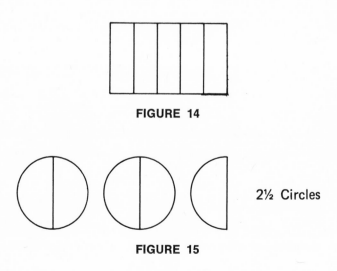

FIGURE 14

2½ Circles

FIGURE 15

As soon as the child has acquired the understanding necessary to perform this task, he should be introduced to fractional numbers greater than 1. These fractions are easily introduced with cutouts similar to those in Figure 15. The child first sees the circles as shown and is asked how many circles he sees. Once an answer (2 1/2) is elicited, the parts are separated as shown in Figure 16. He is now told to count the equivalent parts. He may count 1/2, 2/2, 3/2, 4/2, 5/2, to arrive at his answers. Similar exercises for other fractional parts will be needed to develop this concept.

We can further illustrate this operation by using a number line to show the equivalence, as in Figure 17. Similarly, in Figure 18, we can find

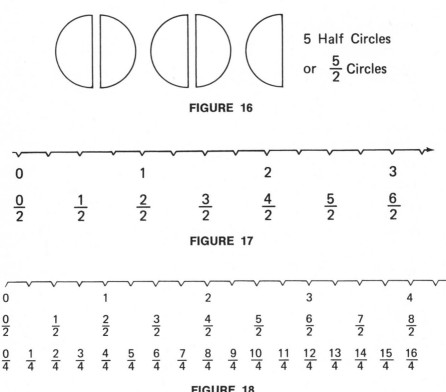

FIGURE 16

FIGURE 17

FIGURE 18

improper fractions equivalent to 3 3/4. By extensive use of the number line the child should be able to change a mixed fraction to an improper fraction and an improper fraction to a mixed number. For example:

$$3\frac{3}{4} = 3 + \frac{3}{4}$$

$$= \frac{12}{4} + \frac{3}{4}$$

$$= \frac{12 + 3}{4}$$

$$= \frac{15}{4}.$$

$$3\frac{3}{4} = \frac{(3 \times 4) + 3}{4}$$

$$= \frac{12 + 3}{4}.$$

$$\frac{15}{4} = \frac{12}{4} + \frac{3}{4}$$

$$= 3 + \frac{3}{4}$$

$$= 3\frac{3}{4}.$$

Equivalent Fractions

The advent of modern mathematics has brought a new interest in vocabulary. Two words that have caused considerable discussion are "equal" and "equivalent." There are no real gains to be made by concerning ourselves with these differences, however, since the only symbol used is that of equality. For instance in $3/4 = 6/8$, we really mean $3/4$ is equivalent to $6/8$, but we still use the equals symbol. The primary concern is that a child realizes he can rename a fractional number with many different symbols: $1/2 = 2/4 = 3/6 = 4/8. \ldots$

Many of the aids can be adapted to developing the concept of equivalent fractions. The number line has already been discussed in this respect. Blocks, checkers, strips of paper, and many other materials can be used in this development. Since their uses are similar, we will discuss the procedure in terms of only one visual aid.

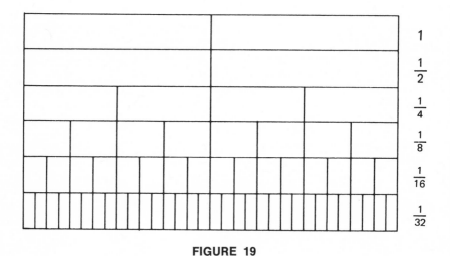

FIGURE 19

Again, the Cuisenaire rods provide a meaningful way to develop the concept of equality. In developing the concept of equivalent fractions we should also be developing a foundation for comparing fractional numbers. This is accomplished by comparing the number of each unit required to cover another. Thus the pupils can conclude many equivalents from the construction shown in Figure 19:

$$\frac{1}{2} = \frac{2}{4} = \frac{4}{8} = \frac{8}{16} \quad \text{and so on,}$$

$$1 = \frac{2}{2} = \frac{8}{8} = \frac{16}{16} \quad \text{and so on.}$$

The child should now be asked to divide the unit rod into thirds, fourths, fifths, and so forth. From these experiences he should be able to generalize that $1 = 1/1 = 2/2 = 3/3 = n/n$ and that it is possible to change any fraction into another equivalent fraction. Not only should he make these generalizations, he should be encouraged to make other interpretations from the table. He should observe that it takes 2 halves to make a whole, 2 fourths to make a half, 4 sixteenths to make a fourth, etc. Once he understands these relationships, he may reason, "Since it takes 2 sixteenths to make an eighth, then it must take 14 sixteenths to make seven eighths." More concisely, since $2/16 = 1/8$, then $7/8 = 2/16 + 2/16 + 2/16 + 2/16 + 2/16 + 2/16 + 2/16$. After the child is able to use this form of logic we can extend the idea to,

$$\frac{7}{8} = \frac{7 \times 2}{8 \times 2} = \frac{14}{16}.$$

Now, using a process similar to the above, the child is able to represent a given fraction in terms of another. He need only determine relationships between the fractional parts in the question and proceed. The pupils can now be confronted with a problem like:

$$\frac{3}{5} = \frac{?}{10} \quad \text{or} \quad \frac{8}{16} = \frac{?}{8}.$$

In this example, the task is to replace the question mark with the whole number that will make the fractions equivalent.

Finally, the child would be expected to arrive at the following generalization: "If we multiply or divide the numerator and denominator by the same nonzero number, the result is a fraction that is equivalent to the original fraction." Thus, he might figure:

$$\text{If } n \neq 0, \quad \text{then} \quad \frac{a}{b} = \frac{an}{bn}.$$

Once division and multiplication of fractional numbers have been developed, the above generalization can be interpreted as a result of the multiplication identity: $(n \times 1 = 1 \times n = n)$. It would also be of future value to stress the special property 1 has with respect to division: $n \div 1 = n$.

Ordering Fractions

The pupils have already been introduced to relative size of two fractions. Through physical comparisons they are able to name the larger or smaller fraction. It is readily seen from Figure 20, for example, that 2/5 is greater than 1/3. This fact can also be demonstrated on the number line, as in Figure 21. Because of his previous experience the child finds this form of comparison relatively easy. The real problem arises when this method is no longer practical.

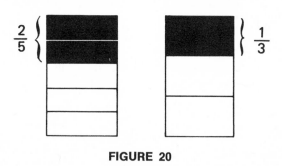

FIGURE 20

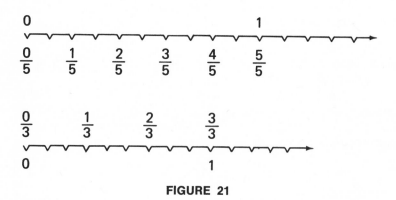

FIGURE 21

The pupils are already capable of abstractly comparing unit fractions like 1/4 and 1/7. They have generalized as follows: "The larger the denominator of a unit fraction, the smaller the fraction." It follows from this that to compare fractions of like denominator, they need only look at the numerator. The fraction with the greater numerator is the larger fraction:

$$\frac{3}{4} > \frac{1}{4} \qquad \frac{21}{37} < \frac{23}{37}.$$

When the numerators are the same, the task is also simple. Since there is the same number of different-sized subsets, pupils need only look at the size of the subsets (denominators):

$$\frac{7}{18} < \frac{7}{8} \qquad \frac{47}{123} > \frac{47}{465}.$$

These examples demonstrate the fact that any two fractions can be immediately compared if they have either like denominators or like numerators. The former method is most prevalent in elementary textbooks, but this should not rule out using both methods. It is obvious, however, that the child should know one method thoroughly before he is introduced to the other.

When asked which fraction is greater, 7/8 or 9/16, the pupil should proceed as follows:

$$\frac{7}{8} = \frac{?}{16} \quad \text{or} \quad \frac{7}{8} = \frac{7 \times 2}{8 \times 2} = \frac{14}{16}.$$

Since 7/8 = 14/16, then 7/8 > 9/16.

In the upper elementary grades it is possible to develop a more efficient means of ordering fractions, a method that relies on the fact that it is only necessary to check numerators if the denominators are the same. Now the child has had considerable experience ordering by this method, so if he is given the fractions 11/17 and 10/17 he immediately knows which is larger or smaller. If confronted with 6/17 and 9/19 he would first change them to like denominators, as follows:

$$\frac{6}{17} = \frac{6}{17} \times \frac{19}{19} = \frac{114}{17 \times 19} \qquad \frac{9}{19} = \frac{9}{19} \times \frac{17}{17} = \frac{153}{19 \times 17}$$

He would then conclude that 9/19 is the greater without evaluating the denominators, since he knows they will be the same. Once he understands this shortcut he can reason: "If 14/21 is going to be greater than 11/19, then when they are changed to like denominator the numerator of the fraction equivalent to 14/21 must be larger than that of the fraction equivalent to 11/19. If 14/21 > 11/19, then

$$\frac{14 \times 19}{21 \times 19} > \frac{11 \times 21}{21 \times 19},"$$

However, since he need only check the numerator, he may conclude: "If 14/21 > 11/19, then 14 × 19 > 11 × 21." He would check by noting $14 \times 19 = 266$ and $21 \times 11 = 231$. Thus $14/21$ is indeed greater than $11/19$.

Addition of Fractions

The introduction of the addition of fractions is best served by depending on materials such as the number line, Cuisenaire rods, and partitioned discs. It has been found to be far easier to first develop the concept of addition of fractions with those fractions that have like denominators and then proceed to other cases. To illustrate this development we will consider the solution of several open sentences by these methods. The first is illustrated in Figure 22, using paper or felt cutouts, and the second with a number line in Figure 23.

$$(a)\ \frac{1}{3} + \frac{1}{3} = \square.$$

$$(b)\ \frac{1}{5} + \frac{2}{5} = \square.$$

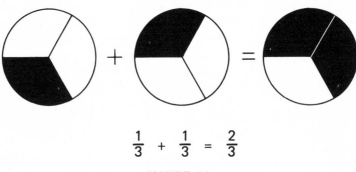

$$\frac{1}{3} + \frac{1}{3} = \frac{2}{3}$$

FIGURE 22

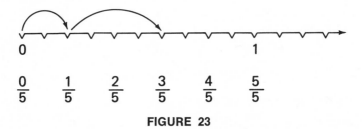

FIGURE 23

By using these interpretations of addition of fractions we can establish the concept of a sum as it pertains to fractions. Therefore, by using an aid, the sum of 5/7 and 4/7 can be found. To avoid difficulties it is advisable to write out the denominators in word form at this stage.

$$\frac{3}{8} + \frac{7}{8} = \square.$$

$$\begin{array}{r} 3 \text{ eighths} \\ + \ 7 \text{ eighths} \\ \hline \end{array}$$

Thus the child may think, "If I add eighths to eighths, then 3 eighths plus 7 eighths is 10 eighths." This is also a prelude to the notion that we must add the same "things" together.

Obviously we cannot work indefinitely with concrete aids. A more efficient computational skill is needed. After a child experiences a number of these examples with aids, he should conclude that when we add fractions with like denominators, we merely find the sum of the numerators and use the common denominator, such as:

$$\frac{2}{11} + \frac{3}{11} = \frac{5}{11}.$$

We now need only be concerned with the addition of fractions with unlike denominators. Since the child has already grasped addition of like fractions and is able to change unlike fractions to equivalent fractions, the task is somewhat simplified. We need only transform the fraction to like denominators and add as before. It may be found to be useful to accompany this development with pictorial interpretation. (See pgs. 110 & 111.)

$$(a) \ \frac{3}{5} + \frac{3}{10} = \square. \quad \text{(Figure 24)}$$

$$(b) \ \frac{1}{2} + \frac{1}{4} = \square. \quad \text{(Figure 25)}$$

Eventually the child should be encouraged to abandon the use of the aids and rely on an algorism. There is, of course, no one algorism for this operation. He might proceed as follows:

$$\frac{3}{4} + \frac{7}{20} = \frac{3 \times 5}{4 \times 5} + \frac{7}{20}$$

$$= \frac{15}{20} + \frac{7}{20}$$

$$= \frac{22}{20}.$$

Since $22/20 = (11 \times 2)/10 \times 2)$, we can rewrite it in the equivalent form of $11/10$ or $1\ 1/10$.

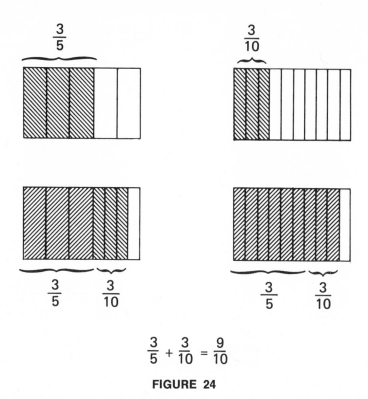

$$\frac{3}{5} + \frac{3}{10} = \frac{9}{10}$$

FIGURE 24

The algorism discussed thus far will take care of all addition of fractions. Both improper and proper fractions can be adopted to this approach. If the number should appear in mixed form, the child has the capability of performing the needed addition.

$$2\frac{1}{3} + 3\frac{1}{4} = \frac{7}{3} + \frac{13}{4}$$

$$= \frac{7 \times 4}{3 \times 4} + \frac{13 \times 3}{4 \times 3}$$

$$= \frac{28}{12} + \frac{39}{12}$$

$$= \frac{67}{12}$$

$$= 5\frac{7}{12}.$$

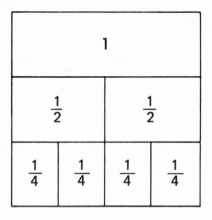

$$\frac{1}{2} + \frac{1}{4} = \frac{2}{4} + \frac{1}{4} = \frac{3}{4}$$

FIGURE 25

As can be seen, this method is somewhat cumbersome. It also presents many opportunities for pupil errors. Since the objective is to teach the child a new concept, the teacher should attempt to reduce the complexity and draw on the past experiences of the child. Thus it is suggested that addition problems presented in mixed form should be handled similarly to whole-number addition in vertical form.

$$47\frac{3}{5} + 65\frac{2}{15}$$

$$47\frac{3}{5} \qquad\qquad 47\frac{9}{15}$$

$$65\frac{7}{5} \qquad\qquad 65\frac{7}{15}$$

$$\qquad\qquad\qquad 112\frac{16}{15}$$

$$112 + 1\frac{1}{15} = 113\frac{1}{15}$$

The child recognizes that 16/15 is greater than 1; therefore he can regroup and add. Drill now becomes the dominant factor in developing his addition skills.

Again we must emphasize the importance of continually relating mathematics to real problems. The teacher should present problems or questions whose solution requires an understanding of the process, as:

James ate 1/4 of a pie, Jean ate 1/6 of it, and Sally ate 1/8 of it. How much was eaten in all?

$$\frac{1}{4} + \frac{1}{6} + \frac{1}{8} = \square.$$

In turn the student should be required, at least in the early stages, to translate a given problem into a story or question. For example, to transform the problem $2/5 + 3/7 = \square$ into a story, the pupil may write: "2/5 of the class ate in the cafeteria and 3/7 of them brought their lunch. What part of the class ate at school?"

Subtraction of Fractions

Once the child has established the concept of addition, subtraction should not pose any new difficulties. As with whole numbers, the teacher should emphasize the inverse relationships between addition and subtraction. The development of the subtraction process should follow a similar pattern to that of addition. That is, we should relate the problems to a practical situation and begin our presentation with some physical or pictorial interpretation.

The first problem encountered will be that of fractions with like denominators. These should not present any trouble. Examples using cutouts or a number line like those illustrated in Figure 26 will soon lead to an efficient algorism.

As was mentioned earlier in the chapter, the rational numbers of arithmetic or positive rationals are not closed with respect to subtraction. Therefore unless the negative numbers are introduced, the sentence $4/7 - 6/7 = \square$ will have no solution.

Open sentences containing fractions with unlike denominators are handled just as they were in addition. By changing the fractions to like denominators we can use the same algorism as the one used above.

$$\frac{12}{16} - \frac{3}{8} = \frac{12}{16} - \frac{3 \times 2}{8 \times 2}$$
$$= \frac{12}{16} - \frac{6}{16}$$
$$= \frac{6}{16}$$
$$= \frac{3}{8}.$$

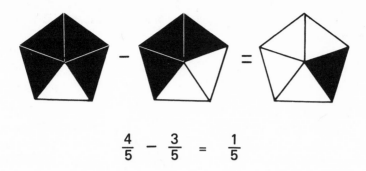

$$\frac{4}{5} - \frac{3}{5} = \frac{1}{5}$$

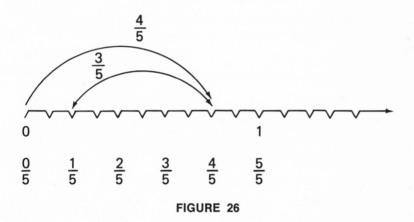

FIGURE 26

Problems with fractions in mixed form should be introduced by using exercises where regrouping is not necessary. We should employ an algorism similar to that of addition, in that we use the vertical form.

$$36 \frac{3}{4}$$

$$- 24 \frac{1}{4}$$

$$12 \frac{2}{4} = 12 \frac{1}{2}.$$

Before introducing a problem where regrouping is necessary, it is wise to review whole-number subtraction. Examples similar to the following help lead the child to develop a clearer understanding of the process of "regrouping."

		2	14
3 feet	2 inches	$\cancel{3}$ feet	$\cancel{2}$ inches
− 1 foot	4 inches	1 foot	4 inches
		1 foot	10 inches

		16	21
17 pounds	5 ounces	$\cancel{17}$ pounds	$\cancel{5}$ ounces
13 pounds	9 ounces	13 pounds	9 ounces
		3 pounds	12 ounces

		3	50
4 months	20 days	$\cancel{4}$ months	$\cancel{20}$ days
2 months	26 days	2 months	26 days
		1 month	24 days

After activities such as the above, we can introduce problems like the following:

$$78\frac{3}{7} \quad = \quad 77\frac{10}{7}$$

$$-36\frac{5}{7} \quad = \quad -36\frac{5}{7}$$

$$41\frac{5}{7}$$

Finally problems in which both regrouping and changing to like denominators are required can be presented:

$$13\frac{2}{7} \quad = \quad 13\frac{8}{28} \quad = \quad 12\frac{36}{28}$$

$$-5\frac{3}{4} \quad = \quad -5\frac{21}{28} \quad = \quad -5\frac{21}{28}$$

$$7\frac{15}{28}.$$

Multiplication of Fractions

Multiplication of fractions probably will cause the pupils more difficulty than any other operations on fractions. Until now all of the operations could be related to some previously learned concept or operation.

This is not always the case when we multiply fractions. Also, as previous examples will illustrate, we have been able to discuss addition and subtraction in the context of the "part of a unit" concept (Figure 27). With

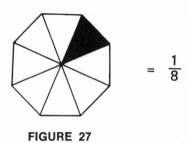

$$= \frac{1}{8}$$

FIGURE 27

multiplication this will not always be possible. In fact, we will have to rely on two different interpretations that refer to a part of a group set (Figure 28).

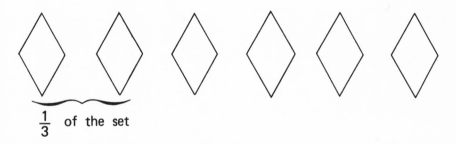

$\frac{1}{3}$ of the set

FIGURE 28

Prior to any formal introduction to multiplication of fractions, the child should be exposed to numerous readiness activities. These should include discussion of a fraction chart in terms of the relationship of one fraction to another (Figure 29). It is readily seen, for instance, that half of a half is a fourth, a fourth of a half is an eighth, or an eighth of a half is a sixteenth. After a brief encounter with this type of fraction chart, we can introduce others showing thirds, sixths, and twelfths from which the child can discover similar relationships.

There are many other such activities from which the child can profit. Included among them are combining equal-size fractional parts of a geometric figure (Figure 30) or employing the number line to perform repeated addition of equal fractions (Figure 31). We can interpret Figure 31 as:

$$8 \text{ sets of } \frac{1}{12} = \frac{8}{12} \text{ or } \frac{2}{3} \text{ or}$$

$$4 \text{ sets of } \frac{2}{12} = \frac{8}{12} \text{ or } \frac{2}{3}.$$

The teacher can also make use of the child's previous experience with addition of equal-size fractions, such as:

$$\frac{3}{16} + \frac{3}{16} + \frac{3}{16} + \frac{3}{16} = \frac{12}{16} \qquad 4 \text{ sets of } \frac{3}{16} = \frac{12}{16} \text{ or } \frac{3}{4}.$$

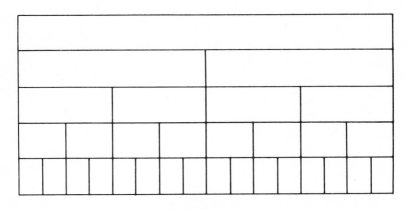

FIGURE 29

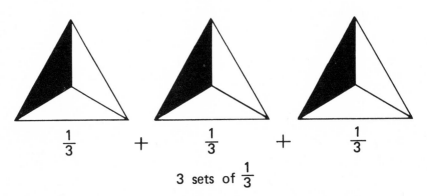

$$\frac{1}{3} \qquad + \qquad \frac{1}{3} \qquad + \qquad \frac{1}{3}$$

3 sets of $\frac{1}{3}$

FIGURE 30

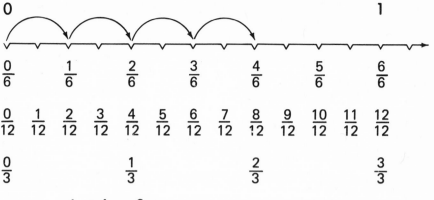

4 sets of $\frac{1}{6} = \frac{4}{6}$ or $\frac{2}{3}$.

FIGURE 31

Basically, multiplication with fractions can be classified or partitioned into six categories:

1. A whole number multiplied by a fraction:

$$\frac{5}{6} \times 6.$$

2. A fraction multiplied by a whole number:

$$6 \times \frac{7}{8}.$$

3. A mixed fraction multiplied by a fraction:

$$\frac{3}{5} \times 2\frac{6}{11}.$$

4. A mixed fraction multiplied by a whole number:

$$7 \times 3\frac{4}{7}.$$

5. A whole number multiplied by a mixed fraction:

$$2\frac{5}{6} \times 9.$$

6. A mixed fraction multiplied by a mixed fraction:

$$2\frac{5}{8} \times 3\frac{4}{7}.$$

It is not the goal in teaching multiplication with fractions to have the child memorize an algorism for each of these cases. On the contrary, the teacher should use the child's experience with each type to arrive at a general algorism for multiplication of fractions. This task may be simplified by strategically introducing the appropriate mathematical properties through the child's activities.

It is logical to introduce multiplication of fractions in such a way that full use can be made of the pupils' prior experiences. Thus, we should begin our development by relating multiplication of fractions as closely as possible to that of whole-number multiplication. This, of course, requires us to begin with problems that have whole-number and fractional factors. We could develop this concept by presenting solutions in varying stages of abstractions, as illustrated by solution of the following problem:

A board is 3/8 inches thick. How high would a stack of 3 boards be?

FIGURE 32

1. We start by showing 3 sets of 3/8 (Figure 32). These are considered together and the product is formed by counting.

$$3 \text{ sets of } \frac{3}{8}$$

$$3 \times \frac{3}{8} = \frac{9}{8} = 1\frac{1}{8}$$

$$\frac{3}{1} \times \frac{3}{8} = \frac{9}{8} = 1\frac{1}{8}.$$

2. By using the number line we can also interpret the problem as serial addition in order to obtain a solution (Figure 33).

$$\frac{3}{8} + \frac{3}{8} + \frac{3}{8} = \frac{9}{8} = 1\frac{1}{8}$$

$$3 \times \frac{3}{8} = \frac{9}{8} = 1\frac{1}{8}.$$

3. If we wish to use Cuisenaire rods or cardboard strips, we need only introduce more than one unit rod (Figure 34).

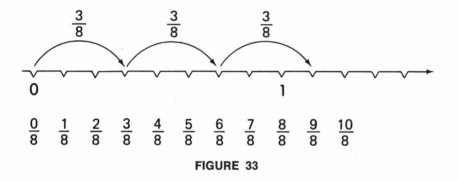

FIGURE 33

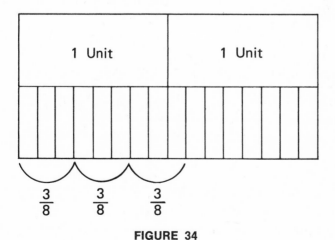

FIGURE 34

As has been the case in all previous developments, we should not continue to use such means indefinitely.   No child should be asked to perform problem after problem with this cumbersome mechanism.   The primary objective of these experiences is to provide a foundation from which a generalization can be made.   In no case should they be used as an intermediate algorism to be committed to memory by the children.

If the teacher has been careful to emphasize the understanding of whole numbers, the pupils will most likely be using the following generalization: "To multiply a fraction by a whole number, we multiply the numerator of the fraction by the whole number and place this product over the denominator of the fraction."

$$4 \times \frac{7}{8} =$$

$$\frac{4}{1} \times \frac{7}{8} = \frac{4 \times 7}{1 \times 8} = \frac{28}{8}$$

This generalization, while crudely stated, may be held throughout the multiplication development.   However, there is no need at this time to confuse this development by verbalizing a more precisely stated rule or generalization.   Let the pupils use their own methods for a while, as long as they are mathematically correct.

The next step is a little more difficult for the child to understand.   It makes sense to interpret $4 \times 7/8$ as $7/8 + 7/8 + 7/8 + 7/8$.   However, the problem becomes more complex if we consider $3/4 \times 4$.   How do we think of 4 as an addend $3/4$ of the time?   It is here that the use of concrete materials such as pictures and geometric shapes becomes a necessity, rather than a convenience.   Let's consider some exercises from which a child can be expected to draw his generalization.

1. Figure 35 employs three steps.   Small cubes lend themselves well to this type of demonstration.
2. To solve the problem given in Figure 36, the child would figure as follows:

$$\frac{2}{3} \times 9 = \frac{18}{3} = 6$$

$$\frac{2}{3} \times \frac{9}{1} = \frac{18}{3} = 6$$

While the product (6) is more easily discovered in the example, the justification for the improper fraction 18/3 is very complex.   Therefore, it is

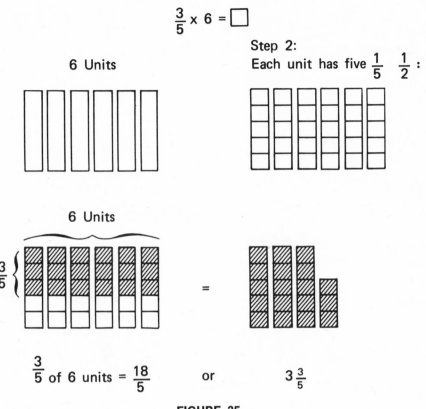

$$\frac{3}{5} \times 6 = \square$$

6 Units

Step 2:
Each unit has five $\frac{1}{5}$ $\frac{1}{2}$:

6 Units

$\frac{3}{5}\Big\{$ =

$\frac{3}{5}$ of 6 units = $\frac{18}{5}$ or $3\frac{3}{5}$

FIGURE 35

suggested that this type of illustration be used in the latter part of the development. This suggestion also holds for the following example.
3. Using the number line in Figure 37, he would employ this process:

$$\frac{2}{3} \text{ set of } 9$$

$$\frac{2}{3} \times 9 = \frac{18}{3} = 6$$

$$\frac{2}{3} \times \frac{9}{1} = \frac{18}{3} = 6.$$

The pupil will usually draw on his past experiences to reason something like this: "Since I want 2 thirds of the set of 9, I must first divide the set

$$\frac{2}{3} \times 9 = \square$$

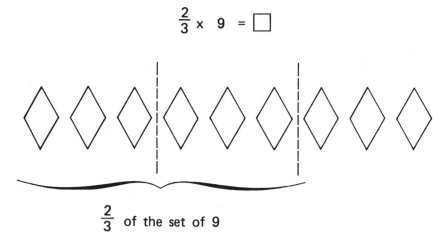

$\frac{2}{3}$ of the set of 9

FIGURE 36

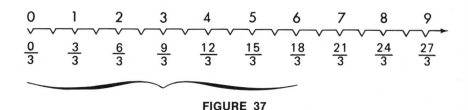

FIGURE 37

into thirds, then take 2 parts of it, or 6 wholes or units." Since each whole is made up of 3 thirds, we have 6×3 thirds or 18 thirds.

Some more able children will most likely have made their own general-izations by this time, and others will be on the verge of doing so. In this case, we can now have the children state the "rule" they have been using for problems like:

$$(a) \ 4 \times \frac{7}{8} = \square.$$

$$(b) \ \frac{3}{7} \times 6 = \square.$$

With teacher guidance and a reminder of the fractional form of whole numbers ($4 = 4/1$ or $6 = 6/1$), we would hope to get the following: "To multiply a whole number and a fraction, I change the whole number to its equivalent fractional form; then I multiply the numerators of the two fractions and divide by the product of the denominators."

$$5 \times \frac{7}{8} = \frac{5}{1} \times \frac{7}{8} = \frac{5 \times 7}{1 \times 8} = \frac{35}{8} = 4\frac{3}{8}$$

Even though one of the denominators will always be 1 in these instances, it makes further development far easier if the child uses this generalization.

Once the child comprehends the multiplication of a fraction and a whole number, the teacher should proceed to multiplication of a fraction by a fraction. In order to keep continuity in the development we should interpret $3/5 \times 2/3$ as $3/5$ of a set of $2/3$. We are no longer referring to the measurement of a unit or whole, but to the partitioning of a set.

The child has already experienced some multiplication of this type through informal readiness activities similar to those in Figure 38. He has discussed relationships such as ½ of ½ is ¼, ¼ of ½ is ⅛. Now we

1 Unit							
$\frac{1}{2}$				$\frac{1}{2}$			
$\frac{1}{4}$		$\frac{1}{4}$		$\frac{1}{4}$		$\frac{1}{4}$	
$\frac{1}{8}$	$\frac{1}{8}$	$\frac{1}{8}$	$\frac{1}{8}$	$\frac{1}{8}$	$\frac{1}{8}$	$\frac{1}{8}$	$\frac{1}{8}$

FIGURE 38

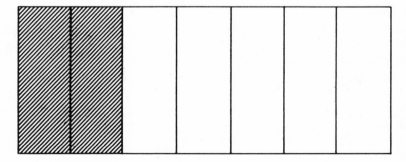

FIGURE 39

need to concentrate on the more abstract or complex example. In the example, $3/5 \times 2/7 = \square$, the pupil begins by dividing a whole into sevenths and indicating two of them as shown in Figure 39. This now becomes the subset he is interested in, and since we need 3/5 of this subset he will first divide it into fifths and then indicate three of them as in Figure 40.

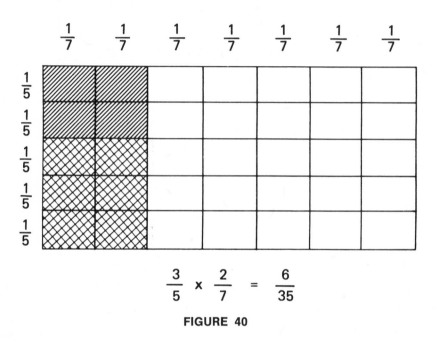

$$\frac{3}{5} \times \frac{2}{7} = \frac{6}{35}$$

FIGURE 40

Now that we have established a method by which we can pictorially solve an open sentence like $3/4 \times 5/6 = \square$, we should provide numerous examples for the class from which they can form conclusions about multiplication of fractions. The pupil should proceed in an orderly fashion, recording the open sentence, finding the solution by the above method, and then recording the answer or product as in Figure 41. Our development might be as in Figure 42.

A display of this nature not only provides a picture of the solutions but keeps all the facts readily available for the child to study so he can discover patterns and draw conclusions. By studying the table and recalling how a fraction and a whole number are multiplied, the child should soon come upon a shortcut or efficient method for multiplying two fractions.

Upon developing the concept or means for finding the product of two

Problem	Solution
$\dfrac{2}{3} \times \dfrac{7}{8} = \square$	$\dfrac{2}{3} \times \dfrac{7}{8} = \dfrac{14}{24} = \dfrac{7}{12}$
$\dfrac{5}{6} \times \dfrac{3}{4} = \square$	$\dfrac{5}{6} \times \dfrac{3}{4} = \dfrac{15}{24} = \dfrac{5}{8}$
$\dfrac{6}{7} \times \dfrac{2}{5} = \square$	$\dfrac{6}{7} \times \dfrac{2}{5} = \dfrac{12}{35}$

FIGURE 41

Problem

$\dfrac{2}{3} \times \dfrac{7}{8} = \square$

$\dfrac{2}{3} \times \dfrac{7}{8} = \dfrac{14}{24} = \dfrac{7}{12}$

$\left(\dfrac{14 \div 2}{24 \div 2} = \dfrac{7}{12} \right)$

$\dfrac{5}{6} \times \dfrac{3}{4} = \square$

$\dfrac{5}{6} \times \dfrac{3}{4} = \dfrac{15}{24} = \dfrac{5}{8}$

$\left(\dfrac{15 \div 3}{24 \div 3} \right) = \dfrac{5}{8}$

Solution

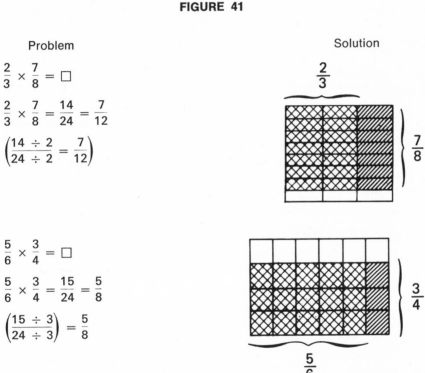

FIGURE 42

fractions, we have the machinery to handle all types of multiplication of fractional numbers, with minor manipulation. This can be stated as follows: If a/b and c/d are fractional numbers, then:

$$\frac{a}{b} \times \frac{c}{d} = \frac{a \times c}{b \times d} = \frac{ac}{bd}.$$

The pupil is not necessarily expected to use this notation to express his generalization. However, by this time he should be able to verbally approximate such a statement.

As noted above, there are six basic types of multiplication of fractions. Up until now we have introduced the first three in the list. However, the ability to work these three forms of multiplication, in conjunction with the child's prior knowledge of the distributive property and his ability to rename a fraction in terms of its equivalent, has prepared him for the other forms. The following are illustrations of the other three types:

$$(a)\ 3 \times 4\frac{1}{3} = \square$$

$$(b)\ 5\frac{1}{2} \times 7 = \square$$

$$(c)\ 5\frac{1}{4} \times 6\frac{1}{7} = \square.$$

Let's consider the most obvious and direct approach first. There is no reason to duplicate our efforts if this is not needed. When a child is confronted with the above problems, we can present or guide him to the following solutions:

$$(a)\ 3 \times 4\frac{1}{3} = \square$$

$$3 \times 4\frac{1}{3} = \frac{3}{1} \times \frac{13}{3} \qquad \text{renaming as improper fractions}$$

$$= \frac{3 \times 13}{1 \times 3} \qquad \text{multiplication of two fractions}$$

$$= \frac{39}{3}$$

$$= \frac{39 \div 3}{3 \div 3} \qquad \text{renaming as equivalent fractions}$$

$$= \frac{13}{1}$$

$$= 13. \qquad \text{division by 1}$$

(b) $5\frac{1}{2} \times 7 = \square$

$$5\frac{1}{2} \times 7 = \frac{11}{2} \times \frac{7}{1}$$ renaming

$$= \frac{11 \times 7}{2 \times 1}$$ multiplication of two fractions

$$= \frac{77}{2}$$

$$= 38\frac{1}{2}.$$ renaming

(c) $5\frac{1}{4} \times 6\frac{1}{7} = \square$

$$5\frac{1}{4} \times 6\frac{1}{7} = \frac{21}{4} \times \frac{43}{7}$$ renaming

$$= \frac{21 \times 43}{28}$$ multiplication of two fractions

$$= \frac{903}{28}$$

$$= 32\frac{7}{28}$$ renaming

$$= 32\frac{1}{4}.$$ renaming $\left(\dfrac{7 \div 7}{28 \div 7} = \dfrac{1}{4}\right)$

It should be easily seen that we are merely using the fact that we can rename a mixed fraction as an improper fraction. Then we employ the same strategy for the multiplication of two fractions that the child has already developed.

After several examples like b and c, where the products of the numerators become quite large, we can discuss the desirability of an easier way to find the required product. When this need has been discovered or realized, we should proceed with examples similar to the following:

(a) $6 \times 9\frac{3}{4} = \square$

$$6 \times 9\frac{3}{4} = 6 \times \left(9 \times \frac{3}{4}\right) \qquad \text{renaming}$$

$$= (6 \times 9) + \left(6 \times \frac{3}{4}\right) \qquad \text{distributive property}$$

$$= 54 + \frac{18}{4} \qquad \qquad \text{multiplication of whole number and}$$

$$= 54 + 4\frac{2}{4} \qquad \qquad \text{renaming}$$

$$= 54 + 4\frac{1}{2} \qquad \qquad \frac{2 \div 2}{4 \div 2} = \frac{1}{2}$$

$$= 58\frac{1}{2}. \qquad \qquad \text{addition of fraction}$$

(b) $\frac{2}{11} \times 7\frac{2}{3} = \square$

$$\frac{2}{11} \times 7\frac{2}{3} = \frac{2}{11} \times \left(7 + \frac{2}{3}\right) \qquad \text{renaming}$$

$$= \left(\frac{2}{11} \times 7\right) + \left(\frac{2}{11} \times \frac{2}{3}\right) \qquad \text{distributive}$$

$$= \frac{14}{11} + \frac{4}{33} \qquad \qquad \text{multiplication}$$

$$= \frac{42}{33} + \frac{4}{33} \qquad \qquad \left(\frac{14 \times 3}{11 \times 3} = \frac{42}{33}\right) \text{ renaming}$$

$$= \frac{46}{33}. \qquad \qquad \text{addition}$$

$$= 1\frac{13}{33}. \qquad \qquad \text{renaming}$$

(c) $5\frac{2}{9} \times 3\frac{6}{11} = \square$

$$5\frac{2}{9} \times 3\frac{6}{11} = \left(5 + \frac{2}{9}\right) \times \left(3 + \frac{6}{11}\right) \qquad \text{renaming}$$

$$= (5 \times 3) + \left(5 \times \frac{6}{11}\right)$$

$$+ \left(\frac{2}{9} \times 3\right)$$

$$+ \left(\frac{2}{9} \times \frac{6}{11}\right) \qquad \text{distributive property}$$

$$= 15 + \frac{30}{11} + \frac{6}{9} + \frac{12}{99} \qquad \text{multiplication}$$

$$= 15 + 2\frac{8}{11} + \frac{6}{9} + \frac{12}{99}$$

$$= 15 + \left(2 + \frac{8}{11}\right) + \frac{6}{9} + \frac{12}{99}$$

$$= (15 + 2) + \frac{8}{11} + \frac{6}{9} + \frac{12}{99}$$

$$= 17 + \frac{72}{99} + \frac{66}{99} + \frac{12}{99}$$

$$= 17 + \frac{150}{99}$$

$$= 17 + 1\frac{51}{99}$$

$$= 18 + \frac{51}{99}$$

$$= 18\frac{17}{33}.$$

When such examples have been presented and discussed, we are ready for the final stage of multiplication of fractions—practice. As has been true for all other operations, a child must not only understand the process, he must be able to use it effectively.

Division of Fractions

No new concept of division will be required to introduce the division of fractions. The open sentence $6 \div 2 = \square$ is asking the question, "How many sets of 2 are contained in 6?" This same interpretation can be used for the sentence $N \div a/b = \square$: "How many pieces a/b units in size can be obtained from a piece N in size?" We can give a concrete or graphic solution to $4 \div 2/3 = \square$ using the number line (Figure 43), just as we did to $6 \div 2 = \square$. The solution of How many 2/3 can be obtained from 4? is 6.

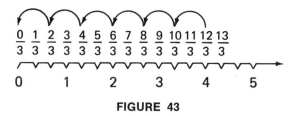

FIGURE 43

However, if we should choose a problem in which the division is not exact, we will have to group for a solution. For example, if we had considered $3/4 \div 1/3 = \square$ ("How many 1/3 can be obtained from 3/4?"), it might be solved as shown in Figure 44. Because the child has had

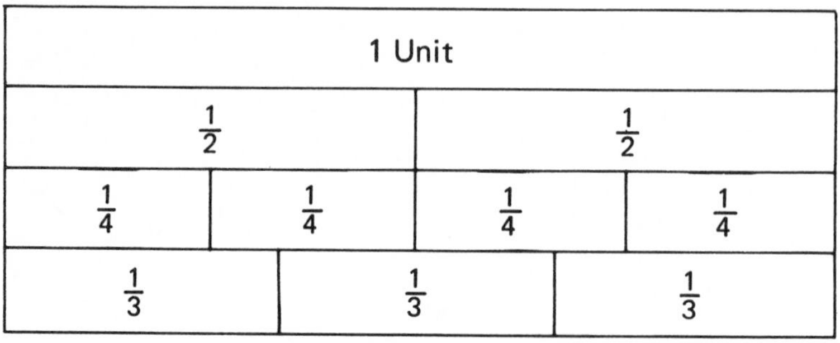

1 Unit			
$\frac{1}{2}$		$\frac{1}{2}$	
$\frac{1}{4}$	$\frac{1}{4}$	$\frac{1}{4}$	$\frac{1}{4}$
$\frac{1}{3}$		$\frac{1}{3}$	$\frac{1}{3}$

FIGURE 44

previous work with the aid, he can begin as shown. However, he soon discovers he cannot immediately arrive at an answer, since the solution is 2 and a part of 1 (Figure 45).

We would direct the endeavor by asking how we might find what "part" of 1/3 is left. This again will invoke some random activity at first. With some directions, the pupils should arrive at the solution shown in Figure 45. The dotted lines indicate how the pupil finds what part of 1/3 is yet to be partitioned. Thus he can find 2¼ thirds in ¾ or ¾ ÷ ⅓ = 2¼.

It is obvious that we can continue to find solutions to such open sen-

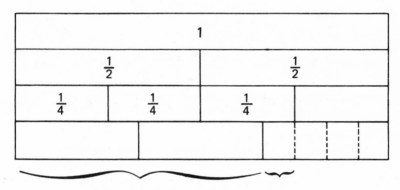

set of 2 thirds and $\frac{1}{4}$ set of a third

FIGURE 45

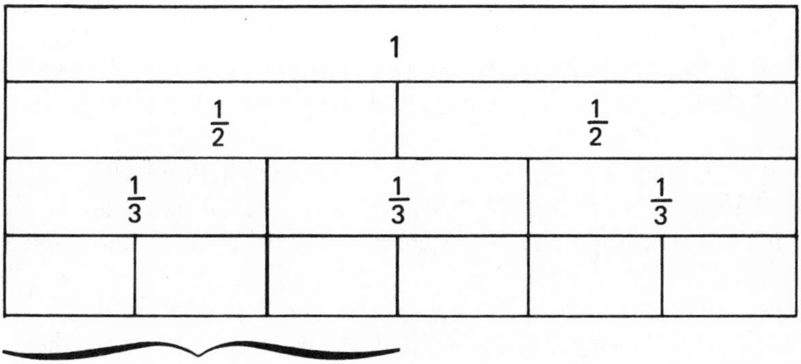

$\frac{3}{4}$ of a $\frac{2}{3}$ segment is $\frac{1}{2}$

FIGURE 46

tences by the illustrated methods. However, these methods are far from being the polished and efficient algorism we need.

Examples similar to the preceding provide a logical stepping stone to the common-denominator method of dividing fractions. With the proper construction with Cuisenaire rods (Figure 46) we are able to determine that the answer to $1/2 \div 2/3$ is $3/4$. Problems like this suggest changing the demoninators to like denominators before dividing (sixths in this case).

$$\frac{3}{4} \div \frac{2}{3} = \frac{9}{12} \div \frac{8}{12} = 1\frac{1}{8}$$

$$1 \text{ set of } \frac{8}{12} \text{ and } \frac{1}{8} \text{ of a set more}$$

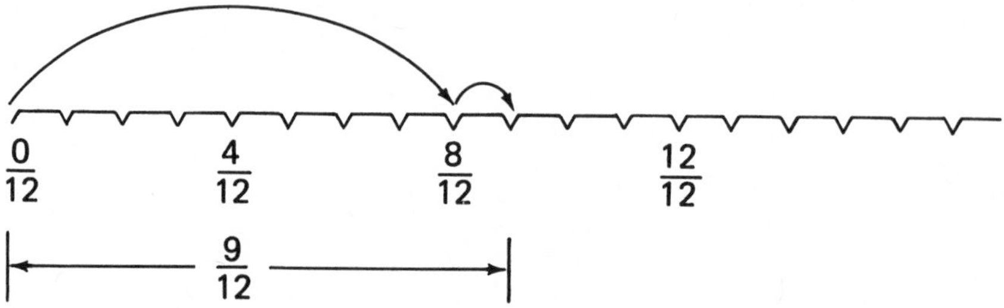

FIGURE 47

Another example can be illustrated on the number line, as in Figure 47. Thus, if a child wishes to divide any two fractions he merely changes them to fractions with like denominators and then finds the quotients of their numerators.

A pattern similar to that used in developing the multiplication algorism should be used, that is, keeping all previously worked examples available for study. This can be done on a chart at the board or by the pupil in a notebook.

Pupils should be presented with several exercises that are readily solvable by physical or semiconcrete methods, as in Figure 48. With these examples we can relate division to multiplication just as we did with the whole numbers. For example we know that $24 \div 6 = 4$, because $4 \times 6 = 24$. It follows that $3/2 \div 3/4 = 2$, since $2 \times 3/4 = 3/2$. This kind of activity leads to a new and more abstract means of solution. If we wish

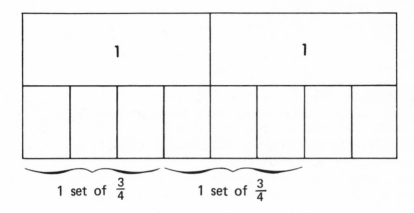

$$\frac{3}{2} \div \frac{3}{4} = \square$$

1 set of $\frac{3}{4}$ 1 set of $\frac{3}{4}$

$$\frac{3}{2} \div \frac{3}{4} = 2$$

FIGURE 48

to find the solution to $4/3 \div 3/7 = \square$, we need only to find the number that when multiplied times $3/7$ will give $4/3$. Thus, if $\square \times 3/7 = 4/3$, then $4/3 \div 3/7 = \square$.

Since every rational can be written in fractional form ($4 = 4/1$, $3\ 1/2 = 7/2$, for example), we can expedite matters considerably if we think of the solution as being in rational form. For example, if, instead of $\square \times 3/7 = 4/3$ we use $\frac{\triangle}{\square} \times 3/7 = 4/3$, then $4/3 \div 3/7 = \frac{\triangle}{\square}$. This solution can be found by trial and error, the common-denominator method, or by using some manipulative materials. The method is not important at this time. We are interested in the child's arriving at a correct solution by a method he understands. Thus, we must use 28 for $\triangle$ and 9 for $\square$. Once a child obtains an answer, he should be required to check it. He should see that $28/9 \times 3/7 = 4/3$ and thus conclude that $4/3 \div 3/7 = 28/9$.

As the pupils discover the quotient of two fractions, they can begin to accumulate the division problems and their related multiplication problems. Once a number of these have been recorded they will begin to see a pattern. For example, if confronted with $5/16 \div 7/11 = \frac{\triangle}{\square}$ and $\frac{\triangle}{\square} \times 7/11 = 5/16$, they may conclude that $\triangle$ is 5×11 and that $\square$ will be 16×7.

After the pupils are consistently finding the answers by this form of renaming, we can concentrate on a more formal discussion of the matter. A suggested development follows:

1. Review the concept of division by 1, through the use of examples in both horizontal and vertical notation:

$$\frac{3}{16} \div 1 = \frac{3}{16} \quad \text{or} \quad \frac{3/16}{1} = \frac{3}{16}.$$

2. Direct the children's attention to the previously developed concept of the reciprocal. Ask questions like, "What must we multiply 3/5 by in order to obtain a product of 1?" After several specific examples, some of the better students will generalize that the inverse of a/b is b/a.
3. Briefly examine problems like

$$\frac{3/4}{2/3 \times 3/2}, \quad \frac{1\frac{5}{8}}{3/7 \times 7/3}, \quad \frac{5/9}{3/1 \times 1/3}$$

to determine if they have all been divided by 1. The child must be guided to a level of understanding that enables them to see that $3/4 \div 2/3 \times 3/2 = 3/4$ or that

$$\frac{1\frac{5}{8}}{3/7 \times 7/3} = \frac{1\frac{5}{8}}{1} = 1\frac{5}{8}.$$

Finally if presented with

$$\frac{317}{931} \div \frac{416}{754} \times \frac{754}{416},$$

the child would conclude without computation that the solution is

$$\frac{317}{931}.$$

4. We can now tie the above steps together and provide the pupils with a method for solving $(9/11)/(7/16) = \square$. He might reason: "If I divide a number by 1, it is unchanged. The divisor to the problem could be made 1 by using the reciprocal of 7/16. $7/16 \times 16/7 = 1$. But if I multiply the denominator of a fraction by a nonzero number, I must

multiply the numerator by the same number, to keep the original value of the fraction unchanged." Thus,

$$\frac{9/11}{7/16} = \frac{9/11 \times 16/7}{7/16 \times 16/7}$$

$$= \frac{9/16 \times 16/7}{1}$$

$$= 9/11 \times 16/7$$

$$= 144/77.$$

Once we have developed this concept with the vertical notation we can more readily transfer it to the horizontal form.

A development of this nature will be of no value unless the pupils are continually encouraged to make generalizations. This type of activity is applicable to both the concrete and abstract levels of development. Also, no child will give forth a polished, complete generalization. Therefore, the process is that of acquiring closer and closer approximations of the ultimate goal. In this case we would like to arrive at $a/b \div c/d = a/b \times d/c$. It is not necessary for the child to write such a statement, for it is conceivable that he could have an excellent understanding of the algorism and not be able to give this general statement.

Decimal Notation

For all practical purposes, once we have established the set of rational numbers, structurally speaking, we will study very little new material. There is, however, a definite need to discuss and study another notation system, decimal notation. At first this topic may appear to be totally new, but with careful study we see that this is far from being true. We are not introducing a new kind of number but merely a new notation. By this stage in a child's study, he has already encountered a subset of the decimal numeral, namely the whole number, such as 4, 46, and so on. The task is thus a matter of extending the notation to those rational numbers less than 1 and in turn to the rational numbers greater than 1. To treat the topic of decimal notation as anything else would surely hinder rather than en-hance the understanding of the decimal numeration system.

By adopting the point of view stated above, we are in a sense finding a new means of recording or symbolizing numbers with which we are already familiar. Thus, 8, .04, and 1.45 are all decimal numerals. In addition to this, there is no need to reestablish such concepts as associativity, commutativity, or distributive properties for the decimals, since the mere altering of symbolization of the rational numbers will not affect their structure.

Extending the Place-Value Notation

Prior to any attempt to further develop the decimal notation, it is advisable to ascertain the present level of student understanding of "place value." It may be necessary to reestablish an acceptable level of familiarity with the column values to the left of the decimal before continuing. Once this has been completed, we can pose the following problem:

If we were to list the column values to the right of the one's place, what would the value of the adjacent column be if we use the same pattern previously established?

$$\ldots \quad | \quad 100 \quad | \quad 10 \quad | \quad 1 \quad | \quad ?$$

We are, of course, relying on the generalization made earlier in our studies of place value and the child's knowledge of operations with fractions. This can be approached in two different ways. The place value of any column is 10 times the one on its immediate right, or one-tenth the column value to its left. Either of these generalizations can be used to conclude that the value of the column in question must be 1/10.

This transition can be more easily accomplished by using coordinate or ruled paper to illustrate physically the place value of the columns (Figure 49). The tens column is represented by a square containing 10 strips, each of which represents 1 unit. The unit is divided into 10 divisions, each of which represents 1/10. By using the coordinate paper, this method of development can be utilized in further development of the decimal notation.

In earlier discussion of the decimal numeration system the multibase blocks were discussed. By reassigning values of 1, 1/10, 1/100, and 1/1000 to the 1000's block, hundreds flat, tens rod, and the ones cube respectively, an excellent aid can be made available for furthering a child's understanding of decimal notation (Figure 50).

It can readily be seen by physically counting that it takes ten tenths to equal one ($10 \times 1/10 = 1$), ten hundredths to equal one tenth ($10 \times 1/100 = 1/10$) and ten thousandths to equal one hundredth ($10 \times$

$$10's \qquad\qquad 1's \qquad \tfrac{1}{10}$$

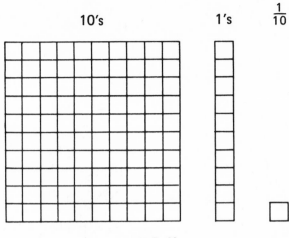

FIGURE 49

$1/1000 = 1/100$). Thus, the pattern of the place value of successive columns can be reinforced and at the same time represented in symbolic form.

The decreasing nature of the column value must not be neglected so as to eliminate the possibility of a more meaningful understanding of the notation. A student should realize before continuing that each column value is also $1/10$ of the column to its immediate left.

Once the place value of the tenth column has been established, the decimal notation can be used to represent rational numbers; for example, 1 1/10, 2/10, 3 3/10 can be written as 1.1, 0.2 and 3.3. It is advisable to use the "0" in the ones place to help avoid possible confusion and to stress that the decimal is only a convenient means to separate the whole numbers from the fractions. This method of separation is already a part of the child's experience on which we should capitalize. The most obvious of these experiences is that of dealing with money.

As was true when place-value notation was introduced for whole numbers, a child must acquire familiarity through proper usage. Considerable practice is needed in reading and writing decimal numerals. It must be clear that the "and" denotes the placement of the decimal point; it should not be used in any other part of the number. Thus "42.5" is read "forty-two and five tenths." The writing of the decimal numeral from oral directions poses both a source of confusion and a possible opportunity for a deeper understanding of the ties between the decimals and rational numbers. When the teacher reads a decimal number for the children to write,

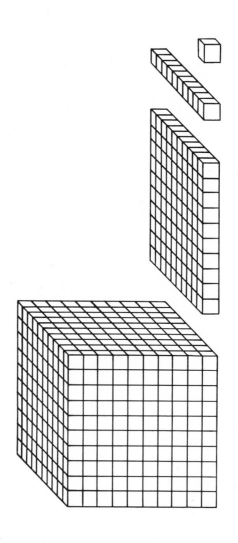

FIGURE 50

such as "three and four tenths," it is not immediately apparent whether they should write 3.4 or 3 4/10. At this time it can be stressed that both numerals represent the same number, and we must indicate which mode we wish to use in recording it.

If proper care has been practiced in developing the first two places to the right of the decimal point, further extension is comparatively easy. When first reading numerals like 3.76 a child may say it as "three and seven tenths and six hundredths" or "three and seventy-six hundredths." The answer can, of course, be given both abstractly or visually. It is desirable in the early stages to rely on the concrete or pictorial interpretation as much as possible. In Figure 51, for example, each large square represents one, each stick is equal to one tenth, and each small square represents one hundredth. The child can be shown or allowed to discover why the numeral 3.76 can be read "three and seventy-six hundredths" by actual count. Each stick contains 10 hundredths or $7 \times 10 = 70$ hundredths plus the 6 hundredths remaining, or 76 hundredths. With such an

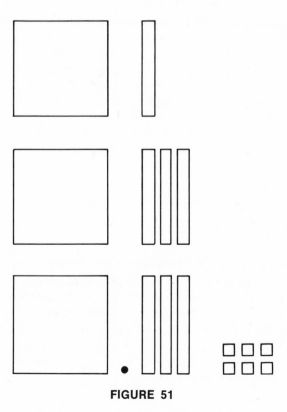

FIGURE 51

	Ten thousands	Thousands	Hundreds	Tens	Ones	Tenths	Hundredths	Thousandths	

FIGURE 52

explanation the child is more apt to acquire insight into the mechanics of decimal notation.

Place-value charts, as formed in Figure 52, are prevalent in most elementary texts. The teacher must be cautioned not to introduce them prematurely. Such a chart could prove to be detrimental by allowing the child to become overly dependent on the aid for reading and writing decimal numerals. Thus understanding would be sacrificed.

Just being able to read and write decimals in the basic form is not a sign of clear understanding. As was true for place-value notation of whole numbers, there are many ways to read and, for the matter, to write the same number. This can be demonstrated by a specific example: We can interpret 7.85 in several different ways, such as "seven and eighty-five hundredths," "seventy-eight tenths and five hundredths," or "seven hundred eighty-five hundredths." Many such possibilities should be explored before advancing to any new material involving decimal numeration.

Algorisms for Decimal Fractions

Addition Algorism

The addition algorism for decimal fractions is virtually the same as that for whole numbers, with the exception of the placement of the decimal point. This should not pose any major problem inasmuch as the addition of decimal fractions is directly analogous to that of common fractions. The teaching of the algorism is also simplified by the fact that the child has already acquired the skills necessary to perform the actual addition process. The concentration, therefore, should be on the above-mentioned analogy. The two examples below can be used to justify decimal placement by utilizing the students' knowledge of addition of fractions with like denominators.

$$(a)\ 57.89 + 2.76 = 57\frac{89}{100} + 2\frac{76}{100}$$

$$= (57 + 2) + \left(\frac{89}{100} + \frac{76}{100}\right)$$

$$= 59 + \frac{165}{100}$$

$$= 59 + 1\frac{65}{100}$$

$$= 60 + \frac{65}{100}$$

$$= 60.65$$

$$(b)\ 3.7 + 4.02 = 3\frac{7}{10} + 4\frac{2}{100}$$

$$= 3\frac{70}{100} + 4\frac{2}{100}$$

$$= (3 + 4) + \frac{70}{100} + \frac{2}{100}$$

$$= 7 + \frac{72}{100}$$

$$= 7\frac{72}{100}$$

$$= 7.72$$

This being true, we need only assure ourselves that like fractions are being added, that is tenths with tenths, hundredths with hundredths, and so on. Because of the nature of decimal notation, this can be accomplished by aligning the decimals of all addends, as follows:

$$\begin{array}{r} 4.67 \\ 24.89 \\ 32.97 \\ \hline 62.53 \end{array}$$

Subtraction Algorism

As was the case for addition there is, for all practical purposes, no new algorism for subtraction.   If like column values are aligned in the minuend and subtrahend, the process of subtraction is exactly that of subtracting whole numbers.   The difficulty of keeping the like column values aligned is eliminated by using ordinary ruled paper, as illustrated below:

2	4.	6	7
	3.	7	1
2	8.	3	8

It is possible to illustrate both addition and subtraction in expanded notation:

$$46.27 = 40 + 6 + .2 + .07$$
$$+ 3.12 = 3 + .1 + .02$$
$$40 + 9 + .3 + .09 = 49.39$$

However, it is not worth belaboring such a justification.   The simplicity of the algorism could be nullified by the cumbersome notation.

In general, pupils should not be required to add or subtract decimals that have a different number of decimal places.   The reasoning for this is based on the way in which decimals are used in practical application. Usually decimals are used in conjunction with a measurement problem and thus involve precision of measurement.   Therefore, to attempt to add numbers of different precision would be misleading.

Multiplication Algorism

Developing the multiplication algorism for decimals presents a fine opportunity for discussion and discovery by the student.   He has, by this time, all the necessary computational skills to perform the multiplication. Hence, we need only lead him to a generalization that will allow for the correct placement of the decimal point.   The formulation of this generalization can result from the child's previous knowledge of multiplication of common fractions.   Thus, when a problem is posed, we merely substitute an equivalent common fraction for its decimal counterpart.

The initial problems that a child is confronted with should be rather basic in nature, since the computation is not our goal at this time. For example, the child can be asked to find the product of 8×0.4. He can be asked, "Is there another way you could write the problem so it is possible for you to perform the multiplication?" Of course we want him to use his understanding of equivalent fractions to write $8 \times 4/10$. He knows the answer to this is $32/10$ and that this can be written as 3.2. After several examples of this nature he may be given a problem similar to $.4 \times .2$. Again, we would expect him to rewrite the problem as $4/10 \times 2/10$ and proceed as before to obtain an answer.

A word of caution is in order with respect to the simplification of the common fraction used as factors in this type of problem. If a child reverts to some previously learned algorism for multiplying fractions, the needed generalization will not be apparent. For example, he could perform the operation as follows:

$$4/10 \times 2/10 = 2/5 \times 1/5 = 2/25 \qquad \text{or}$$

$$2\overset{1}{\cancel{4}}/1\cancel{0} \times \underset{5}{\cancel{2}}/1\cancel{0} = 2/25$$
$$5 \phantom{/1\cancel{0} \times }5$$

While this is not incorrect, it can obscure the wanted outcome. We obviously would prefer the child to conclude the answer was $8/100$ and proceed to record it as 0.08. After computing and recording several examples similar to the above, the child will begin to generalize as follows: "I disregard the decimal to perform the computation needed. To find the correct decimal placement, I multiply the denominator of common fractions and write the answers in equivalent decimal notation." This generalization is not entirely correct mathematically, but it is a good first step in the child's formulation of the generalization.

Pupils may encounter difficulty if we rely entirely on an abstract or symbolic development. It is therefore desirable to utilize a variety of presentations or interpretations to obtain the solution to decimal products. A geometric illustration can help clarify the product of $.4 \times .2$ where all else fails (Figure 53). Such an illustration was used earlier to demonstrate that in multiplication of fractions less than 1 the product will always be less than either factor. By inspecting the area of Figure 53, it is readily observable that this is true for decimal fractions also. Other demonstrations of this nature can be performed with multibase blocks or small cubes.

Once the child becomes proficient in working and interpreting multiplication examples like the above, he is ready to formalize his thinking into

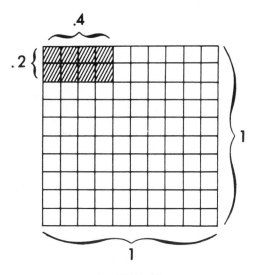

FIGURE 53

a general rule for finding the product of decimal numbers. The first stage is a systematic observation of the relationship between the decimal product and the equivalent product written in common-fraction form. For example:

(a) 2.45 × 3.2   →   245/100 × 32/10
(b) 47.89 × .02 → 4789/100 × 2/100
(c) 3.141 × 1.2   → 3141/1000 × 12/10

The child has already observed that the numerical portion of his answer is found by multiplying the numerator of the two fractions. Thus he should be directed to concentrate his efforts on the denominator or decimal placement. This can be accomplished by oral means or problems similar to the following:

(a) .48 × 1.4   48/100 × 14/10   = 672/? = 672
(b) 1.71 × .004   171/100 ×   4/1000 = 684/? = 684

In such problems, the child must locate the decimal correctly in the final answer.

The next stage is transitional in nature and provides a bridge between such developmental examples to an algorismic rule. At this time the child can arrive at the correct decimal product as long as he can use the common fraction form as an intermediate step.   That is, if he can see the denominators, he is capable of locating the decimal point correctly.   For example:

$$3.4 \times 2.55 = 34/10 \times 255/100 = 8670/1000 = 8.670$$

Of course, this procedure is entirely too restrictive to be used indefinitely.   What is needed is an easy and accurate means to establish the correct number of decimal places in the product.   In order to do this we must observe the relationship between the number of decimal places in a decimal numeral and the denominator of its equivalent common fraction.

4.6	$= 46/10$	tenths (one decimal place)
2.75	$= 275/100$	hundredths (two decimal places)
0.456	$= 456/1000$	thousandths (three decimal places)

We can further observe that the number of zeros in the denominator will also give us the number of decimal places in the numeral.   Skill in finding the correct number of decimal places should be acquired before actual products are introduced.   Hence the child may be asked:

If we multiply tenths by tenths the result will be in the _____ ?

After extending this to several other decimal places, we may wish to record our conclusion as follows:

tenths by tenths	hundredths
$.1 \times .1$	$.01$
tenths by hundredths	thousandths
$.1 \times \quad .01$	$.001$
.	.
.	.
.	.

The final stage in the development, before actually finding a decimal product, should be ample practice in placing the decimal in a provided product or factor.   Examples are:

$$
\begin{aligned}
(a) \quad 4.8 \ \ \times 7.65 &= 36.72 \\
(b) \quad 0.467 \times 0.204 &= \quad .095268 \\
(c) \quad 46.7 \ \ \times \ .24 &= 11.208
\end{aligned}
$$

Upon attaining sufficient skill in all of the above stages, the students should be provided practice with actual decimal products such as 3.78 $\times$

42.5. Decimal products should be presented in as many problem situations as possible to illustrate the practicality of such notation. Examples used could include measurement problems, percents, money, or even newspaper articles containing decimal notation.

Division Algorism

There are several ways to teach the algorism for division of decimal numbers. The most consistently used method is that which relies on the student's knowledge of the fundamental principles of fractions. This is also in line with our development of decimals as merely symbolic representations of rational numbers.

This approach is dependent on the child's knowledge of division of whole numbers and how to interpret a division problem in fractional form. For example:

$$(a)\ 36\overline{)780}\ \Rightarrow\ \frac{780}{36}$$

$$(b)\ 4\,\frac{3}{10} \div 2\,\frac{3}{10} \Rightarrow \frac{4\,(3/10)}{2\,(3/10)} \Rightarrow \frac{43/10}{23/10}.$$

It is essential that these skills be reviewed prior to any consideration of division with decimal fractions.

When the teacher has been assured that the above skills do exist, he can confront the child with the first division problem containing a decimal fraction. The goal is to relate all decimal division to that of whole numbers and thus keep new and unnecessary learning to a minimum. Hence the teacher begins with the obvious type of problem, that which has a whole-number divisor and a decimal dividend. When confronted with $7.85 \div 5$, the child may be guided to a strategy similar to that used in developing multiplication. Thus, $7.85 \div 5 = 785/100 \div 5$, which is equal to $785/100 \times 1/5 = (785 \div 5)/100$, thus yielding a quotient in the hundredths. Similarly $37.4 \div 4 = 374/10 \div 4$ or $(374 \div 4)/10$, yielding a quotient in tenths; $.478 \div 2 = 478/1000 \div 2$ or $478 \div 2/10$, yielding a quotient in thousandths.

By continuing this process, we can arrive at a rule for locating the decimal point in a quotient. When the divisor is a whole number, that is, when a decimal fraction is divided by a whole number, there are as many decimal places in the quotient as there are in the dividend.

Upon reaching this generalization, we are ready to advance to division problems that have both decimal fraction divisors and dividends. This extension can be accomplished by leading the pupils through the following sequence.

First, present the class with a division problem that contains a decimal divisor such as $.4\overline{)12}$ and ask what they would have to change in the problem so that previously learned skills would allow them to perform the operation. We are, of course, hoping for the reply, "If the divisor was a whole number, I could find the quotient." Once this is recognized we are ready for the most crucial step in decimal division, that of acquiring a whole-number divisor. There is a tendency to treat this process much too lightly, thus sacrificing all chances for understanding.

Second, the whole-number divisor can be obtained, as we all know, by "merely" multiplying the divisor and the dividend by the appropriate number. In the example:

$$.4\overline{)12} \rightarrow 4\overline{)120}$$

You would multiply both .4 and 12 by 10. How many times have you heard someone use the word "merely" or "simple" to describe a concept, and yet you are at a total loss as to what was happening? This will be the case in the above if proper care of development is not taken. We should begin by drawing an analogy between decimal divisors and division of common fractions, in examples such as the following:

(a) $.5\overline{)12.5}$ $\longleftrightarrow$ $12.5/.5$

(b) $.12\overline{)4.8}$ $\longleftrightarrow$ $4.8/.12$

(c) $1.6\overline{)4.8}$ $\longleftrightarrow$ $4.8/1.6$

(d) $11.04\overline{)2.208}$ $\longleftrightarrow$ $2.208/11.04$

The class should now be asked, "Is there any way that the divisor (.5) in the problem 12.5/.5 can be made a whole number?" If an answer cannot be found, a further hint may be given by asking, "Can I multiply .5 by a number so it will become a whole number?" There are several possibilities, such as 2, 4, 6, 8, or 19. Our instinct at this time would be to say, "We want to use the 10, since . . ." However, this is not what we are concerned with at the present time. The important idea is finding an equivalent division problem with a whole-number divisor. Once we have selected a number by which to multiply the .5, we must draw on the child's knowledge of common fractions. If we multiply .5 by 2, we must also multiply 1.25 by 2. Several examples like the following should be used to entrench the notion of equivalent division problems.

$$(a) \ \frac{1.25}{.5} \Rightarrow \frac{1.25 \times 2}{.5 \times 2} \Rightarrow \frac{2.5}{1} \Rightarrow 1\overline{)2.5}$$

$$(b) \ \frac{.049}{.07} \Rightarrow \frac{.049 \times 100}{.07 \times 100} \Rightarrow \frac{4.9}{7} \Rightarrow 7\overline{)4.9}$$

As more examples are encountered, the child will soon see the utility in selecting multiples like 10, 100, or 1000, when finding the whole number divisor. Also, you should gradually move from

$$.7\overline{)1.23} \Rightarrow \frac{1.23}{.7} \Rightarrow \frac{1.23 \times 10}{.7 \times 10} \Rightarrow \frac{12.3}{7} \Rightarrow 7\overline{)12.3} \quad \text{to} \quad .7\overline{)1.23} \Rightarrow 7\overline{)12.3}$$

In the latter example, the transitional steps are omitted. However, if a child has difficulty, he should be capable of going back to this strategy.

Third, before any division of decimal fractions is actually performed, it is advantageous to assure ourselves that the child really believes he is working with equivalent problems. For example, if he doesn't think or understand that $.4\overline{)\,.205}$ is equivalent to $4\overline{)2.05}$, we will encounter considerable difficulty extending the division algorism. This hurdle can be overcome by a series of problems similar to the following:

$$4\overline{)12}^{\,3} \qquad 40\overline{)\,120}^{\,3} \qquad 400\overline{)1200}^{\,3}$$

$$2\overline{)\,6}^{\,3} \qquad 8\overline{)24}^{\,3}$$

$$1\overline{)3}^{\,3} \qquad 1/3\overline{)1}^{\,3} \qquad 28\overline{)84}^{\,3}$$

Once a child has acquired an intuitive feeling for the fact that regardless of what we multiply both divisor and dividend by, we will not change the quotient, we are free to encounter actual decimal division.

Fourth, we can now pose simple problems for the child to work, such as:

$$(a) \ .04\overline{)\,.12} = 4\overline{)12}^{\,3}$$

$$(b) \ .05\overline{)2.5} = 5\overline{)250}^{\,50}$$

At this stage we should use only problems where the quotient will be greater than or equal to 1.

Fifth, when sufficient skill has been acquired in finding quotients like the above, the student is prepared to encounter the final two hurdles in the decimal algorism. These hurdles are difficulties posed by (a) problems where the divisor is larger than the dividend, like $48.2\overline{)24.7}$, and (b) problems where a remainder exists, such as:

$$
\begin{array}{r}
218.23 \\
.17\overline{)37.1} \rightarrow 17\overline{)3710.00} \\
34 \\
\hline
31 \\
17 \\
\hline
140 \\
136 \\
\hline
40 \\
34 \\
\hline
60 \\
51 \\
\hline
9
\end{array}
$$

Problems like (a), where the divisor is larger than the dividend, can be handled through demonstrating the work as follows:

$$
\begin{array}{r}
.512 \\
48.2\overline{)24.7} \rightarrow 482\overline{)247.000} \\
2410 \\
\hline
600 \\
48\ 2 \\
\hline
1\ 1\ 80 \\
964 \\
\hline
216
\end{array}
$$

To keep the division algorism analogous to that of whole numbers, the dividend must be larger than the divisor. Thus we annex zeros after the decimal and continue as before. Since the decimal is not placed in the quotient until the division has been completed, we need only apply the whole-number division algorism to $482\overline{)247.000}$. The number of zeros annexed depends entirely on the precision required by the situations being encountered.

For problems like (*b*), remainders can be illustrated as follows:

$$
\begin{array}{r}
.2 \\
8.0 \\
10.0 \\
200.0 \\
.17\overline{)37.1} \rightarrow 17\overline{)3710.0} \\
\underline{3400.0} \\
310.0 \\
\underline{170.0} \\
140.0 \\
\underline{136.0} \\
4.0 \\
\underline{3.4} \\
.6
\end{array}
\qquad 218.2 \text{ R.6}
$$

It should be stressed through the use of the above method that the remainder is not a whole, as it would appear, but a decimal fraction. This process should be repeated for several other examples where the remainders can be expressed as hundredths, thousandths, and so on. For example:

$$
\begin{array}{r}
.10 \\
7.00 \\
.14\overline{)1.00} \rightarrow 14\overline{)100.00} \\
\underline{98} \\
2.00 \\
\underline{1.40} \\
0.60
\end{array}
\qquad 7.10 \text{ R. } .60
$$

We should extend our analogy between fractions and decimals by rewriting the decimal remainders in their equivalent common fraction forms. The quotients in the examples above would appear as:

(*a*) 218.2 and .6/17   or   218.2 and 60/170
(*b*) 7.10 and .60/14   or   7.10 and 60/1400 = 7.10 and 3/70

Exercises such as these will give some insight into the common usage made of decimals like 33.3 1/3 or 66 2/3.

The final step in the acquisition of this algorism should be its application to practical problems involving measurement.

Chapter 5

TEACHING GEOMETRY AND
MEASUREMENT

Geometry

The mere mention of the word geometry has the ability to arouse fear in the most stouthearted elementary teacher. The way the study of geometry is remembered, it is formidable enough to cause many students to avoid any further mathematics. This is a poor commentary for a subject that, if given a chance, can provide the intrinsic motivation for the study of mathematics.

Children invariably enjoy the study of geometry, provided it is not restricted to meaningless regurgitation of terms and definitions. Geometric vocabulary is of little value at this level and may in some instances retard a child's learning in the subject. To make the study of geometry enjoyable and productive, the teacher need only rely on the child's imagination and his natural instinct to explore. By providing enough guidance the teacher can channel the child's exploration toward a productive end.

The study of geometry in the elementary school is only the beginning of a child's study of the subject and should be treated with this in mind. A geometric concept introduced at this time will not be totally mastered by the child. He will, however, continue to refine and polish his acquisition over the years in order to obtain a more precise definition or concept. A pupil should learn more each year about previously studied topics as well as encounter new ideas in geometry. The continuous developmental nature of geometric concepts makes it essential that a long period of informal or intuitive exposure to a topic precede its formal presentation.

Methods of Teaching Geometry

Historically speaking, geometry has suffered in the elementary schools, either from neglect or from a very superficial consideration. Both approaches are detrimental to a child's learning of the subject. When geometry is considered in the elementary grades there is a tendency to become impatient for observable results and to "hurry" through the conceptual development, which is very complicated at best. This brings about three major errors in teaching that can hamper the child's ability to grasp the concepts involved: (1) overemphasis on vocabulary, (2) too rapid an introduction to formalized interpretation of geometric concepts, and (3) too little time provided for the child to engage his intuition in the learning process.

The authors have examined many elementary textbooks and workbooks to review what is being taught about geometry in the elementary schools. The topics usually presented include: lengths of lines, measurement, perimeters of rectangles and squares, volume, and area of surfaces. If developed properly, these topics are not only valuable to the child for future reference but can be rewarding in themselves. However, very few elementary texts devote ample time to the intuitive-exploratory development of a concept before providing the child with a rule, formula, or definition. For example, considerable time is spent on the memorization of words such as "triangle," "square," and "rectangle" so the child can identify a set of objects. This time could be better spent in making observation and comparisons of the objects with little regard to the names. As the child matures and grows a refinement of these observations and descriptions should lead into precise definitions.

Thus the teacher should not start out with definitions of geometric figures. He should use models that the child can see and feel. Children learn to classify objects according to shape, size, number of sides, and so forth. A child may forget the word "triangle," but he will recognize that it belongs to the set of objects having three sides. The vocabulary of geometry should be developed in the same way as the general vocabulary; that is, development must be gradual. We should not expect a child to acquire instant adult-level proficiency.

Throughout the elementary grades geometric figures should be things that can be seen or felt. The abstractness of a point, for example, is usually beyond the comprehension of an elementary child. Study must be maintained on the concrete level of development. The child should be able

Is the big fish *inside* or *outside* the bowl?

FIGURE 1

to pick up a solid figure, touch it, count the corners, and make comments about it without being tied to a rigorous vocabulary. For example, a first-grade child made the following observation when asked to compare a sphere and a cone: "It would hurt if you sat on that pointy thing, but not on the round one."

Developmental Strategy

The level of sophistication of geometry content in most elementary text-books is usually such that study is relegated to memory work. While the topics presented are appropriate, not enough time is allowed for intuitive investigation and organization of experience by the child. Most textbooks provide a good content outline of geometry, and a teacher is well advised to follow this general course of study. He should, however, supplement these offerings with appropriate foundational activities which are in the most part omitted from elementary texts.

The authors feel that most elementary teachers are more than capable of following a text's presentation of vocabulary, definition, and technical terms used in geometry. The teacher's challenge is to provide the back-ground necessary for a child to grasp the subtle geometric concepts. Pupils should be allowed to have considerable experience with geometric terms before these terms are formalized. They do not need to know that a square is a quadrilateral in order to observe that it has four sides. Such terms as "inside," "outside," and "on" a figure may be introduced quite naturally to primary children through their own perceptual experience (Figure 1). Later such experiences may be gradually transferred to the geometry mode.

The authors do not feel that a mathematics *methods* text is the place to teach geometry content. The scope of such an endeavor would not be feasible when the topic is restricted to a few pages. The goal of this chapter is to provide some suggested activities and explorations to furnish the child and the teacher with the necessary informal foundation for studying geometry. The teacher should consider the following activities as pretext-book offerings and not as a substitute for a more formalized presentation. We are more concerned with concentrating on a general method of teaching geometry than with trying to cover every aspect of the subject.

Point and Line

The geometry studied in elementary school is based on sets of points. A line segment, a line, or a square are sets of points. However, the concept of a point is very elusive and abstract, to say the least. No matter how small a point we make it still contains an infinite number of points. In fact there is no way to construct, draw, or show a point, since it has no dimensions. We cannot hold it, touch it, or even see it. It therefore follows that since every entity in geometry is sets of points, we cannot really see any of them but must study them through the use of models or representative approximations. It is not essential that the child comprehend this concept in its entirety, but he must be made aware of the distinction through activities similar to the following.

Suggested Activity

For this activity the children should be asked to bring to school pictures of animals, which they may display on the bulletin board.

Materials:

Feltboard and felt cutouts (see Chapter 9 for discussion of selection and use of feltboards).

Arrangement:

Class works as a group.

Procedure:

1. Have each child show his pictures to the class and tell what the picture shows. The teacher may want to display the pictures on the board. As each child tells about what he has brought, it should be stressed that these are pictures of animals and not the actual animals. This activity is designed to introduce the word "represents." We say that the picture represents the animal.

2. A similar procedure should be used with the felt cutouts.

Models

The use of models is essential to the study of geometry. In the beginning, these are for the most part produced by the teacher. However, in most cases the child can take an active role in his learning, and this is usually more successful.

One means of accomplishing this is to have the child illustrate the figure from which discussions may be generated. Initially, the free-hand drawings by the children will suffice for superficial observations. As the discussion progresses so should the accuracy of the drawings. Figure 2 shows a drawing of a triangle by a first-grade child. The figure does approximate a triangle inasmuch as it appears to have three sides, and it is a closed figure.

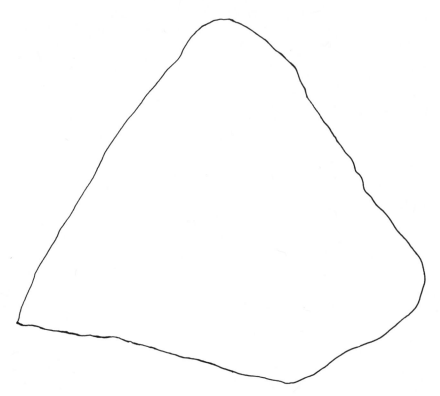

First - Grader's Concept of a Triangle

FIGURE 2

It does not lend itself well to discussing or observing that the triangle has three vertices or "pointy places," as a child might say. Since we want the child to make his own drawings whenever possible, it seems natural that we should provide him the means to produce a more accurate representation.

Suggested Activities

Activity 1

Materials:

Dot-to-dot coloring book or ditto copy similar to Figure 3, pencil, crayons.

Arrangement:

Individual work at pupils' desks.

Procedure:

Have the children draw lines from point to point on a figure such as
that in Figure 3, starting with the point labeled "1" and then proceeding to

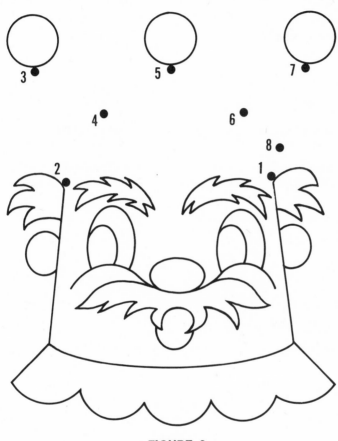

FIGURE 3

connect the rest of the points in order. Most children have already been
introduced to this type of activity, but there may be a need to give an example on the board. Be sure the children do not use straightedges to connect the dots.

Activity 2

Discuss with the children the fact that their lines in Activity 1 were not
always straight. Ask them if they know of any way they could make them

straighter.   The students will most likely make some recommendation such as the use of the edge of a book.

Materials:
    Straightedge (not a ruler), dot-to-dot picture (Figure 3).

Arrangement:
    Individual desk work.

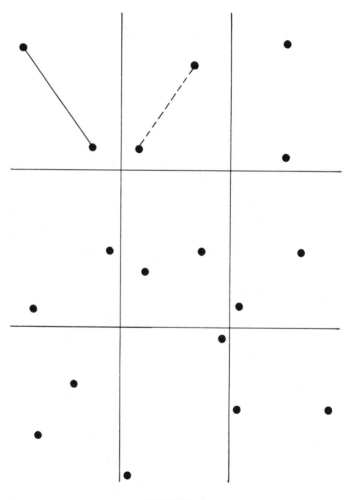

FIGURE 4

Procedure:

1. Give each child a straightedge (6″ piece of lattice or molding, not a ruler). Use a page similar to Figure 4 and use the first three or four frames as examples of how to draw a straight line between two points. You may wish to have the children number the frames as in the pages of a book.

2. Now, let each child complete the remaining frames by himself, with as much individual help as needed. Help the children acquire a functional technique for using the straightedge. In giving instructions, say something similar to: "Draw the line between the two points" or "Draw a line from one point to the next."

Observation and Classification

There is no denying that vocabulary plays a primary role in the study of geometry and should be given the attention fitting its importance. Such a development should be gradual in nature and related to the child's experience whenever possible. The teacher must build a child's vocabulary on words and phrases that the child already knows and should not immediately expect precise definitions. With this as our premise, it is possible to proceed with the development of new geometric concepts even if the child does not have a total grasp of the vocabulary.

Merely learning vocabulary will prove to be an insufficient basis for further study if the child does not grow in other skills essential to the learning of geometry. This is true of all mathematics, for that matter. A child enters school eager to learn in most cases and willing to express himself about many topics. These topics are, of course, not always relevant, and the enthusiasm is soon dampened in the name of order and discipline. It appears that rather than direct this exuberance toward the goal of learning, we suppress it and let it go to waste.

A child must be encouraged to observe and compare geometric figures from his point of view before we impose a more rigorous description or analysis on him. As he becomes more adept in his observational skills, we can develop his skill in the classification of geometric figures. At this stage, the child will begin to see emerging patterns and will make some attempt to form generalizations. It takes the total awareness of the teacher to weed out the improper conclusions without dampening the child's willingness to continue. A teacher with such awareness can help the child increase his ability to make and verbalize observations from a set of given experiences.

Suggested Activities

Activity 1

This activity is given as an example of how the teacher can use the child's general vocabulary as a basis for geometry.   It also provides an opportunity to elicit class discussion.

Materials:

Figure 5, crayons.

Arrangement:

Individual work.

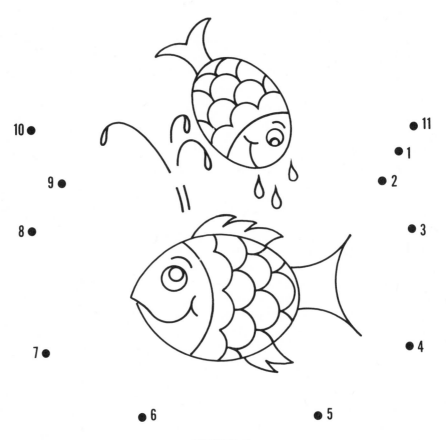

FIGURE 5

Procedure:

Have the children complete the picture (Figure 5) by drawing the lines from dot to dot. Once they have completed the figure have them color the largest fish red and the smallest fish blue. Upon completion of this task, ask, "Which fish is *inside* the bowl? Which fish is *outside* the bowl?" This activity is to provide the child with an intuitive encounter with the words "inside" and "outside," which will be used later in a more mathematical setting.

Activity 2

This activity can be used for the following purposes:
1. To introduce comparison activities by discussing triangles, quadrilaterals, and other polygons.
2. To continue the development of skills in using the straightedge.

Note: In this activity the burden of discussion should be left to the students; the teacher's role is that of moderator. You'll find that in the early comparison activities considerable work will be needed for the children just to understand the words "same" and "different."

Materials:

Figure 6, straightedge.

Arrangement:

Class works as a group.

Procedure:

Have the children complete the drawing in Figure 6 by using their straightedges. Once they have completed this task, follow up by asking questions such as the following: "Are all the figures the same? How are they the same? How many sides does each have? Can you draw a *picture* of a point *inside* the figure? Can you draw a *picture* of a point *outside* the figure? Draw a *picture* of a point *on* the figure."

Activity 3

This activity will call for discussion similar to that used in the two previous activities. Each comment by the children should be discussed by the teacher in a positive manner, whether it is right or wrong. The incorrect answer may be as instructive as a correct one. Our primary concern in the introduction is that of comparison by number of sides. Also, while these figures are quadrilaterals, we should not necessarily use the word at this time.

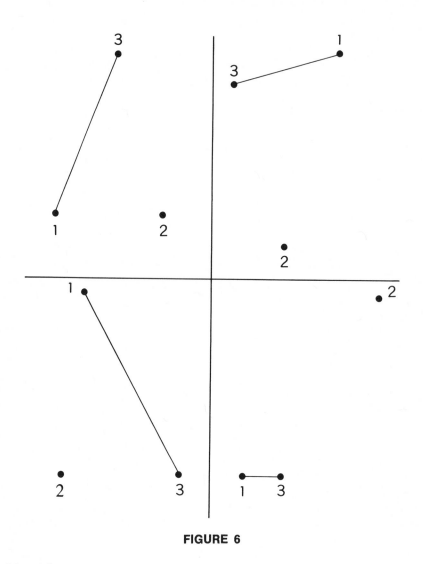

FIGURE 6

Materials:

Figures 7 and 8, straightedge.

Arrangement:

Class works as a group.

Procedure:

Have the children complete designs such as in Figures 7 and 8, using a

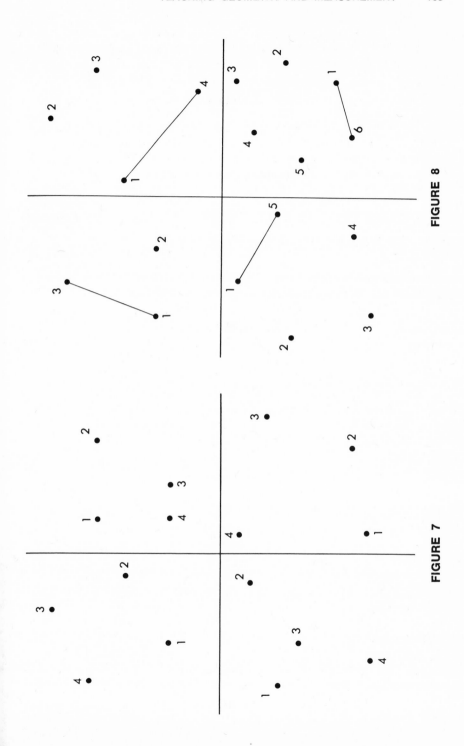

FIGURE 8

FIGURE 7

straightedge, draw the line segments between the dots.   Upon completion, questions similar to those in the previous two activities should be used.

Activity 4

This activity is to be worked by each child individually.   A group discussion of the task may follow if needed.   The primary interest is in making the numerical distinction between polygons.   The teacher can use the word polygon but should not require the children to do so.

FIGURE 9

Materials:

Figure 9.

Arrangement:

Individual desk work.

Procedure:

1. Give each child a copy of a worksheet similar to Figure 9. After a brief introduction, ask the children to:

(a) Place an (X) inside each four-sided polygon.
(b) Place a (T) inside each three-sided polygon.
(c) Place an (*) inside each five-sided polygon.

2. Check the page for accuracy. You will want to talk about the circle and how many sides it has. (None, since a side must be a straight line.)

Congruence

The concept of congruence may be introduced as soon as a child has a firm grasp of the concept of size and shape. Theoretically congruence is a distance-preserving mapping. (In two congruent figures the distance between any two corresponding points will be equal.) This sort of definition is asking a little bit too much of an elementary child. We should be content to have them think of two figures being congruent if the two figures fit exactly on one another or if we could use the same pattern to draw both figures. Cutouts, tracing paper, and a geoboard can be used effectively to teach this concept.

Activity 1

In this activity we expect that the children will make many different geometric shapes on their geoboards. Also, it is natural for them to want to share what they have made (created) with other children. At first, this may take the form of showing their neighbor, which should be encouraged as long as the class is not too chaotic. Ultimately this need to share can be channeled into class discussions.

Materials:

Geoboard, rubber bands. (Suggestions for selection and/or preparation of geoboards are included in Chapter 9.)

Arrangement:

The class may be divided into small groups after the initial introduction of the apparatus.

Procedure:

Provide each child with a geoboard and three rubber bands. Once the children have the geoboard, allow them a reasonable amount of free time to create any kind of picture they wish by encircling pegs with rubber bands. As this free play continues it will lend itself to discussion of their pictures. Let the children describe the pictures as they see them; there is no reason to force mathematical descriptions. This exercise has no definite time schedule but is terminated as the teacher sees fit. Remember we only want to familiarize the pupil with the apparatus and to provide for free discussion of what he sees and produces.

Activity 2

This activity will provide a prime opportunity to recall previous class discussion of polygons. The child must draw upon his verbal understanding of past vocabulary. The use of the geoboard offers an opportunity for a wide variety of shapes to be created and discussed by the children. They are no longer restricted to figures that the teacher makes up.

Materials:

Geoboard; rubber bands. If you do not have access to a geoboard, use a paper with equally spaced dots, as shown in Figures 10 and 11.

Arrangement:

Class arrangement is left to the discretion of the teacher.

Procedure:

Each child will use his own geoboard for this activity. The goal is to have the children follow simple oral directions. Ask each child to make a triangle with a rubber band on his geoboard. It should be noted at this time that all the triangles are not the same (congruent), but that they all have three sides (see Figure 10). A similar activity and discussion can and should be used for the rectangle and the square (quadrilaterals), as in Figure 11. The activity should be continued for figures with four, five, six, etc., sides so that the student learns there are geometric figures other than those with common names. Note that vocabulary is important only to the extent that the teacher uses it correctly.

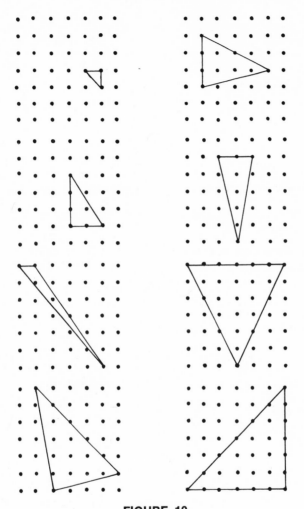

FIGURE 10

Activity 3

We are interested in introducing the phrase "copy exactly," but we are not looking for proficiency in its use. The teacher should not feel that each child must perform the task correctly. Accuracy will come only with time and experience.

Materials:

Geoboard, rubber bands.

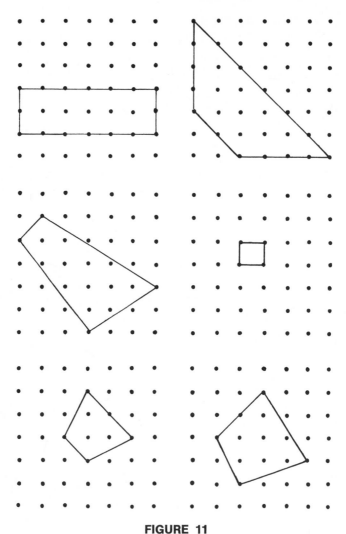

FIGURE 11

Arrangement:

Class as a group.

Procedure:

The teacher will make a square on her geoboard and then ask the students to *copy it exactly*—that is, the copy must be congruent to the figure the teacher has made. At this point, class discussion will focus on what we mean by "copy it exactly." While we are looking for an intuitive understanding of congruence, some verbalization of its meaning will naturally appear in the class discussion.

Since the children are copying the figure from the teacher's geoboard, we will need a method for determining if the figures are exactly the same. The children may suggest ways of doing this. Usually they will copy the figure on a piece of paper and then see if it fits the teacher's figure. This activity should be repeated with other figures such as the triangle, rectangle, or any other figure (Figure 12).

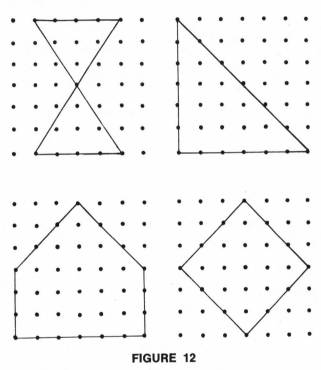

FIGURE 12

Activity 4

This activity will help further the notion of congruence through actual physical manipulation of figures.

Materials:

Cardboard cutouts (Figure 13), chalk.

Arrangement:

Small groups.

Procedure:

Trace around one of the cardboard figures (see Figure 13) on the floor; then place all the figures on the desk. Now, ask one child to find the figure that *fits inside the lines exactly*. Once he finds it and selects a figure, he must check it by placing it inside the traced lines.

The first few times the figures should be placed face up, that is, with the side of the paper on which the tracing was done facing upward. Then it should be shown that if we traced one of the shapes in Figure 13 and

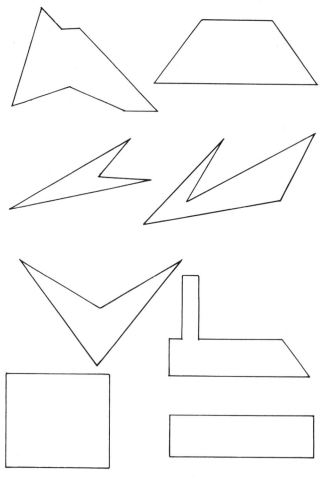

FIGURE 13

turned it over, it would not fit inside the line.   This type of activity will give the child an intuitive idea of checking congruence by superposition.

Similarity

Similarity, in the early stages of its development, can be thought of as meaning "the same shape as."   To acquire the precise definition of similar figures, we need measurement, but this does not eliminate the opportunity for an intuitive understanding of the concept.

Activities similar to those employed to teach congruence can also teach similarity.   Prepare squares or circles, no two the same size.   The child can maneuver the figures to place the smaller inside the larger until the border is the same all the way around (Figure 14).   Activities of this kind can be

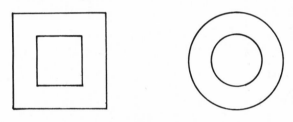

FIGURE 14

carried out with numerous regular polygons, such as equilateral triangles, hexagons, and so on.

Suggested Activities

Activity 1

The intuitive "feel" for similarity of irregular figures should not be neglected.   This may be presented in many interesting ways.   When scale drawings or models are constructed properly, the figures will be similar.

Materials:

Geoboard, graph paper.

Arrangement:

Class as group.

Procedure:

Give each child several sheets of graph paper (1/4″ size is fine). Now construct any desired figure on the geoboard and ask the children to copy the figure on their papers (Figure 15). Most children are familiar with

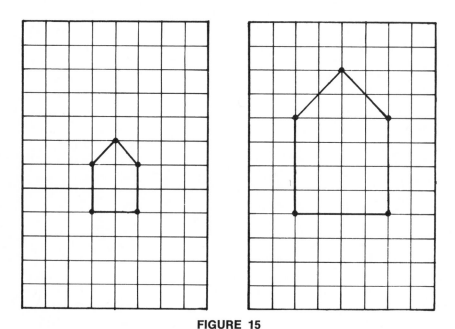

FIGURE 15

Figure on Geoboard (left) is Reproduced by Student on Graph Paper

model cars and planes and realize that the model is just like the real thing, with the exception of size. A discussion at this time based on this idea can help convey the notion of similarity.

Activity 2

Materials:

Overhead projector.

Arrangement:

Class as group.

Procedure:

Have ready several overhead transparencies of regular and irregular polygonal figures. Project the image on the screen and discuss the shape and size of the image in relation to the original figure. If there is no distortion, the figures are similar.

Symmetry

A child in first grade can begin the study of symmetric figures if the topic is handled properly. He can begin by looking at the world around him and discussing what he sees. His body is symmetrical with respect to a vertical line through his nose. Some leaves are symmetrical, many trees are symmetrical, and so on. From these observations he may be asked to make a symmetrical design with blocks or other materials.

Once the child has grasped the notion that a figure is symmetrical if it is "balanced," that is, "What's on one side must be on the other side," we can begin a more formal development. The following developmental activities should give rise to many other appropriate ones.

Suggested Activities

In the following three activities we want the child to be able to identify and draw symmetric figures and to be able to sketch the lines of symmetry of a symmetric figure.

Activity 1

Materials:

Figures 16–19, tracing paper, ruler, pencil, scissors.

Arrangement:

May use large group or individualized instruction.

Procedure:

1. In this lesson the child will use tracing paper to make symmetric figures. A dashed line indicates the line of reflection, and a dot on the line will be used as a reference point. Instruct pupils as follows:

(a) Cover with tracing paper and trace the figure.
(b) Trace the dashed line and reference dot (Figure 16).
(c) Turn the tracing paper over; be sure the dashed line and its tracing match, and the reference dot and its image match.
(d) Mark over the figure on the tracing paper to get an impression (Figure 17).
(e) Remove the tracing paper, then darken the impression marks. The original figure and its image now form a symmetric figure (Figure 18). Do you see why?

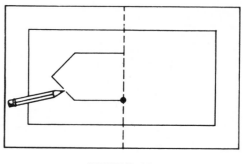

FIGURE 16

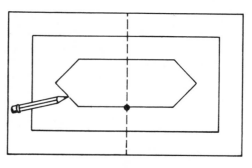

FIGURE 17

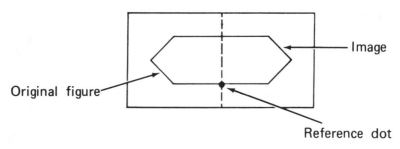

FIGURE 18

2. Point out that besides these points matching, all the corresponding sides are equal.

3. Instruct pupils to follow the above procedure and make symmetric figures by drawing the images of the figures in Figure 19.

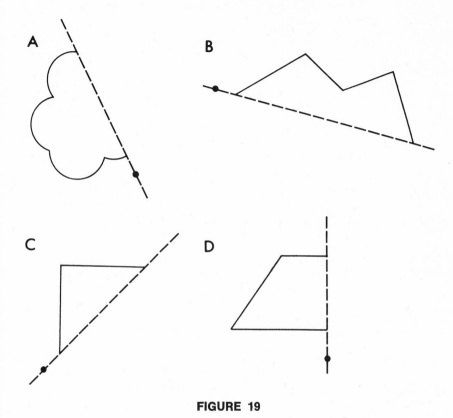

FIGURE 19

Activity 2

One way to determine if a figure is symmetric is to trace the entire figure and then turn the tracing paper over. If when the tracing paper is turned over it can be made to match the original figure, the figure is symmetric.

Materials:

Figures 20 and 21; tracing paper, ruler, pencil.

Arrangement:

Group size to be determined by the teacher and progress of students.

Procedure:

1. Instruct pupils to try the test given above on the examples in Figure 20.

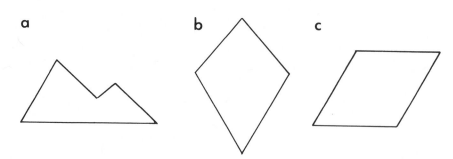

A. This figure *is not* symmetric. No matter how you flip the tracing paper it will not match the original figure.

B. This figure *is symmetric.* Did you get the image on the tracing paper to match?

C. This figure *is symmetric.* Did you find the correct way to flip the tracing paper?

FIGURE 20

2.   Then instruct pupils to indicate whether the shapes in Figure 21 are or are not symmetric by checking the appropriate response.

Activity 3

Another way to determine if a figure is symmetric is to fold the figure on an estimated line of symmetry.   If the two halves of the figure match, that is, coincide with one another, the figure is symmetric.

Materials:

Figures 22–25.

Arrangement:

Same as for Activity 2.

Procedure:

1.   Instruct pupils to consider Figure 22.   Point out that if this figure is symmetric, the dashed line BF might be the line of symmetry.   If this figure is symmetric and line BF is a line of symmetry, then point E must match point D and points A and C must match.   This may be checked by folding the figure on the proposed line of symmetry.

2.   Using Figure 23, instruct pupils to sketch what they believe to be a line of symmetry, using a dotted line, and then indicate whether the shapes are or are not symmetric.

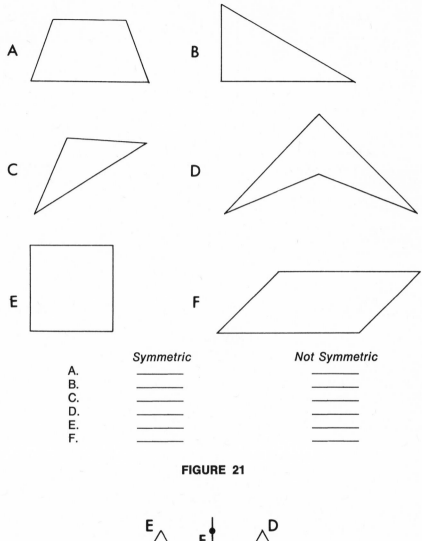

FIGURE 21

FIGURE 22

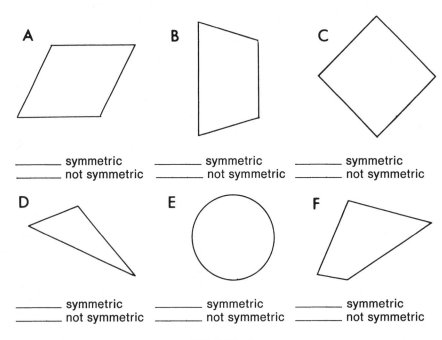

FIGURE 23

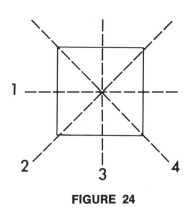

FIGURE 24

3. Use Figure 24 to demonstrate that some symmetric figures have more than one line of symmetry. A square, as shown in the figure, has four lines of symmetry.

4. In Figure 25, have pupils indicate all possible lines of symmetry by drawing dotted lines on the figure. If the figure is not symmetric, that is, if

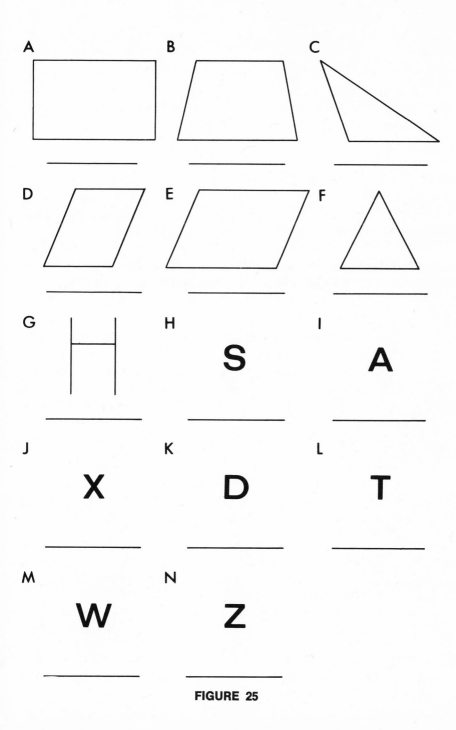

FIGURE 25

there are no lines of symmetry, they should write "not" in the space provided.

Activity 4

In order to review symmetric figures with your students you could play a game of "Who Am I?" in which they would try to identify figures by their descriptions.

Materials:

Cards.

Arrangement:

The arrangement of the group size is dependent on student progress.

Procedure:

To prepare for this game, write clues such as those given below on cards. A student picks a card, reads the clues, and tries to name the figure described, thus earning a predetermined number of points for his team.

Sample:
I am a triangle with exactly one line of symmetry. Who am I? Answer: isosceles triangle.

(a) I am a special parallelogram with exactly four lines of symmetry. Who am I?_____

(b) I am a special kind of parallelogram with exactly two lines of symmetry which are not diagonals. Who am I?_____

(c) I am a triangle with exactly three lines of symmetry. Who am I?

_____

(d) I am a special kind of quadrilateral with exactly one line of symmetry. Who am I?_____

(e) I am one of the four letters below. I have no lines of symmetry. Which letter am I?_____

A   Z   M   B

(f) I am a special kind of parallelogram. I have exactly two lines of symmetry, both of which are diagonals. Who am I?_____

(g) I am two of the five letters below. I have exactly two lines of symmetry. Who am I?_____

B   X   U   S   I

Answers: (a) rectangle; (b) square; (c) equilateral triangle; (d) regular trapezoid; (e) Z; (f) rhombus; (g) X and I.

Linear Measurement

Elementary textbooks are more than adequately supplied with exercises pertaining to linear measurement, but they are typically lacking in developmental activities in the same category. The topic of measurement is thrust upon the child in the form of a ruler, with little if any prior introduction to what measurement is all about. The following sequence is suggested as groundwork prior to giving the child a standard measuring instrument.

The authors believe the child must be aware of each of the following concepts before meaningful work can be accomplished with any form of measurement.

1. Measurement is a means of comparison.
2. What is meant by a "common unit."
3. What is meant by a "standard unit."

Suggested Activities

Activity 1

This activity relies on the child's natural desire to compare, for example: "I'm bigger than James," or "Michelle is shorter than Billy." This comparison is a basic form of measurement where the unit of measure is the individual himself or any nearby object. Such activities will allow the child to become familiar with such comparative terms as "shorter," or "longer."

Materials:

Yarn, string, pencils, rope, etc.

Arrangement:

Class observes while individuals perform certain tasks.

Procedure:

Select two students from the class and ask which is taller. Once the answer has been given, ask pupils how they know their answer is correct. We would expect some kind of comparison to be made. The students will probably need some help in stating that they compared one student to the other, but they must be allowed ample opportunity to express their thoughts. Once this comparison and discussion have taken place, similar activities should be used with objects such as pencils, chalk, and strings of different length.

Activity 2

This activity attempts to show the child that in measurement we must always begin with a common origin. Another concept to be taught is that changing the position of an object does not alter its length, but it may change its appearance. A young child should not be told this; he must learn such a concept by experiencing many comparative activities.

Materials:

Yarn, rope, or string; feltboard.

Arrangement:

The class plays the game as a group.

Procedure:

1. Prepare several lengths of yarn, rope, or string, one of which is as long as your desk or some other convenient object. Place the yarn or string on the bulletin board in patterns such as those shown in Figure 26

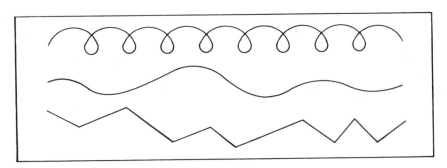

FIGURE 26

and ask the students if they think any of the pieces on the board are as long as the desk (or other convenient object you have selected). They should be allowed to guess, and as each child answers, his guess should be confirmed or shown false by taking the string he chose from the bulletin board and comparing it with the desk. Several wrong answers will most likely be given because of the way the pieces are arranged on the board. This could be discussed in terms of how we compare lengths. In this example, we must stretch out the rope or string first (Figure 27).

FIGURE 27

2. Again, set up a bulletin board similar to the above. However, this time the strings will represent the length or height of several different objects in the room. Ask the children to identify the rope or yarn that is as long as the cabinet or some other object. Each guess should be verified by actual comparison.

Activity 3

This activity is a continuation of the preceding comparison activities, with one addition. We are now introducing measurement by a secondary comparison; that is, we no longer compare objects with each other, but by using a representation of their length. This concept is far more difficult than it appears and should not be treated lightly.

Materials:

Masking tape and adding machine tape or string.

Arrangement:

Class observes selected individuals performing assigned task.

Procedure:

1. Give each child a piece of string or strip of paper and ask him to cut it the same length as some object in the room, such as a book or pencil. Have several pupils show their string or strip and ask how they know the length is correct.

2. Have two children show how tall a third child is by using a piece of string to measure him. Then help the students tape the length of string to

the board and put the student's name by it.   Repeat the process for a second child.   After completing both measurements ask the rest of the class to tell, by looking at the board, who is the taller.

3.   Send one child into the hall and ask another to step to the front of the room.   Now ask the class who is the taller, the child outside or the one in front of the class.   This should help children recognize the need for measuring each child by some means other than physical side-by-side comparison; that is, a measurement strategy similar to that used in procedure two.

4.   After completing the above activities, the children may find it interesting to *represent* all their heights on one of the chalk or bulletin boards. This can be done by having the children measure each other with string or yarn, cutting off the appropriate length, and placing it on the board with the name under it (Figure 28).   This type of activity can be thought of as

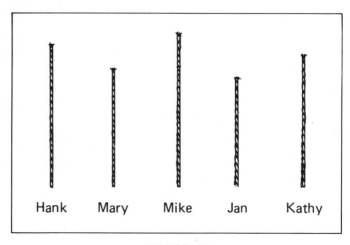

| Hank | Mary | Mike | Jan | Kathy |

FIGURE 28

the first readiness activity for graphing.   You may want to make a new graph later in the year to show change, so the original graph can be stored for later use.

Activity 4

With this activity we hope to develop the notion that many different objects can serve as a unit of measure.   We have listed only a few items that can be used.   The teacher should feel free to use any additional units of measure she finds appropriate.

Materials:

Rope, string, paper clips, chalk, etc.

Arrangement:

Class observes as selected students or small groups perform.

Procedure:

1. Have as many as possible of the above-mentioned items available on a table for the children's use in measuring. A record should be kept for each of the following five activities.

(*a*) List each object and its length, for example, "The desk is 5 ropes long."

(*b*) Select a child to help measure the length of your desk with a piece of rope. Ask, "How long is the desk?" Then measure the desk by placing the rope along the desk and having the child mark the end of the rope with his finger. Move the end of the rope to his finger and continue as before. Of course, your answer will be approximate.

(*c*) Pick other children to help in measuring different objects with different *units of measure*, until you think they have mastered the mechanics of measurement.

(*d*) Now have the students measure the same object with different units of measure. Record the answers as suggested and then discuss the reason for the difference in the answers. For example, "The desk is 4 ropes long, but it is 7 strings long."

(*e*) After using many different examples similar to the two above, the child should conclude that in order to have measurements which are understood by everyone, we should use the same *unit of measure* or we should measure with the same thing.

Activity 5

This activity not only continues to develop the last concept in Activity 4 but is a readiness activity for the standard units of measure, inch, foot, and yard.

Procedure:

Ask the class how far it is across the room. Do not immediately suggest a way to measure it, but let the children discuss how they would want to do it. After talking about several ways, you can suggest the number of steps as one means of measuring. Have a child tell how many steps he thinks it would be, then have him try it. Once he obtains a number, count the number of steps it takes you to walk across the room (this will be different from the student's). At this point, ask why we got different answers.

Next, measure the same distance by placing one of your shoes immediately in front of the other. Have the students count the number of times you use your shoe and then select a student to do the same type of measurement. Again, we should discuss why we get a different number of steps. Keep a record of each measurement on the board.

Perimeter

The perimeter of a plane figure should be an outgrowth of linear measurement. The children should have measuring instruments, such as a ruler, available. We need only touch briefly on what we mean by perimeter before we continue. Like any other topic discussed thus far, we should begin with something other than a problem in the textbook.

Suggested Activities

Activity 1

Materials:

Geoboards, worksheets, rubber bands.

Arrangement:

To insure that each child is introduced to the concept correctly, it will be advisable to have groups of four to six children for this activity. Also, since the activity has several parts, it is possible that it may not be completed in a single class period.

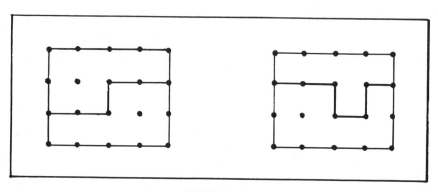

FIGURE 29

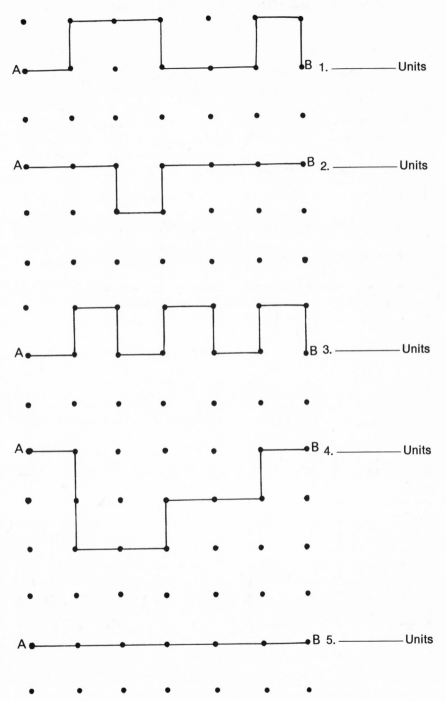

1. _____ Units

2. _____ Units

3. _____ Units

4. _____ Units

5. _____ Units

FIGURE 30

Procedure:

1. Construct a square on your geoboard and ask how long each side is. Let the answers vary as far as the name of the measure is concerned. It might be so many spaces, nails, etc.

2. Construct a rectangle and proceed as above, but guide the children into using the term "unit," that is, "It is 6 units long."

3. Construct paths on your geoboard similar to those shown in Figure 29. Ask the children how many units long each of the paths is.

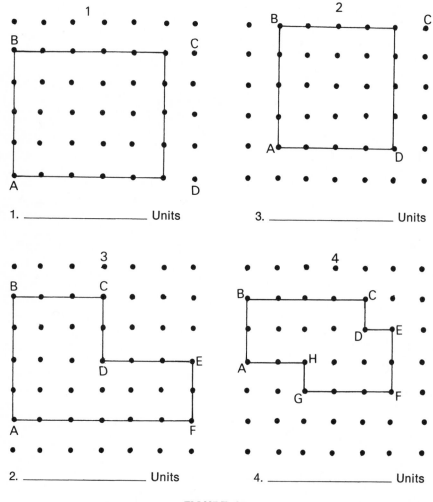

1. _____ Units

3. _____ Units

2. _____ Units

4. _____ Units

FIGURE 31

4. Present the children with a work sheet similar to Figure 30. Work the first two examples with the class and then let them finish alone.

5. Using an activity similar to Figures 30 and 31, ask the children: "How many units is it from A to B? How many units from B to C? How many units from C to D? How many units from D to A?" Then ask how many units is it if we go all the way around, starting at A and ending at A. Record this answer on the line below shape 1. Do the same for 2 and let the children work 3 and 4 by themselves.

Volume and Solids

The following sequence of activities has been selected because they provide examples which can be used for the introduction of geometric solids and the measurement of volume. A parallel development could also apply to the measurement of area.

Objectives of these activities are twofold:

1. To provide such sequencing of activities as will enable the child to become familiar with dimensional objects naturally.
2. To give the child an intuitive concept of volume as the amount contained or held in something.

Suggested Activities

Activity 1

The purposes are to give the children experiences with different types of three-dimensional objects and to help them discover what attributes a three-dimensional object has before learning its name.

Arrangement:

Divide the class into groups of three to six children per table.

Materials:

On each table place a wide variety of three-dimensional objects. In particular, be sure that there are different sizes of each kind of material to be used in the entire unit. Don't put balls on one table, blocks on another, and so forth.

Procedure:

1. Give the children a few minutes of free play. Visit each table and make a kind of game of describing the various objects in as many ways as possible.

2. Now, shift the emphasis in the game. Go from table to table, select an object, and see if any child at any particular table can properly identify it. After it has been named correctly, hold it up for the class to see and have the class repeat the name in unison. Make sure that a *large* cube or a *small* cube is still recognized as a cube. Make a list of the objects you feel the children should be able to name when the class later discusses different items. Remember that correct names for objects are as easily learned as incorrect ones.

Activity 2

This activity is designed to give children experiences in manipulating three-dimensional objects to illustrate that they can hold something; that is, they are containers.

Materials:

On each of the pupils' tables there should be various measuring devices as well as various small containers. In particular have some small balls, marbles, blocks, small boxes, jars, coffee cans, and milk cartons on each table. In front of the class where all can see have boxes larger than those on the children's tables, large cans, a wastepaper basket, volley ball, baseball, stack of books, and so forth.

Arrangement:

Children remain at their tables as for Activity 1.

Procedure:

1. Ask a series of questions which the children can answer by actual selection of three-dimensional objects:

(*a*) "Find me a container on your table that I can use to carry sand to the play yard." Insure that each child selects an open container, not a solid one.

(*b*) Hold up a baseball and ask the children to find on their table a container in which they can carry the ball to the play yard. Not all children will be able to have different objects due to the limited amount of material on each table.

(*c*) Clear all containers from the children's tables and choose a stack of books to be carried to another room. Then direct the attention of the class to the larger containers near your desk and invite the children to choose a container suitable for the books. It is hoped that a square box will be selected, not the wastepaper basket.

(*d*) Continue to set up similar situations and ask questions that will force the children to focus attention on the holding capacity of the various containers.

2. With children working in small groups at a table or desk, have them experiment to find which container will hold the different kinds of objects. This can also be an individual project.

Activity 3

Purposes are to relate the *holding ability* of a container to its size and to begin to introduce the notion of *estimation* and how it can be discovered, particularly whether an estimate is correct or close.

Materials:

Same as Activity 2, except the teacher will need each of the various objects and containers on or near her desk.

Arrangement:

Children remain at their tables as before.

Procedure:

1. Involve the entire class by holding up objects so that all can see and asking questions:

(*a*) Hold up a baseball and a half-gallon milk carton and ask, "Will this container hold the ball?" After the children have responded, let one come up and try. Do this with several objects and containers, letting the object drop into the container each time.

(*b*) Choose a container that is just a little too small to hold the ball and repeat the experiment, each time making sure some child has a chance to verify the estimate.

(*c*) Have two containers which seem to be of the same size but are such that one holds the ball and the other does not. Allow several children to experiment with fitting the ball into the container while questions are asked as to why one holds the ball and the other does not.

(*d*) Now, at a little more abstract level, hold up a pint milk carton and ask: "Will this hold a marble? Will it hold a baseball?" Do not show the object, that is, the marble or the ball.

2. Visit each table and choose an object. Then request the children at that table to pick a container which will hold the chosen object. Be sure to let each child try his container to see if he is right or wrong.

3. Hold up various sizes of objects so that all may see and ask children to select containers from their table which will hold these objects. Again, be sure to include one object that no container will hold and try to elicit why this is so from the children.

Activity 4

This activity is concerned with measuring with the same-sized container but different-sized measuring devices. After becoming familiar with the idea that a three-dimensional object can *hold* something, the children should be ready to begin determining how much or how many of certain objects a container will hold. Whenever possible, preface each activity by having the students estimate and, if appropriate, record their estimates. In a sense the real activities will be the checking of their estimates by the children.

Objectives of this activity are to give the students experiences leading toward the conclusion that:

1. Two containers of the same size hold more of one kind of object than they do of another, and this difference is due to the size (and possibly the shape) of the measuring material.

2. Different-sized containers hold different amounts of objects or materials of the same size.

3. Sand is a better measuring medium than marbles or balls.

Materials:

A wide variety of measuring materials such as cubes, marbles, balls, and sand; and a variety of containers such as small boxes, milk cartons, jars, and coffee cans at each table.

Arrangement:

In groups at tables as before.

Procedure:

1. Select from each table a container and have the children estimate how many marbles or small balls it will hold.

(*a*) Record the estimates, and then let students fill the containers, counting and recording as they fill.

(*b*) These activities should be followed by a class discussion as to why the containers hold more marbles than Ping-Pong balls. Note: If children have not reached the stage of counting and recording, then select two containers of the same size and shape and have them fill them alternately, one marble, then one ball. The idea of "one to one" should bring out that more marbles than balls are needed.

2. To lead into more abstract thinking, follow Activities 1 and 2 with questions such as "Will this can hold more peas or baseballs?" You can use any well-known objects as long as they are in sight of the students.

3. At some stage in this activity, select two different containers of the

same size and repeat the above experiments.   Again, use different-sized measuring devices in an attempt to bring out the idea that we need a uniform measuring device.

Activity 5

In this activity children will measure with the same measuring device as in Activity 1, but using different-sized containers.

Materials:

As in Activity 4, but the use of sand as a measuring device is especially recommended during the later stages of this activity.

Arrangement:

As in Activity 4.

Procedure:

1.   Select two containers of different sizes for each table.   Elicit from the children that the sizes are different and let them fill the containers with marbles, sand, etc., to check the idea.   Then have a class discussion as to why different numbers of balls or cupsful of sand are needed to fill the container.

2.   Repeat the above with various types of measuring devices and containers, but at some stage be sure to shift to sand as a measuring device and glass jars as containers.   Try to elicit from the student why the sand made a better measuring medium than marbles or balls.

3.   Select jars or containers that students can see through.   Lead the discussion as before: "How many cupsful of sand will this one hold?"   Let students fill the containers to check their estimates, and have them record their findings.   In doing this, use at least two different-sized measuring cups to fill the containers.   Through class discussion, again bring out that sand *filled* better than marbles and so forth, but the class is still faced with the problem of having to choose measuring cups of the same size.

Activity 6

Learning the concepts of *bigger* and *smaller* as related to volume is the topic of this activity, which is a continuation of previous activities but introduces a few more subtle ideas for the children to grasp.   It seems natural to start comparing three-dimensional objects on the basis of how much or how many they *hold*.   Without formally introducing the word *dimension*, it is hoped that the idea becomes clear that capacity is changed if the height or base size is changed.   Also, children should be aware that there are objects which have no holding capacity.

Objectives are:

1. To give students experiences in classifying three-dimensional objects according to their holding capacity.
2. To help students learn to order containers according to how much they hold.

Materials and Arrangement:

Same as previous three activities.

Procedure:

1. Before class, select two milk cartons of the same capacity (i.e., both may be pints), but cut the tops off so that one will hold more than the other. Do this for each table.

   (*a*) Have children estimate how many cupsful of sand each could hold, record the estimates, and then check by filling.

   (*b*) Through class discussion, elicit that we can say that one container is *bigger* or *smaller* according to how much sand they hold.

2. Repeat the above, using different-shaped containers, for example, a detergent bottle and a coffee can. Be sure to let the students examine the containers first and then check their estimates by filling with sand.

Activity 7

Ordering by volume.

Materials and Arrangement:

As above.

Procedure:

1. Using three different-sized containers such as milk cartons, coffee cans, and jars, have the students fill the containers and arrange them according to which holds the most sand. Be sure these containers can be differentiated, i.e., A, B, and C, or red, yellow, and blue. The teacher must not identify them by size. Now class discussion can be started with questions such as: "Does B hold more than A? Why? Does C hold more than B? Why? What do we know about A and C? Why?" It is not expected that the transitive property will be noted, and no attempt should be made to force it.

2. After repeating the above with different materials and containers and in various ways, have the children fill preselected containers of the same size and ask them to arrange them as in earlier lessons. It is hoped that the idea of *same size as* will come forth just as *bigger than*, etc., did before.

3. Now place from three to five different-sized containers on each table and let the children estimate their volume and arrange them according to size. Record this arrangement, and then let the children fill the containers with sand to check their estimates.

Activity 8

Experiments in varying dimensions.

Materials:

Models similar to Figures 32 and 33.

Prepare containers of at least four different heights but all having the same base, as in Figure 32. Have the children fill the containers with

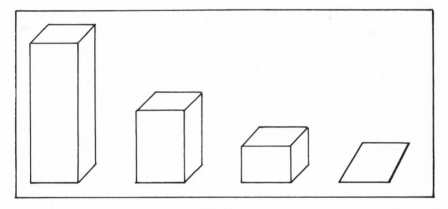

FIGURE 32

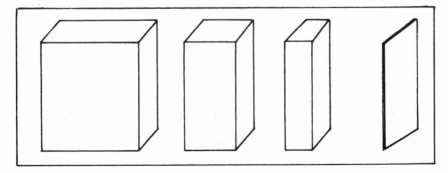

FIGURE 33

various materials (marbles or sand), and see if the idea occurs to them that the volume change is due to the change in height.   Check also for the idea that certain objects can hold nothing.

Prepare a second set of containers, letting the height remain constant while the base varies (Figure 33).   Again engage the class in activities until change in volume is associated with the change in base.

PART II

The Teacher's Role

Chapter **6**

DEVELOPING TEACHING SKILLS

Introduction

Much has been written since the early 1960s concerning the "new" mathematics in the elementary school, and it has been the subject of numerous national studies involving leaders in mathematics in the United States and abroad. As a result teachers now have available elaborate pupil textbook series prepared by teams of authorities. At the same time the mathematics curriculum was being studied and revised, technological advances were providing new types of equipment for use in the classroom. Listening centers, digital computers, overhead projectors, transparencies, film loops, number lines, games, individualized card-type laboratories, Cuisenaire rods, and a multitude of manipulative aids are now readily available from commercial sources.

During the past decade, also, as curricula have been studied and as publishers have marketed varieties of resource materials, there have been attempts to develop new or adapted teaching procedures or organizational arrangements for teaching mathematics in the elementary school. Such terms as discovery method, Montessori plan, open school, English primary school, and computer-assisted instruction are commonly noted in the literature relating to the teaching of mathematics.

The question to be considered by both the prospective and the experienced elementary school teacher is: How can I best teach mathematics in today's elementary schools to today's children?

Objectives of Teaching

The methods of teaching elementary school mathematics will be determined largely by the overall objectives of the mathematics program. These objectives usually are stated in the school system or state curriculum guide, as well as in the teacher's editions of the pupil textbooks available in the school.

In actual practice, however, what goes on in the classroom is dependent upon the teacher's own objectives, which may or may not be in accord with any stated list of goals for the elementary school. For example, one teacher in the fourth grade may feel that memorizing multiplication tables is the priority goal for the age group, and his day-to-day teaching will stress 100 percent achievement of this objective. Another teacher may have the general objective of completing the textbook, as reflected in the teaching procedure of "covering" a prescribed number of pages per day. A teacher who himself experienced difficulty with mathematics may have as his objective explanations of every new topic or operation in minute detail; his teaching procedures will take on an expository approach.

Two recent studies of elementary school classrooms stress the apparent disparity between objectives agreed upon by authorities and the actual objectives and teaching procedures used in the classroom. John Goodlad and Frances Klein found little evidence of implementation of educational reform exhibited in a sample of classrooms from 13 states. Trained observers visited over 150 classrooms in the late 1960s to look for evidence of currently accepted educational practices, such as emphasis on discernible objectives. The researchers noted that "general or specific goals were not identifiable to observers. Instruction was general in character and not specifically directed to diagnosed needs, progress, and problems of individual children. Teachers shot with a shotgun, not a rifle." [1]

"Mindlessness" is a term repeatedly used by Charles E. Silberman to describe what occurs in our American public schools. He infers that because teachers do not have clearly formulated objectives, what happens in the classroom is largely ineffectual.[2]

The necessity for teaching mathematics in the elementary school is not questioned, and when it comes to stating objectives most authorities are in agreement. Differences exist in the way objectives are stated, but more important are the differences in emphasis teachers and mathematics educators give to certain objectives. The classroom teacher does not necessarily

---

[1] John Goodlad and Frances M. Klein, *Behind the Classroom Door* (Worthington, Ohio: Charles A. Jones Publishing Co., 1970).

[2] Charles E. Silberman, *Crisis in the Classroom* (New York: Random House, 1970), p. 11.

need to memorize someone else's set of objectives, but he should give careful thought to what he hopes to accomplish in general with a particular group of learners during the school year, and specifically day by day.

The overall objectives of a mathematics program in the elementary school that are generally recognized by most authorities include the following four points:

First, instruction in mathematics should seek to free children to learn, to make their own discoveries, and to develop their own skills in learning how to learn. This is what school is all about. The experiences provided by the school should free the child, not restrict his learning. Observers of preschool children are impressed with their curiosity and their desire to explore their environment, but these same children can quickly become bored or frustrated with first grade in some schools. The mathematics taught in the elementary school can be a challenge to the learner; the processes used in learning to think and communicate with numbers should contribute to the overall school goal of fostering growth in learning how to learn. Measuring, manipulating, exploring shapes, comparing, estimating, seeking solutions to real problems, piling up, constructing, or in some cases "messing around" with a geoboard or other device are to be encouraged as important aspects of the mathematics curriculum. The means of learning mathematics is, therefore, an objective.

Related to this objective, and of critical importance in the elementary school, is the second goal, developing and maintaining favorable attitudes toward learning about mathematics. Unfortunately many elementary school teachers have developed feelings of personal inadequacy over the years with regard to mathematics which can be consciously or unconsciously transmitted to another generation. The elementary school mathematics program and procedures used should be such that children will, in general, feel positive with regard to the area of mathematics and will be willing if not eager to avail themselves of opportunities to expand their mathematical knowledge and skills year by year.

The third goal of elementary school mathematics should be that of helping children acquire an appreciation for the order, the beauty, and the power of mathematics. John Dewey expressed this goal thus:

It is true of arithmetic as it is of poetry that in some place and at some time it ought to be good to be appreciated on its own account—just as an enjoyable experience, in short. If it is not, then when the time and place come for it to be used as a means or instrumentality, it will be in just that much handicapped. Never having been realized or appreciated for itself, one will miss something of its capacity as a resource for other ends. . . .[3]

---

[3]John Dewey, *Democracy and Education* (New York: The Free Press, 1930), p. 240.

Surely mathematics serves a useful purpose, but the decimal system or Hindu-Arabic numerals can provide pupils many opportunities for sensing beauty and for realizing satisfactions that result from developing an awareness of orderly relationships. While we can enjoy a painting or a recording without ever having studied art or music, some first-hand acquaintance with art or music instruction can sharpen our capacity for such enjoyment. Similarly in mathematics some guided learning experiences can open new areas of appreciation for what our number system is, the international nature of contributions to it by mathematicians, and what it has done and can do.

Fourth, the development of certain basic computational skills continues to be a primary goal of elementary school mathematics. By the time a typical learner completes sixth grade he should be able to add, subtract, multiply, and divide whole numbers with reasonable speed and almost 100 percent accuracy. Hopefully he will have developed similar competency in working with rational numbers, including decimals, and measurements. The skillful teacher will seek to achieve this objective, *but not at the expense* of neglecting the overall objectives. It is possible that by spending considerable school time daily on drill practices, a teacher can get a high percentage of learners to compute well, but at the same time their attitudes and interests in mathematics may become so negative that they will avoid, if possible, future mathematical studies. Similarly a teacher who does not have a sound understanding of the learning potential or stage of development of the learners may provide instructional practice in computational activities for which they are not ready or which could be learned much more efficiently at a later stage.

Behavioral Objectives

The teacher is guided by the overall objectives for the teaching of mathematics in the elementary school. But just as a trip from New York to San Francisco by car benefits from the setting of daily objectives, so also does the teacher need more specific objectives for each week and each day. With a class of 10-year-olds a teacher should have as one goal the improvement of computational skills. But this is a broad objective. At some time during the year he might have as a specific objective: "To improve the mathematics skills of these fourth-grade students in adding unlike fractions, so that on the unit test which accompanies the text 80 percent of the class will get at least 21 out of 25 correct answers." Or a teacher of seven-year-olds might have as a general objective the development of an understanding of the number system. At some specific time his objective might be: "Given three different two-place numerals, the pupil should, with 75 percent accuracy, be able to write the answers to oral questions about the meaning of each numeral such as (1) How many tens have been counted? (2) How many ones were left over after grouping the tens? (3) How many ones were counted all together?"

The preceding are examples of behavioral objectives—objectives intended to bring about a change in the learner's behavior. A behavioral objective should identify the learner and the program variable and imply some type of learner behavioral change that can be evaluated as an outcome.

Instructional objectives use action verbs—words which describe observable behavior. Most teachers are accustomed to objectives using such verbs as "learn," "write," "answer," and "compute." The effective teacher in planning for mathematics learnings also will use verbs such as the following:

1. Identify (Pick up or choose one from many to identify objects, properties of objects, or specified changes in objects.)
2. Distinguish (Select one from others that have properties or characteristics that are potentially confusing in identification.)
3. Construct (Make or finish making a drawing or construction that identifies a particular object or set of conditions.)
4. Name (Say or write the name of the object or property of a class of objects.)
5. Order (Arrange according to a specified category—time, importance, size, etc.)
6. Describe (Write or tell enough that the identification of the object, property, or event is considered to be sufficiently communicated.)
7. State a rule (State it not necessarily in technical terms but so that the generalization or conclusion is given accurately, naming all objects or events relevant to the situation.)
8. Apply a rule (Use a rule to solve a problem in a new situation, employing a systematic process to arrive at the solution.)
9. Demonstrate (Show how to use all the steps needed in the application of a rule.)
10. Interpret (Apply a series of rules as a means of explanation.) [4]

The teacher's edition of the pupil text usually states the overall objectives for each chapter or topic and specific objectives for each page or section. It is desirable for the teacher to restate these objectives as needed into measurable objectives for his class.[5]

---

[4]Elizabeth J. Boisclair, "Preparing and Using Instructional Objectives," in *Teaching Mathematics in the Elementary School* (Washington, D.C.: National Association of Elementary School Principals and National Council of Teachers of Mathematics, 1970), p. 21.

[5]Assistance in writing objectives is given in David E. Hernandes, *Writing Behavioral Objectives: A Programmed Exercise for Beginners* (New York: Barnes and Noble, Inc., 1971); H. H. McAshan, *Writing Behavioral Objectives: A New Approach* (New York: Harper and Row, Publishers, 1970); and Robert F. Mager, *Preparing Instructional Objectives* (Palo Alto, Calif.: Fearon Publishers, Inc., 1962).

As the teacher plans for the school year, he will refer to the guide provided by the local school system, examine the teacher's edition of the pupil textbook series provided and learn as much as possible about his particular group of learners. This information will help him develop his overall objectives for the school year and more specific weekly and daily objectives.

Instructional Procedures

Sound instructional procedures do not just happen; they are the result of careful, thoughtful planning. Good instruction is deliberately designed to support the objectives of instruction and to be consistent with the learning requirements of students. Procedures for the teaching of mathematics in the elementary school are based upon the same principles of learning as are those in other subject areas. The differences are chiefly in objectives and materials.

Basic principles of learning have been stated succinctly by James E. Russell:

First, learning is the art of the learner, not of a teacher.
Second, the learner learns when he makes a response.
Third, the thing he learns is the total response he makes.
Fourth, the making of a response calls for an expenditure of energy.
Fifth, a pupil tends to expend energy in terms of his intentions of where he is going—rather than our intentions of where we want him to go.
The teaching act consists of creating circumstances in which learners can make learning responses which the teacher thinks will teach them things worth learning. To do this, a teacher must be able to bring himself to the child as the child is, must respect the child for what he is, and must have hope for the child for what he can become. The teacher must plan a situation appropriate to that child's capacity to make the responses that are hoped for; the teacher must know what the chances are that these responses may be elicited in those circumstances; and the teacher must then relate his day-to-day decisions to this vast background of information about the child.[6]

Applying these principles to the teaching of mathematics, the effective teacher attempts to provide a learning environment in which pupils can learn the mathematics appropriate to their capacity to learn. The learning environment includes the material items (textbooks, charts, posters, manipulable aids) available in and out of the classroom, as well as the atmosphere

---

[6]James E. Russell, "Preparation for Teaching: A Modest Proposal," *Journal of Teacher Education*, 17 (Winter 1966): 505.

of the classroom—ideally, an atmosphere which challenges students and encourages them to succeed at their learning tasks. To create this environment the teacher must continue to be a student of mathematics and of learning and must be capable of constructing, revising, or altering situations that will facilitate effective learning.

Instructional procedures should be consistent with the overall objectives of the teacher. If an objective is to develop understanding rather than to give pupils a formula to memorize for the area of a rectangle, for example, the teacher will help them to use square units (or other shapes) to find the area and will delay the introduction of the formula until they understand what is meant by the term "area." If an objective is to allow children to discover or to explore, the teacher will encourage his pupils to find answers to his questions (or their own questions) in a variety of ways. For example, in developing the basic multiplication fact of 6 × 8, some children may manipulate six sets of eight objects and regroup in sets of ten; others might know that five eights are forty, and six eights would be 40 + 8; and other pupils might think, "Three eights are 24, and 24 and 24 are 48."

If an objective is to contribute to positive attitudes toward mathematics, the teacher should plan to use related procedures. Games and puzzles appropriately used present challenges, provide enjoyment of mathematics, and develop computational skill. An inventive teacher will develop a collection of interesting activities such as the one shown in Figure 1.

In each circle place one of the numerals 1, 2, 3, 4, 5, 6, 7, 8, 9 so that the sum of the three numbers represented in each line will be 15.

One solution:

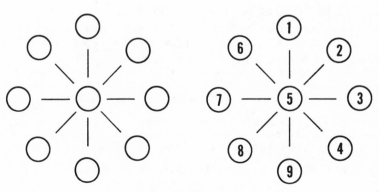

FIGURE 1

Avoid using procedures that contribute to excessive frustration, failure, or boredom. Certainly some seatwork sheets are needed, but overuse or misuse can cause children to respond, "Do we have to?"

The Discovery Approach

Supporters of discovery learning, which suggests that the learner be allowed to explore a situation in his own way, have been articulate in their praise of the procedure:

Discovery methods . . . are the natural and preferred way of learning for man.[7]

This rather mystical motivating power is unique to discovery learning.[8]

Discovery learning promotes better learning and retention.[9]

Discovery learning leads one to be a constructionist and it avoids the kind of information drift that fails to keep account of the uses to which information might be put.[10]

The discovery approach . . . is invaluable in developing creative and independent thinking in the individual.[11]

Older textbooks provided a diagram or chart or a procedure and then asked the child to apply the rule or directions to a set of examples. The discovery procedure involves the child directly in uncovering the principle to be learned.

The teacher utilizing a discovery approach must be extremely skillful in providing appropriate materials and in setting the stage for the children's participation. He must be capable of introducing ideas when appropriate and when the class needs direction. He must be able to allow children to make mistakes and yet must lead them to an awareness of misleading statements. At the optimum time, the teacher must see that summary statements are made. One of the teacher's most difficult tasks is to avoid instant rejection of statements he did not anticipate or want. The classroom environment must be of such a nature that a pupil does not fear expressing his findings or thinking related to mathematics. Even though the ideas may be half formed or contrary to the teacher's, they can still help the student move to a higher level of mathematical thinking.

---

[7]E. Paul Torrance, "Conditions of Creative Learning," *Childhood Education*, 39 (1963): 367.

[8]Robert Kersh, "Learning by Discovery: What Is Learned," *The Arithmetic Teacher*, 11 (1964): 226–31.

[9]Robert Gagné, *The Conditions of Learning* (New York: Holt, Rinehart, and Winston, Inc., 1965), p. 168.

[10]Jerome S. Bruner, "The Act of Discovery," *Harvard Educational Review*, 31 (1961): 21–32.

[11]Cambridge Conference on School Mathematics, *Goals for School Mathematics* (Boston, Mass.: Houghton-Mifflin Co., 1963), p. 17.

A class which has been accustomed to daily teacher-made assignments in a basic textbook may have difficulty adjusting to a teacher who provides them freedom to discover certain mathematical concepts or relationships. For this reason "guided discovery" is suggested. In this procedure, the teacher provides assignment cards which say, for example:

(1) How many acorns balance the big pebble?
(2) How many ways can you fold these shapes so that one half matches the other half?
(3) Use the geo-board and rubber bands to make as many shapes as you can with an area of 6 squares.

As children suggest investigations of their own interests, the assignment cards can be discontinued.

Although considerable opportunity is provided in the elementary school for discovery of the basic facts, the meaning of the operations, the development of concepts of measurement, and so forth, direct teacher presentation of material is also necessary. The effective teacher balances discovery learning with teacher-directed learning activities.

Interaction with Learners

There is little research evidence to indicate that any one teaching procedure is significantly more effective than another. The teacher is the key to effective instruction. As teachers differ as individuals, teaching procedures will differ. Each teacher, therefore, needs to study, select, try out, and continuously revise the procedures most useful to him in helping the learner achieve the objectives of mathematics instruction.

Study of research over the years on the learner, the teaching-learning process, the curriculum, and teaching materials can enable the teacher to utilize his teaching strengths more effectively. For example, numerous researchers have taped mathematics classes and analyzed the nature of the interaction between the teacher and the learner. Ned A. Flanders found that in the typical classroom two thirds of the time someone is talking, and two thirds of that time the person doing the talking is the teacher. When he analyzed the type of teacher talk he noted that teachers who are classified as more indirect than direct obtained the better results in terms of their pupils' achievement. "Indirect teachers," as defined by Flanders, tend to use verbal behavior showing acceptance of the learner's feelings and ideas, offer praise or encouragement, and ask questions to a greater degree than they use verbal behavior classified as lecturing, giving directions, or criticizing. Flanders's research also indicated that better teachers are most indirect when introducing new content materials or when setting goals with learners and most direct when goals have been set and work is in progress.[12]

Asking Questions

One teaching procedure used extensively by many teachers is that of asking questions. Flanders concluded from his research that teachers typically ask questions from 8 to 15 percent of the time they are teaching. There is a marked difference in the competence of teachers in the art of asking questions, however.

Probably the type of question asked most frequently in a mathematics class will be a *memory* question, one where the pupil provides a basic fact or an answer where the learner must recall a statement from his text or some other source. Such questions are:

(1) What is the product of 8×6?
(2) What is a parallelogram?

Mathematics teachers should also use convergent, divergent, and evaluative questions, in order to achieve objectives other than those related to factual learnings. *Convergent* questions require the learner to analyze and compare given data. The answers to such questions are predictable but broader than simple memory questions. Examples are:

(1) In what ways is this triangle like that triangle?
(2) In which months do more children in this room have birthdays?

Divergent questions call for pupils to be more creative and imaginative. Examples are:

(1) How many different ways can you show "8"?
(2) Who can find a way different from Susan's to do this problem?
(3) On this matrix of the multiplication facts, what relationships can you discover?
(4) That's one idea, now what are some others?
(5) How many ways could you bring me a quart of milk?

Another type of question deals with matters of judgment, values, and choices and is called an *evaluative* question. Examples are:

(1) Would you prefer the metric system of weight to our present system?
(2) Why is the Hindu-Arabic system of numeration more useful than the Roman system?
(3) Is this line segment longer than that line segment?
(4) What do the rest of you think about what Jack said?

---

[12]Ned A. Flanders, *Teacher Influence, Pupil Attitudes, and Achievement,* United States Department of Health, Education, and Welfare, Office of Education, Cooperative Research Project No. 397 (Minneapolis: University of Minnesota Press, 1960).

Research has shown that the kinds of questions teachers ask determine the kinds of responses pupils make.[13] The effective teacher or the one who seeks to improve his teaching consciously attempts to vary the type of questions used and to strengthen their quality. One way to do this is to tape-record a lesson once a week. By listening to his own teaching, he can easily note the pattern he follows in questioning. Each week an attempt should be made to use appropriately convergent, divergent, or evaluative questions.[14]

Motivation and Reinforcement

Interest and attitude towards mathematics can be improved if realistic, obtainable goals are established and pupils experience success and are aware of their progress in reaching them.

For various reasons not all children will be enthusiastic in their attitude toward mathematics. One of the teacher's functions is to increase the pupil's interest in learning the subject. What the teacher says (and how he says it) has been found to be most important. Praise is a highly effective motivation. When a pupil responds correctly, the teacher can at least say "Good," "That's correct," or "Right." Even more effective is an occasional comment like "I like the neat way Jimmy presented his problem on the chalkboard," or "That's good thinking, Mary Jane. Now I wonder who can find another way to show us . . . ?"

The use of rewards such as tokens which can be traded for candy, toys, or school-related items has been tried as a means of stimulating the achievement of necessary mathematics competencies. Several studies have shown that achievement gains do result when children are rewarded immediately with candy or tokens for correct responses rather than given knowledge of results 24 hours later. Verbal praise, physical contact, a pat on the shoulder, or the facial expressions of the teacher are other ways of providing reinforcement when correct responses are made. The key to the increase in achievement probably lies more in the positive attitude of the teacher in recognizing children's correct responses rather than in the value

---

[13]James J. Gallagher and Mary Jane Aschner, "A Preliminary Report on Analyses of Classroom Interaction," *The Merrill-Palmer Quarterly of Behavior and Development,* vol. 9, no. 3 (1963).

[14]Suggestions for improving verbal interaction are given in the following references: Edmund J. Amidon and Ned A. Flanders, *The Role of the Teacher in the Classroom* (Minneapolis, Minn.: Association for Productive Teaching, Inc., 1967); Edmund Amidon and Elizabeth Hunter, *Improving Teaching: The Analysis of Classroom Verbal Interaction* (New York: Holt, Rinehart and Winston, Inc., 1967); Gallagher and Aschner, "Analyses of Classroom Interaction"; Norris M. Sanders, *Classroom Questions: What Kinds?* (New York: Harper and Row, 1966).

of the candy or token. Too frequently the emphasis in the classroom is on calling attention to the incorrect response.

Much research on learning deals with reinforcement of learning. A child's learning is reinforced when he is given knowledge of his results and provided scores or correct answers immediately or soon after he responds. This is one of the reasons programmed instruction or computer-assisted instruction is so effective. The teacher should devise a plan to provide pupils with answers to assignments in the text, teacher-prepared exercises, or tests as soon after the child completes his work as possible. Some mathematics textbooks provide answer sections in the back of the text or in a separate booklet. Teacher aides, pupil assistants, or pupils themselves can be utilized to extend the services of the teacher in providing this immediate reinforcement.

Organizing the Classroom

In the typical elementary school the teacher needs to make decisions as to the best way to organize the class for mathematics instruction. If the classroom is self-contained (one teacher with the same group of children most of the day), the children will be on varying levels of achievement. There is a need to group children for mathematics instruction, as in reading. The problem is that in mathematics there is usually only one textbook available for class use, while for reading multilevel materials are available. If this is the case, the teacher should begin the year using the review chapters of the textbook to help determine which pupils are going to be able to use the text efficiently, which will need an enriched program to supplement it, and which will need a variety of practice materials because the text will generally be above their learning level.

Some teachers will be able to use the text at times for whole-class instruction, as in a geometry or measurement unit, with varied types of practice materials developed in terms of pupil ability levels. But for other textbook units, such as one in long division, some pupils will need to continue with subtraction and multiplication instruction and practice, and delay work with the more advanced concept.

In schools that are departmentalized, teachers might expect to be able to teach the whole class as one group with one textbook. However, research does not show any great difference in pupil achievement resulting from grouping children by ability, as is usually the intent of a departmentalized organization. In fact, no conclusions can be drawn from research studies regarding the superiority of any one method of mathematics instruction. Achievement differences are affected more by other variables than by the organizational pattern. The most important implication from research studies is that good teachers are effective regardless of the nature of the classroom organization.

Organization of the classroom to utilize the available space most efficiently is another challenge to the teacher. In a departmentalized classroom to which children come for mathematics intruction, he needs to be ingenious in devising an optimum learning environment. One area of the room could be designated for materials for independent exploration with geometric models, attribute blocks, multibase blocks, abaci, Madison Project independent exploratory shoe boxes, or Nuffield Mathematics Project activity cards. Another area could contain games and puzzles such as checkers, dominoes, Kalah, or tangrams. Still another area could have calculators, geoboards, metric rules, slide rules, and trundle wheels. A table could be supplied with reference books, biographies, and other contemporary publications featuring number stories. Ideally an area of the room will be available for listening and viewing stations for filmstrips, film loops, and films, preferably in carrels. Arrangements such as these suggest that the creative teacher will find less need for arranging pupil desks in standard rows. Instead the classroom will utilize space in ways conducive to individual or small-group learning activities.

The self-contained classroom should have similar facilities for stimulating mathematics learning. Of necessity, less space will be available for mathematics activities exclusively.

Individualizing Instruction

The current groundswell of support for the English primary school is causing many teachers to reconsider traditional procedures which rely heavily upon a textbook. In English primary schools, as well as in an increasing number of American schools, teachers organize mathematics programs and instruction in relation to the unique needs and abilities of individual children. In some cases small groups of children work on a mathematics activity, while in others each child is involved in independent study.[15]

How can a teacher make the change over from total group instruction to individualized or small-group learning? One way might be to choose one afternoon a week when the time schedule can be relaxed and one or two problems involving mathematics-related activities pursued. For example, one Friday afternoon the teacher could have a collection of pieces

---

[15]Suggested References on individualized and small-group learning include Nuffield Mathematics Project, *I Do and I Understand* (New York: John Wiley & Sons, Inc., 1967), and Vincent R. Rogers, *Teaching in the British Primary School* (London: The Macmillan Company, Collier-Macmillan Ltd., 1970), pp. 154–79.

of ⅜″ plywood, nails, rulers, and hammers ready with which the children could be allowed to work in groups of two to make individual geoboards. Then he could use directions on cards, such as "How many square shapes can you make with four rubber bands?" to guide the children in exploring possible uses of the board.

Another procedure could be the provision of a mathematics corner or table in the classroom or even in the corridor adjacent to the classroom. Materials on the table should be provocative and supplemented with a few cards posing questions concerning the materials. A card might ask:

(1) How many cupfuls fill the jug?
(2) Measure your neck, wrist, and waist. How many wrist measurements will go around your neck? How many neck measurements will go around your waist?

A third procedure could be to allow one group of three or four children per day to be involved in individualized or small-group activity while the rest of the class continues regular textbook-based arithmetic. By the end of the week or two weeks all children would have had at least one opportunity for exploratory activities. This procedure also keeps teacher planning within manageable limits. After a few weeks, the teacher may wish to try two groups per day.

Diagnostic tests are available to assist the teacher in determining errors pupils are making. By observing and questioning the children as they work the teacher can ascertain what thinking procedures they are using. Thoughtful teacher observation can supplement testing in providing the teacher with information as to what and how to teach a specific child.

Various commercially developed programs for individualizing instruction in mathematics are increasingly being made available to school systems. Performance Contracting, Individually Prescribed Instruction (IPI), and Computer-Assisted Instruction (CAI) are examples of these.

Problem Solving

Many children need help in achieving success with the story problems or work problems which are a part of every textbook. These problems are included in the mathematics program with the intention of helping the learner apply mathematical ideas and skills to the solving of real-life problems.[16]

---

[16]For help with problem solving, see National Council of Teachers of Mathematics, *Hints for Problem Solving*, Topics in Mathematics for Elementary School Teachers, booklet 17 (Washington, D.C., 1969).

Learners who have success in problem solving tend to possess these desirable characteristics: (1) ability to note likenesses, differences, and analogies, (2) understanding of mathematics vocabulary and concepts, (3) ability to visualize quantitative facts and relationships, (4) skill in computation, and (5) skill in reading comprehension.

The teacher's edition of the textbook usually includes suggestions appropriate for a particular grade level to assist the teacher in developing problem-solving skill. Some specific techniques which have been found to be helpful suggest that the teacher:

1. Plan to provide for individual differences by locating problems at various levels of difficulty. If the textbook material is too difficult or irrelevant, use local data as a source of problems.
2. Help children to write the mathematical or number sentence implied. Encourage pupils to estimate the answer.
3. Allow the learner to prepare his own problems which can be dramatized, placed on the board, or projected via a transparency for solution by other class members.
4. Encourage pupils to make drawings or diagrams as an aid to problem solution.
5. Present problems orally or on tape to eliminate the reading problem, if this is the major difficulty.
6. Prepare problems in which essential data are missing or those that have unnecessary data.
7. Prepare problems which can be solved without paper and pencil. Allow opportunity for children to discuss procedures used to obtain a solution. Encourage and accept creative procedures while at the same time helping learners to utilize most efficient methods.
8. Allow children on occasion to work together in preparing problems or finding solutions to problems based upon local data, newspapers, stores, and field trips.

As children work with word problems from their textbooks or those involving locally obtained data, opportunity may be presented for value clarification. The teacher might be using problems from an old edition of a textbook, so that children begin to laugh at the prices for traditional items: "Find the cost of two loaves of bread at 10¢ a loaf; a pound of butter for 35¢; and three pounds of steak at 69¢ a pound." The teacher might ask pupils to study newspaper advertisements to find today's prices and then explore with them such questions as:

(1) Why have prices changed?
(2) What did people earn as weekly wages at earlier periods?
(3) Would it be beneficial if we could return to the "good old days"?

Another problem might state: "Bob gets an allowance of two dollars per week. If he buys this item and this item, how much will he have left for savings?" Some child may raise a question as to the size of Bob's allowance, which could lead to a discussion of what is a reasonable allowance for a fourth-grade pupil or what the pupil should be expected to pay for out of his allowance—should it include his school lunch money? Or the concern might be for the desirability of a savings account.

Problems such as these present invaluable opportunities for teaching values which the teacher should capitalize upon but not abuse. Reasonable amounts of time can be spent exploring pupils' questions with value connotations. Teachers can introduce problem situations which stimulate this type of learning. Needless to say the teacher will use good judgment and not allow his personal biases to develop into sermons on our political and financial systems.

Some suggested problem situations which could develop into discussions on values are:

1. Have children keep logs of how they spend their time from school dismissal to bedtime or on weekends. Questions will arise as to the value of certain activities, for example, TV viewing versus outdoor play.
2. Plan a class party for one of the holidays. As discussions as to costs develop, determine how much each pupil should contribute. Questions will arise as to what the class should do if all pupils do not bring their share or what else might be done with this amount of money if the class doesn't have the party.
3. The school lunch program offers other opportunities. Could the menu be improved at current prices? Where does the money come from to support the lunch program?

Mental Computation

Part of each day should be devoted to some type of "mental arithmetic" in which the learner solves arithmetical questions without pencil and paper. Mental arithmetic has regained much of its popularity during the past decade, as evidenced by suggestions in teacher's editions of pupil texts. It is valued for:

1. The emphasis placed upon thinking with numbers, which is frequently called for in daily living.
2. Its psychological impact—pupils who make errors are not affected gradewise.
3. Its efficiency in time usage—time for copying exercises is eliminated.

4. Its economy—no expense for materials is involved.
5. Its adaptability to the tape recorder and other types of audiovisual presentation.

An obvious disadvantage of mental computation is the difficulty of adjusting the presentation of examples or problems to the individual differences in children. One example at a time cannot provide for differences in speed or level of ability. This is also a problem for the teacher in the choice of written exercises, however.

An excellent aid to the teacher is the pupil response card (Figure 2). He can make a pocket card holder for each pupil from a piece of tagboard or manila file holder approximately 4½" × 6". The 6" side is folded up about ½" to make a pocket. Then for each pupil a set of 2" × 3" cards is prepared from tagboard with the numerals 0 through 9. Some duplicates will be needed.

Pupils arrange their numeral cards on their desk top and hold the pocket card in their hands. In the primary grades the teacher can expose a set or group of objects on the flannelboard. The children are asked to show the numeral card that names the number of the set. Each child selects the appropriate card, inserts it in his pocket holder, and holds the pocket holder at his chin facing the teacher. As the teacher notes those responding correctly, a nod or smile can indicate to each child that he can

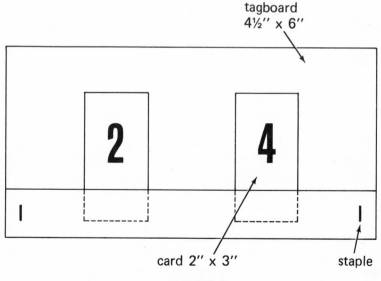

tagboard
4½" x 6"

card 2" x 3"   staple

FIGURE 2

put his card holder down. The teacher might follow up with another question, such as "What is the number which is two more than this?"

The pocket card holder can also be used for mental computation in other ways, such as for: (1) story problems read to the class by the teacher, (2) flash cards with the basic facts, (3) the naming of numbers portrayed on an abacus, or (4) converting base-five numerals to base ten. When not in use, the holders and cards can be kept in individual envelopes in the mathematics text.

The advantages of this device are that it enables the teacher to see at a glance that all pupils are participating, to note which pupils need special help, and to eliminate the confusion which sometimes arises when pupils wildly wave their arms to get the teacher to call on them.

Some other types of activities which help children think with numbers are activities such as the following:

1. "What's My Rule." One pupil stands, calls on a classmate to name a number, and thinks of a rule he is going to follow. For example, Bill might think that he will double the number, so if Mary says 10, Bill says 20. If Jane says 4, Bill says 8. The others in the class try to determine Bill's rule. As children have the freedom to create rules, considerable practice in adding, subtracting, multiplying, and dividing is possible.

2. "Twenty Questions." One pupil stands and thinks of a number. The other pupils have to determine the number by asking questions. Is it larger than 10? Is it between 50 and 100? Is it an odd number? The object is to be logical in questioning rather than to make random guesses.

Ideas such as the above should be recorded on cards and kept readily available at the teacher's desk.

The Place of Drill

One of the objectives of a mathematics program in the elementary school is helping the learner reach as high a level of efficiency as possible in basic computation skills. The term "drill" is often used to describe the type of activity devised to achieve this objective. From numerous research studies a major guiding principle has developed: Drill must be preceded by a thorough teaching program aimed at the building of meanings and understanding.

The basic addition, subtraction, multiplication, and division combinations are examples of mathematics learnings elementary pupils are expected to master. Mastery implies not merely knowing but being able to recall rapidly and with 100 percent accuracy. Some children will reach this goal with little practice, while others require frequent, varied drill activities. The teacher must know and study individual children to determine the specific needs, types of drill materials, and optimum time requirements for each student. The procedure of placing "early morning" work on the board, the same for all pupils, may serve the purpose of keeping them quiet, at least for a while. Yet the practice afforded by such a procedure may be unneeded by some and too difficult for others. Or the procedure of requiring all 30 pupils to do the 24 long-division examples on page 69 in a 30-minute work period, for example, may be appropriate for the 5 or 6 pupils who can work those problems at this rate but may provide little or no challenge to the 10 students who can do the exercises in 10 minutes. And it will frustrate those who can do only a few, if any, of the exercises in the time allotted.

Research has indicated that achievement is increased when the amount of time spent on developmental activities is increased. While the ideal amount of time to spend on drill will vary, research studies suggest that *more* than 50 percent of class time should be spent on developmental activities.

Part III includes many suggestions for teacher-made and commercial materials which are useful in providing practice.

Homework

Research, as well as good judgment, has pointed out the need for specific objectives for homework assignments. Homework can be related to the daily activities in mathematics or individually prescribed in terms of pupil needs. Indifferent, routinized assignments imposed by the teacher and opposed by the pupil are not apt to result in growth.

There is evidence that an increase in computational skill can be achieved through regularly assigned homework in the middle and upper grades. However, research studies offer little support for the improvement of problem-solving ability through regularly assigned homework problems.

Teachers should encourage homework assignments which provide the learner an opportunity to enrich the learnings developed at school. For example, pupils can be asked to: (1) find pictures or newspaper clippings to be used in original story problems, (2) make simple surveys involving number experiences, (3) make a list of geometric shapes seen between school and home, (4) count the number of blocks they live from school, and so forth, and (5) find or read books which feature numbers, such as "The Six Foolish Fishermen," "Yertle the Turtle," or "How Big is Big?"

The Disadvantaged Learner

As other pupils, the disadvantaged profit from well-designed materials utilized wisely by the teacher. The availability of federal funds enabling special attention to be given the learner who is labeled disadvantaged has provided increased support in recent years for such programs. The term "disadvantaged," although used in various ways, refers to learners who may be disadvantaged due to environmental factors such as socioeconomic level as well as to those who are academically disadvantaged. The latter type includes learners who are low achievers (low third of population in mathematics or general achievement) and slow learners (IQ of 75 to 90). In many cases learners are both environmentally and academically disadvantaged.

Programs that provide success experiences, careful development of concrete to abstract levels, use of simple language, reduced reading level and load, field trips, individual and small-group work, programmed texts, recordings, tapes, pupil or adult tutors, and a variety of manipulable aids have resulted in improved achievement as well as attitude.

Although there is much to be learned about the teaching of the disadvantaged, current research suggests the following principles:

1. Methods and materials of instruction must be adapted to these pupils.
2. More closely guided discovery approaches are helpful, although direct teaching of "rules" may be needed for low achievers.
3. More active physical involvement with mathematics aids that can be manipulated is beneficial.
4. Individualized instruction is helpful, since these students are not all disadvantaged in the same way.

Use of Materials and Media

The work of Jean Piaget provides support for the use of manipulative materials in mathematics. He identifies four stages of development: the sensory-motor stage, the preoperational or representational stage, the concrete operations stage, and the formal operations stage.[17] According to Piaget, the child reaches the stage of concrete operations at about age 7 and remains in it until he is approximately 11 or 12 years old. These are the years in which he typically attends elementary school. During this stage of development, the fundamental concrete operations, such as clas-

---

[17]Barbel Inhelder and Jean Piaget, *The Growth of Logical Thinking* (New York: Basic Books, 1958).

sification, serialization, and reversibility, should be derived from the child's interaction with his environment.

In acquiring mathematical concepts a four-step approach is usually recommended:

1. Begin with a real situation to help the learner see the need for a new learning.
2. Use concrete materials (real objects) to demonstrate and discover the new learning.
3. See the new learning and discover it through the use of semiconcrete materials, pictures, drawings, tally marks, or representations of objects.
4. Perform the new learning in the abstract, using traditional number symbols, signs, or algorisms until mastery is attained.

Examples are provided throughout this book of steps 2 and 3, particularly in Part I. Teacher-made and commercially-prepared teaching-learning aids to be used in this process are described in considerable detail in Part III.

One type of commercial aid, Cuisenaire rods, has been the subject of numerous research studies. These studies have generally indicated that primary-age children using the Cuisenaire materials learn more than those in conventional programs.

The use of manipulative aids is not limited to the primary grades. Whenever mathematical concepts are presented, learning activities ranging from the concrete to the abstract will be useful to most learners. However, all pupils do not need to use the same instructional materials concurrently. Those who require little time with manipulative materials should be moved to learning centers in the classroom where tape recordings, filmstrips, slides, and study sheets are available to help them to develop mastery of the concept.

There is some research to indicate that in certain situations teacher demonstrations with concrete materials are as effective as having each pupil actually manipulate the materials. Although many types of effective materials are available, the quality of learning which takes place depends more on the teacher than on the materials used.

Diagnosing Pupil Learning Difficulties

The effective teacher is constantly alert to the progress his pupils make in reaching objectives. At the same time he seeks to determine the specific difficulties the children are having. Rather than scolding a child for a paper containing many errors, the teacher tries to determine what is causing the difficulties. Is the child careless? Did he understand the directions?

Is the process used one that he understands? Does he have a mastery of the operations needed to solve the example?

Several methods are available to the teacher who wants to know the "why" of what a pupil is doing. First, the teacher should observe the child at work. Does he use inefficient methods such as counting on fingers or making tallies on a paper? Is he accurate but too slow for the amount of work expected? Is he having vision problems—can't see the chalkboard to copy the numerals accurately? Watching the child at work will provide meaningful clues. Second, the teacher can listen to the child as he explains his work or as he responds to teacher questions. His responses may reveal inability to read correctly, to see the necessary steps in sequence for solving a particular problem, or to understand a particular basic operation.

A third procedure to use in diagnosing an individual pupil's difficulties is to analyze his written work. Perhaps his writing is such that he makes his numerals incorrectly or illegibly, resulting in computation errors. On an exercise where the teacher dictates 30 basic facts and the pupil writes his responses, the teacher should be able to note which basic facts have not been mastered. On a test from the textbook, a standardized test, or a teacher-made test, the teacher can examine not only correct answers but the computation used for those exercises that are incorrect. The child may be having trouble with the zero facts or the decimal point, for example.

Finally, when arithmetic classes are individualized or pupils are working independently on assignments or activities, the teacher can take time for personal interviews with those who appear to be having difficulties. If on a test a child has made numerous errors, the teacher working individually can have him rework an incorrect exercise and, while he works, note his work method, attitude, and understanding. A few minutes spent individually with a pupil may be much more profitable than trying to hold the attention of the whole class while the teacher goes over errors class members have made.

The teacher should always keep in mind that, because pupils differ in mental ability and language development, instruction must be appropriately adjusted to the needs of the pupil. Observation, listening, analyzing written work, and personal interviews will permit the teacher to learn much that will assist in determining appropriate teaching or reteaching strategies.

Evaluating Pupil Achievement

A variety of procedures related to the varied objectives of the mathematics program can enable the teacher to evaluate pupil achievement in elementary school mathematics. Perhaps the most pertinent evaluation is that done by the teacher as he notes pupils' responses to questions, studies daily written work, and observes enthusiasm, interest, confidence, and resourcefulness. Each child should have a folder in which weekly samples of written work are placed. A periodic review of the folder by the pupil, teacher, and parent provides one type of evidence of progress and achievement.

The teacher can prepare a progress record in the form of a check sheet which allows spaces for listing of pupils' names on one axis and lists the specific competencies to be observed on the other. For example, at the second-grade level the check sheet would include columns for such items as "knows sums 2 through 8," "knows sums 9 and 10," and "can read and write numerals through 999."

Accompanying the pupil textbook and at intervals in the text are tests which can be used for diagnosis or measuring achievement. These are particularly helpful because the items have been selected with relation to the objectives and content of the chapter or chapters being studied. If possible the teacher should have these tests duplicated rather than requiring pupils to copy the items from the text page. Chapter 7 discusses other uses of the textbook tests.

Another type of test used for evaluation of achievement is the standardized test. These tests have been carefully developed by textbook or educational publishers to enable the teacher, pupil, and parent to compare the pupil's achievement with national norms for a particular grade level. Standardized tests are one way for a school system to account to the public on the quality of the schools. A comparison of results from year to year enables those concerned to note the progress as well as the level of achievement. Standardized tests should be examined carefully prior to selection for use in an effort to select an instrument most closely related to the objectives of the school system. A teacher administering a standardized test needs to be exact in following the directions in the accompanying manual.

Teacher-made tests offer advantages in that they can be constructed for the specific objectives of the teacher for a particular unit and group of children. A disadvantage is that considerable time is required for a teacher to construct a valid test. Too frequently teacher-made tests measure computation skills but overlook other worthwhile goals of the mathematics program. Some items might be included which require pupils to evaluate several ways to obtain a solution; others could have several answers, with the student asked to select the best response.[18] The following are illustrations of test items:

---

[18]An excellent reference to aid the teacher in the improvement of test item construction is the 26th Yearbook of the National Council of Teachers of Mathematics, *Evaluation in Mathematics* (Washington, D.C., 1961). Frederick G. Brown, *Measurement and Evaluation* (Itasca, Ill.: F. E. Peacock Publishers, Inc., 1971), discusses many aspects of elementary school teacher-made and standardized tests.

1. Which of the following measurements has the greatest precision?
(a) 3 1/3 in.; (b) 3 3/4 in.; (c) 3 5/7 in.; (d) 3 4/5 in.; (e) 3 3/10 in.
2. To subtract in this problem 37 we must:
$$-18$$
(a) Carry.
(b) Regroup the 3 tens.
(c) Regroup the 1 ten.
(d) Subtract without doing anything else first.
3. In the number 631, the 6 has a value that is:
(a) Two hundred times the value of the 3.
(b) Six times the value of the 1.
(c) Twice the value of the 3.
(d) Twenty times the value of the 3.
(e) Sixty times the value of the 1.
4. In the number 60, the zero:
(a) Doesn't have to be there.
(b) Means nothing.
(c) Holds the ones place.
(d) Holds the tens place.
5. The number of X's below is written in numerals in four different number bases. Which numerals are correct?
XXXX XXXX XXXX XXXX
I. 31_{five}; II. 14_{twelve}; III. 20_{eight}; IV. 1110_{two}
(a) Only I is correct.
(b) III and IV are correct.
(c) All are correct.
(d) I, II, III are correct.
6. How would you draw a diagram to show how many square feet are in a square yard?

Summary

The elementary school teacher who is effective in teaching mathematics will have the following characteristics:

1. Has developed and continuously reexamines the overall objectives he anticipates his pupils will achieve.
2. Is guided by specific behavioral objectives for each unit or topic taught.
3. Creates an optimum learning environment in his classroom and also utilizes the out-of-class environment for appropriate learning situations.
4. Plans and skillfully presents lessons for the entire class or part of the class through lecture, discussion, and demonstration with visual aids of various types.
5. Balances discovery learning by the learner with teacher-directed learning activities.

6. Provides pupils a wealth of opportunities to make discoveries, classify ideas, generalize, verify by using manipulative materials or symbolic materials, and verbalize their understandings.
7. Attempts to vary the type and strengthen the quality of his questions.
8. Uses praise or other appropriate verbal and nonverbal responses to provide reinforcement.
9. Utilizes the textbook appropriately in terms of his understanding of the needs and capabilities of the learners.
10. Encourages pupils to progress at varying rates and through different levels of learning tasks through independent assignments.
11. Balances total group instruction with individualized or small-group learning activities.
12. Devotes part of each day to some type of "mental arithmetic."
13. Balances drill-type activities with developmental activities.
14. Relates homework to daily activities and to individual needs of learner.
15. Utilizes well-designed materials, either teacher-made or commercially prepared, that are appropriate to the learning task.
16. Keeps adequate records to support evaluations of pupil progress in achieving objectives.

Chapter 7

USING A TEXTBOOK

Probably the greatest single resource for the teacher in communicating mathematical concepts is the pupil textbook. Most of the major textbook publishing companies offer mathematics textbook series for kindergarten through grade six. Thus one series provides for a sequential development of mathematical concepts throughout the elementary school years.

Considerable time is devoted to preparation of such textbook series by teams of carefully selected writers. The writing team typically consists of mathematics specialists, experts on child development and learning theory, and representatives of the public schools. Before placing a series on the market, it is usually tested in public school classrooms.

Teacher's Editions

Although pupil texts are increasingly being organized in such a way that the average pupil can proceed independently in his learning, there remains a real need for the teacher's edition. When used thoughtfully, this is the most valuable aid the beginning teacher can obtain for the development of a sound mathematics instructional program. Every conscientious teacher preparing for the school year will make sure that he has a copy of the teacher's edition of the mathematics text for use in the classroom.

Organization of Teacher's Editions

Teacher's editions of mathematics textbooks are organized in various ways. Most include lists of objectives for the grade level, mathematical

224

SETS

ONE
- Idea of a set as a collection or group of things
- Idea of a member of a set
- Comparing sets
- Idea of one-to-one correspondence
- Equivalent and non-equivalent sets
- Associating a number with a set
- Ordering sets according to their rank
- Showing pictures of sets
- The empty set
- Joining disjoint sets
- Partitioning a set into disjoint subsets

TWO
- Idea of a set as a collection or group of things
- Idea of a member of a set
- Idea of a subset
- Comparing sets
- One-to-one correspondence
- Equivalent and non-equivalent sets
- Associating a number with a set
- Joining disjoint sets—relating to addition
- Partitioning a set into disjoint subsets—relating to subtraction
- Joining equivalent disjoint sets—relating to multiplication
- Partitioning a set into equivalent disjoint subsets—relating to division
- Fractional parts of sets

THREE
- Notation in braces
- Empty set notation
- zero as number of
- Naming a set
- Subsets
- One-to-one correspondence and equivalent sets
- Set union
- Concept of infinite set
- Relation of addition to the union of disjoint sets
- Relation of subtraction to partitioning a set
- Relation of multiplication to union of equivalent disjoint subsets
- Relation of division to partitioning into equivalent disjoint subsets

FOUR
- Notation in braces
- Empty set
- zero as number of
- Naming a set
- Subsets
- Equivalent sets
- Concept of infinite set
- Concept of intersection
- Sets of multiples
- Sets of fractional numerals
- Sets of points in geometry
- SUPPLEMENTARY TOPICS
- Replacement set
- Solution set

FIVE
- Infinite set
- Finite set
- Disjoint sets
- Set union, notation
- Subsets
- Every set as subset of itself
- Equivalent sets
- Set intersection
- Venn diagram
- Pairing elements of two sets to form couples; product set
- Sets of prime factors
- Average of set of numbers
- Geometric figures as sets of points
- Intersection of sets of points
- Sets, set elements, and fractional numbers
- Intersection of sets of factors

SIX
- Infinite sets
- Finite sets
- Equivalent sets
- Equal sets
- Disjoint sets and subsets
- Replacement set, notation
- Solution set, notation
- Set union, notation
- Set intersection, notation
- Pairing elements to form couples; product set
- Sets of multiples and factors even and odd numbers
- Sets of equivalent ratios
- Disjoint subsets in geometry
- Intersection of sets in geometry
- Union of sets in geometry
- Sets of points

SEVEN
- One-to-one correspondence
- Equivalent and equal sets
- Finite and infinite sets
- Empty and non-empty sets
- Subsets
- Union and intersection
- Disjoint sets
- Replacement set
- Solution set
- Complement of a set
- Dense set
- Set of factors, multiples, primes and points
- Finite and infinite sets of numbers
- Subsets of lines, planes, half-lines, half-planes
- Union of geometric figures and their interiors
- Graphing subsets on number rays and on finite lattices

EIGHT
- Replacement set
- Solution set
- Universal set
- Infinite sets numbers points
- Sets and probability
- Union and intersection with geometric figures
- Graphs of solution sets on the number line
- Union and intersection of sets on finite and infinite lattices
- Subsets of planes rays lines half-planes parabolas
- Set descriptions of straight-line graphs

Scope and Sequence Chart
Source: Eugene D. Nichols et al., Teacher's Edition 4, *Elementary Mathematics: Patterns and Structure* (New York: Holt, Rinehart & Winston, Inc., 1966), pp. XXII–XXIII.

FIGURE 1

background information for the teacher, descriptions of materials needed, vocabulary to be stressed, suggested time schedules, copies of tests to be reproduced locally, and suggested supplementary activities. Page-by-page directions are provided to assist the teacher in daily planning and in selecting appropriate teaching procedures. These directions may be found in a separate section of the teacher's editions, but frequently they are superimposed in color on a reproduction of the page in the pupil text.

Scope and Sequence Charts

Most teacher editions include a scope and sequence chart which details the topics to be considered at various grade levels. The teacher needs to be acquainted with the mathematical topics covered in the years preceding the present grade level as well as what will be taught by teachers in following years. Figure 1 is an excerpt from a teacher's edition of a mathematics series indicating grade placement of mathematics topics for the area "Sets." The scope and sequence chart states, for example, that "the idea of a set as a collection or group of things" is to be developed in grades one and two; the "idea of a subset" in grade two, and "subsets" in grades three, four, and five.

Using the Teacher's Editions

Study the Objectives

In using the teacher's edition, the teacher should first of all become familiar with the stated objectives—for the school year as well as for each chapter. A fourth-grade teacher might find the goals for one chapter stated in this way:

The objectives of this chapter are:
1. To have the children develop an understanding of some basic geometric concepts, including these:
a. Point
b. Line
c. Ray
d. Line Segment
e. Angle
2. To have the pupils understand that there is a distinction between a geometric concept and a pictorial representation of it
3. To have the pupils gain some experience with the concept of an unlimited (infinite) number of points as the opportunity arises naturally within the basic development
4. To recognize each of these closed figures: triangle, parallelogram (including such special cases as the square, the rectangle, the rhombus), circle,

rectangular prism (called a "box-like figure" in the pupils' material), cylinder, and sphere

5. To have pupils define the various closed plane figures in their own words and describe the difference between such figures as a square and a rectangle that is not a square

6. To be aware of the fact that every geometric figure is a set of points

It is important that children attain the first objective. These basic geometric concepts form the foundation on which their future geometric work is based. Each concept that is developed is, in turn, made a part of the development of the next concept.[1]

Adjust the Objectives to the Local Situation

In some school systems the teacher will need to compare the statement of objectives to be found in the local system curriculum guide or the state curriculum guide with the one in the teacher's editions. A comparison of objectives will enable the teacher to know what additional topics may need to be added and which topics in the text could be deleted or receive less emphasis in his yearly plans. Local school conditions, including grouping procedures, promotion policies, and the prior experiences of the pupils to be taught, also guide the teacher in the choice of objectives.

Review the Mathematics for the Grade Level

Once the objectives for a grade level and for a chapter are clear to the teacher, his understanding of the mathematics involved must be reviewed. Teachers who have recently completed their undergraduate or graduate preparation for teaching hopefully will have had two or more courses in mathematics. Many school systems provide periodic in-service programs in the content of mathematics for the elementary teacher. With the continuing changes taking place in the field of mathematics, however, teachers need to review and update their mathematical background frequently.

Teacher's editions of recently prepared pupil textbook series state quite succinctly the mathematical concepts the teacher must comprehend in order to teach effectively. In some cases, this background is given in a special section of the teacher's edition. In other cases the necessary mathematics information is included in connection with each chapter or each lesson. In the first grade a lesson might have as its purpose: "The child learns to recognize paths that represent closed curves and open curves." Note in Figure 2 how a teacher's edition presents this background material for the teacher.

---

[1]Edwina Deans et al., *Teacher's Annotated Edition of Understanding Mathematics, 4* (New York: American Book Co., 1968), p. G–12.

1 through 25. Therefore, the set of numbers 3 through 10 is a subset of the numbers 1 through 25. The set of numbers 20 through 30 is not a subset of the numbers 1 through 25 because each member of the set of numbers 20 through 30 is not a member of the set of numbers 1 through 25.

The branch of mathematics known as geometry can also be organized in terms of sets, since it deals with sets of points and relationships between sets of points. Formal definitions are not given for some elemental geometric ideas, but the meaning of an idea can usually be developed by using physical representations to suggest the idea. As an example, no attempt is made in most geometries to define *point*. Thus, point is accepted as an undefined term. The dot you draw on paper suggests a point and can be used to develop the idea of a point. However, the dot is not the point, because a point, as a geometric idea, cannot be seen or drawn.

Space is the set of all points. The atmosphere suggests what is meant by space. All sets of points are subsets of space. One such subset of space is a *plane*. The surface of a flat object, such as a mirror, a chalkboard, or the top of a table, suggests or represents a plane. We think of a plane as having no beginning and no end.

A *curve* is a set of points and is a subset of space. All the curves and subsets of curves that are presented in *STA 1* are also subsets of a plane. A path, a river, and a piece of string are a few of the physical objects that represent curves or subsets of curves. In this Teacher's Edition, we use the word *path* to mean the sketch, drawing, or physical object that represents a curve or a subset of a curve.

Two subsets of a plane, *closed curves* and *open curves,* are presented in *STA 1*. You will note in the following paragraphs that the child is not expected to learn precise mathematical definitions of closed curves and open curves. Instead, he learns a meaningful way of deciding which a path represents, a closed curve or an open curve.

A closed curve is a set of points and is a subset of space, as well as a subset of a plane. Closed curves can be represented by paths similar to those in the drawings below.

The child learns that a path represents a closed curve if, when he selects a starting place and traces with a finger along the path, he can get back to the selected starting place without retracing any part of the path.

An open curve is also a set of points and is a subset of a plane. Open curves can be represented by paths similar to those shown below. Note that each path that represents an open curve has a beginning and an end.

The child learns that a path represents an open curve if, when he selects a starting place and traces along the path, he must retrace part of the path in order to get back to his starting place.

Observe that the paths in the pictures just shown do not cross. The paths in the first picture represent *simple closed curves,* and the paths in the second picture represent *simple open curves.* The paths shown below represent some curves that are *not* simple curves because each of these curves crosses itself.

Only simple curves are studied in Grade 1. Therefore, from now on in this Teacher's Edition, when we refer to "closed curves" or "open curves," we are referring to simple closed curves or simple open curves. Keep in mind that the only open curves studied in Grade 1 are those that have a beginning and an end.

Each closed curve that is presented in *STA 1* is a subset of a plane. Each open curve is also a subset of a plane. Any path that you can draw on the chalkboard that is similar to those in the first two pictures shown represents a subset of a plane.

Many of the physical representations of geometric ideas are familiar to the child in Grade 1. Therefore, it seems sensible and educationally sound to begin the study of geometry with some of the fundamental ideas that can be related to the child's physical world. Note that, in the presentation of each geometric idea, the learning experiences progress from situations that are familiar in the child's world to situations that are not related to his world.

Page from Teacher's Edition Explaining Mathematical Ideas
Source: Maurice L. Hartung et al., Teacher's Edition, *Seeing through Arithmetic, Book 1* (and Practice Tablet 1). Copyright © 1968 by Scott, Foresman & Co., p. 25. Reproduced by permission of the publisher.

FIGURE 2

Clarify Your Use of Terminology

Because the ability to read the text materials can be a factor in achievement in mathematics, the vocabulary of the pupil text is carefully controlled. The teacher's edition usually describes the efforts made by the authors to use mathematical terms correctly and to control the readability of the text. The teacher's oral and written use of terms and symbols should be in agreement with that of the text. If a glossary is provided, the teacher will find it helpful to examine it to be certain he understands the terminology and is consistent in his usage of the terms as the authors define them.

At the primer or first-grade level very few words are required. Pictured situations are utilized to help the children learn to think about arithmetic ideas. In one textbook series the first-grade text has only 22 printed words, of which 11 are word names for numerals such as one, two, and three. The sixth-grade text of this series has a total vocabulary of 1,176 words, 841 of which appeared in the preceding books of the series.

Most teacher's editions list the new words which should receive special attention from the teacher at the beginning of the notes explaining each new topic.

Consider Suggested Time Schedules

The teacher's edition frequently suggests a time schedule for teaching the chapters and pages in the pupil text. While teachers should be aware of these proposed time allotments, differences in abilities of children and class groups will determine the amount of time devoted to specific pages and chapters. By keeping in mind the need for mastery of one mathematical concept or skill before introducing a new one, the teacher will avoid the frustration or undue pressure of maintaining a rigid schedule that calls for completion of a prescribed number of pages per week.

One commercial mathematics series teacher's edition provides a table which summarizes the suggested average length of time in weeks for teaching the chapters in a certain grade to three groups of learners: reluctant, modal, and eager. A total of 36 full usable weeks in the school year is assumed. The suggested schedule for Grade 5 is shown in Figure 3.

Look for Testing Suggestions

A feature of some teacher's editions is the assistance provided the teacher in the form of tests related to the philosophy, purposes, and mathematical content of the pupil text. The tests not only enable the teacher to evaluate pupil achievement but, when used for diagnosis of learning difficulties, can be utilized in planning further instruction. Test results for the

Group\Chapter	Reluctant Learners	Modal Learners	Eager Learners
1	4	4	3
2	4	3	2
3	3	3	2
4	4	3	3
5	4	4	4
6	4	4	4
7	6	5	5
8	4	3	3
9	3*	3	3
10		4**	3
11			2
12			2***

* End Minimum Course
** End Average Course
*** End Extension Course

Time Schedule
Source: Walter J. Sanders, Tina Thoburn, Jo McKeeby Phillips, J. Franklin Fitzgerald. Teacher's Annotated Edition, *Developing Mathematics Five* (New York: The Macmillan Co., 1971), p. ii. Copyright © 1971 by The Macmillan Co.

FIGURE 3

entire class and for individual pupils can provide a guide for reteaching and for individualizing instruction.

If the tests are included in the teacher's edition, a statement is usually included permitting the teacher to reproduce the test for use by classes without violating copyright protection. If the tests are published separately by the publisher in a test booklet, the teacher does not ordinarily have the legal right to reproduce the copyrighted material.

Pupil tests may be intended for specific purposes. Some teacher's editions include inventory tests for use at the beginning of the school year; achievement and diagnostic tests to be used at the ends of chapters or sections of the text; and mastery tests for use at mid-year or at the end of the school year. Figure 4 is a sample of a third-grade mid-year mastery test.

NAME _____ DATE _____

TEST 4 Midyear Mastery Test, Part 1

To follow page 161   ANSWERS

— Read each sentence carefully. Decide if it is a true sentence or a false sentence. Then write *true* or *false* in the answer column.

1. The Roman numeral XI names the number *eleven*.

1. *True*

2. A rectangle is made up of four segments that meet to form square corners.

2. *True*

3. The next even number after 14 is 15.

3. *False*

4. A temperature of 85° is warmer than a temperature of 58°.

4. *True*

5. Thirty-six inches make one yard.

5. *True*

6. A quarter is worth more than 3 dimes.

6. *False*

7. John had 50 rabbits. He sold 32. To find how many he has left, you should add 50 and 32.

7. *False*

8. One fourth of a candy bar is less than one half of a candy bar.

8. *True*

9. There are 31 days in June.

9. *False*

10. The sum of 21 and 38 is nearer to 60 than to 50.

10. *True*

11. A plane has no thickness.

11. *True*

12. A rectangle is a symmetric figure.

12. *True*

13. The number 14 makes this number sentence true.
$$32 + n = 46$$

13. *True*

14. $50 + 30 > 80$

14. *False*

15. $300 + 30 + 3 = 333.$

15. *True*

(Items 16 through 20 omitted)

Source: From *Elementary Mathematics* 3, 2nd Edition, *Teacher's Edition*, by Joseph N. Payne et all., copyright © 1968, 1966, by Harcourt Brace Jovanovich, Inc., and reproduced with their permission.

FIGURE 4

For this test the teacher might prepare an item-by-item analysis of class achievement, such as the following, to provide for reteaching and assisting individual pupils.

Question Number	Number of Pupils Missing the Item (class of 30 pupils)
1	2
2	4
3	0
4	3
5	18
6	5
7	4
8	3
9	20
10	6
11	24
12	21
13	3
14	5
15	0
16	8
17	6
18	2
19	5
20	1

A quick review of this tabulation would indicate to the teacher that many pupils had difficulty with items 5, 9, 11, and 12. Items 5 and 9 deal with the understanding of types of measurement. Items 11 and 12 are geometrical concepts. Before proceeding to new concepts in these areas the teacher will find it profitable to do some review and reteaching. He should use teacher-made materials to amplify the concepts and teaching plans that will develop the ideas in a different manner from the method formerly used.

Collect Teaching Aids

A careful study should be made of the teacher's edition to determine the teaching aids suggested for particular grade levels. For effective use of the pupil text, the teacher will need to have available a basic set of teacher demonstration items and sets of materials for individual pupil use. These should be collected or ordered sufficiently in advance so they are on hand at the time the text suggests their use.

For grade three one teacher's edition suggests the following materials:

A minimum number of teaching aids is necessary to carry out this program and many substitutions are possible. For example, activities suggested for the flannel board may be adapted effectively to the chalkboard or to other suitable display materials. You are the best judge of the kind of aids your pupils need.

For the Teacher
   Acetate to cover charts
   Adhesive labels
   Aluminum-foil pie plates
   Apron
   Blindfolds, 2
   Boxes, gift size, 3
   Bucket of sand
   Calendar
   Candy bars
   Candy kisses, wrapped
   Clothesline
   Clothespins, 10 each of 3 colors
   Coins, pennies to half-dollars, real or play
   Colored chalk
   Containers (cup, pint, quart, and gallon) to demonstrate volume
   Corrugated cardboard
   Counters (papers disks, bottle caps, or buttons)
   Cubes (sugar or wood) to demonstrate volume
   Demonstration abacus
   Demonstration grid
   Demonstration number line
   Discarded purse
   Empty cans, 46 oz, 12 oz, 6 oz, and 3 oz sizes
   Felt geometric shapes in at least 2 colors
   Felt objects, symbols, and numerals
   Felt squares and circles that show fractional parts
   Felt ten-strips, 1 by 10 inches marked into 10 units
   Felt-tip marker
   Felt units, 10, 1 by 1 inch
   Fiber-tip pen
   Flannel board
   Floor tiles or other squares to demonstrate area
   Glass tubing
   Grid paper, ¼-inch ruled
   Hundred board, commercial; or 100 paper-fasteners, 100 key tags and 3-by-3-foot cardboard
   Hundred squares, felt, 10 by 10 inches marked into 100 units
   Ladies' gloves, 1 pair
   Large die

Large pan (such as a roaster)
Library-card pockets, 30
Local maps
Menus from restaurants and cafeterias
Milk cartons
Newsprint
Numeral cards, 2 sets of 20 each, two-digit numerals
Objects to demonstrate fractions (licorice or rope candy, felt strips, strips of
   paper)
Objects to demonstrate place value (pencils, sticks, pipe cleaners)
Objects to demonstrate product sets (different colored cups and saucers,
   colored-paper cutouts)
Objects to demonstrate sets and subsets
Objects to demonstrate three-digit place value (marbles, bottle caps, cork
   disks, bread tabs)
Overhead projector (if available) and transparencies
Paper bags, 4 sizes
Paper cups
Parquet blocks
Pipe cleaners, rubber bands, or string
Poster board
Rubber cement
Sale advertisements from newspapers and catalogs
Shoe box
Small test tube
Soda straws
String
Tagboard
Tape, cloth
Tape measures, cloth and steel
Thermometer
Toothpicks
Wheel
Wire or rope to show arbitrary units for measurement
World almanac
Yardstick
Yarn

For the Children
   Adding machine tape
   Book with corner that clearly forms a right angle
   Canceled postage stamps or old Christmas seals
   Colored construction paper
   Crayons
   Discarded magazines or catalogs
   Discarded newspapers
   Envelopes
   Flashcards, commercial or tagboard
   Graph paper
   Index cards, 3-by-5 inch, 10 per child

Paste
Rulers, inch and centimeter scales (if available)
Scissors
Sets of beads or blocks
Straightedges
Unlined paper [2]

The teacher's edition may also indicate that the text is only one part of a multimedia program offered by the publisher. Some textbook publishers, for example, provide workbooks, charts, cards, manipulative aids, single-concept film loops, and spirit duplicating masters. The teacher should inquire as to the availability of these.

Study the Recommended Teaching Procedures

The bulk of the teacher's edition is devoted to specific directions for use of each page of the pupil text. The format varies from one publisher to another but usually includes a statement of purpose, a review of mathematical content, suggestions for prebook teaching, procedures for using the pupil page, correct answers to the pupil page, and supplementary suggestions to provide further experience with the concepts and skills of the lesson. Some teacher's editions include specific exercises for faster or slower learners.

Figure 5 is an illustration from a pupil textbook of a page on numeration. The directions from the teacher's edition for developing the lesson using this page are reproduced in Figure 6.

Summary

The pupil textbook available to the elementary school teacher is probably the teacher's single most valuable resource. Although textbooks are now prepared so that many children can make satisfactory progress in their study of mathematics with little teacher guidance, the teacher's edition enables the teacher to make efficient use of the textbook. To use the pupil text without consulting the teacher's edition is somewhat like starting out on a long automobile trip without considering appropriate road maps and travel information.

To use the textbook most effectively the teacher should:

1. Obtain a personal copy of the teacher's edition of the textbook provided the pupils.

---

[2]Teachers Edition, Book 3, *Elementary School Mathematics*, Second Edition, by Robert E. Eicholz and Phares G. O'Daffer, pp. xviii–xix. Copyright © 1968 by Addison-Wesley Publishing Co., Inc. All Rights Reserved.

PRACTICE WITH NUMERATION

Part 1 Copy. Write four numerals as indicated for the number of each set.

	Base Two	Base Five	Base Seven	Base Ten
1. .	1	1	1	1
2. :	10	2	2	2
3. :.	11	3	3	3
4. ::	100	4	4	4
5. ::.	101	10	5	5
6. :::	110	11	6	6
7. ::::.	111	12	10	7
8. :::::	1000	13	11	8
9. :::::.	1001	14	12	9
10. ::::::	1010	20	13	10
11. :::::::	1011	21	14	11
12. :::::::	1100	22	15	12
13. :::::::	1101	23	16	13
14. :::::::	1110	24	20	14
15. :::::::	1111	30	21	15
16. :::::::	10000	31	22	16
17. :::::::	10001	32	23	17

Part 2 Write an answer for each question below.

1. How many digit symbols are needed for base-five numeration? *five*

2. How many digit symbols are needed for base-two numeration? *two*

3. How many digit symbols are needed for base-ten or decimal numeration? *ten*

4. How many digit symbols do you think are needed for base-three numeration? For base-four numeration? *three; four*

5. If some number b is the base number of a numeration system, how many digit symbols are needed? b

Can you do this? To change 132_{five} to a base-seven numeral, you can first change 132_{five} to a base-ten numeral. Then change the resulting base-ten numeral to a base-seven numeral.

Copy and change each numeral as indicated.

	a	b
	101010	10
1.	$132_{five} =\underline{\quad}_{two}$	$101_{two} =\underline{\quad}_{five}$
	32	20
2.	$23_{seven} =\underline{\quad}_{five}$	$24_{five} =\underline{\quad}_{seven}$
	1011	10
3.	$14_{seven} =\underline{\quad}_{two}$	$111_{two} =\underline{\quad}_{seven}$
	21	141
4.	$1011_{two} =\underline{\quad}_{five}$	$64_{seven} =\underline{\quad}_{five}$

Source: Bernard H. Gundlach et al., Teacher's Edition, *Mathematics 6* (River Forest, Ill.: Laidlaw Brothers, 1968), p. 26. Reproduced by permission of the publisher.

FIGURE 5

TEACHING HELPS for Page 26

PURPOSE

To provide pupils with review and practice in using positional numeration.

MATHEMATICAL BACKGROUND

Pupils have already learned how expanded notation can be used to change a numeral like 201_{five}, 3456_{seven}, or 1001_{two} to a decimal numeral. They have also learned how division can be used to change a decimal numeral to a numeral in another base.

By combining these two procedures, we can change a non-decimal numeral to a non-decimal numeral in some other base. For example, to change 22_{seven} to a base-five numeral, we could first use expanded notation to change 22_{seven} to a decimal numeral.

$$22_{seven} = (2 \times 7^1) + (2 \times 7^0)$$
$$= (2 \times 7) + (2 \times 1)$$
$$= 14 + 2 \text{ or } 16$$

Then division can be used to change 16 to a base-five numeral.

$$5^0 = 1 \qquad 5 \,\overline{)\,16\,}\, 3$$
$$5^1 = 5 \qquad \; 15$$
$$5^2 = 25 \qquad 1 \,\overline{)\,1\,}\, 1$$
$$ \underline{1}$$
$$ 0$$

Therefore, $16 = 31_{five}$.

Since $22_{seven} = 16$ and $16 = 31_{five}$, we know that $22_{seven} = 31_{five}$.

TEACHING THE LESSON

Prebook Activities

Review briefly each of the various positional numeration systems studied in this chapter.

Using the Page

Explain carefully the instructions for *Part 1, Part 2,* and *Can*

Source: Bernard H. Gundlach et al., Teacher's Edition, *Mathematics 6* (River Forest, Ill.: Laidlaw Brothers, 1968), p. T 26. Reproduced by permission of the publisher.

FIGURE 6

you do this. After allowing pupils sufficient time to prepare answers for the exercises in each part and in *Can you do this,* discuss these answers as a class activity.

Postbook Activities

Have pupils prepare a chart similar to the chart in *Part 1* for the whole numbers eighteen through twenty-five.

ENRICHMENT ACTIVITIES

Extension

Display cards like the following or show such cards on the chalkboard or via the overhead projector.

A		B		C		D	
1	9	2	10	4	12	8	12
3	11	3	11	5	13	9	13
5	13	6	14	6	14	10	14
7	15	7	15	7	15	11	15

Have a pupil choose a number from 1 to 15 and select the card or cards on which the numeral for that number appears. The sum of numbers named in blue on all the cards the pupil selects is the number the pupil chose. For example, if the pupil selects cards **B, C,** and **D,** add 2, 4, and 8 and tell the pupil the number he chose was 14.

After repeating the process with several other pupils, explain that the cards make use of the base-two numeration system as follows. Card **A** lists all numbers in which the base-two numeral would have a 1 in the 2^0 position, card **B** lists all numbers in which the base-two numeral would have a 1 in the 2^1 position, and so on for cards **C** and **D**. Therefore, it is possible to add the powers of two for each card selected to find the number chosen.

Allow pupils to copy the cards and show the trick to their parents and friends.

2. Become thoroughly acquainted with the philosophy of the authors concerning the teaching of mathematics and with the objectives for the year.
3. Compare scope and sequence of textbook with local and state curriculum guides.
4. Review the background materials in the teacher's edition before using the pupil text.
5. Obtain the necessary teaching aids.
6. Plan each lesson, using the teacher's edition as a guide to correct vocabulary, mathematical concepts, prebook teaching, use of the pupil pages, and recommended follow-up activities.
7. Utilize teacher observation and the testing materials recommended in the teacher's edition for evaluating and for diagnosing group and individual learning difficulties.
8. Finally, avoid being a slave to the textbook. Use it as a valuable resource, but adapt its use to the needs, backgrounds, and interests of the particular group of learners.

Chapter **8**

UNDERSTANDING THE
DEVELOPMENT OF
MATHEMATICS CURRICULA

In considering what mathematics should be taught in the elementary school, the teacher is immediately concerned with decisions as to what to teach in a sixth grade, a third grade, a kindergarten, or a nongraded class of seven-year-olds. He understandably relies upon the textbook and the learning materials readily available in the classroom in shaping the mathematics curriculum for a particular group of learners.

To understand the development of an appropriate mathematics curriculum for the elementary school, the teacher must be acquainted with the historical background of instruction in the subject, from ancient to contemporary times. Experimental projects of the 1950s and 1960s resulted in a virtual revolution of content and method and led to the formulation of national curriculum recommendations. A study of elementary school mathematics curricula must also consider the contributions of educators and psychologists to a theory of learning on which the curriculum can be based.

Historical Development

Arithmetic probably had its genesis when man first sought an answer to *how many?* The process of counting originally utilized a one-to-one

correspondence between fingers or stones and other objects. There is evidence of such a need for the use of numbers from 50,000 to 125,000 years
ago.[1]

Because primitive man used parts of his body as a basis for counting,
the present base-ten number system developed quite naturally. Since man
has five digits per hand, it is probable that the quinary or base-five system
was the first one used. The needs of primitive man dictated the degree to
which he developed his number system. Base ten has endured as most
useful, although base five and base twenty were also popular at times.

Probably the first dated event in recorded history was the introduction
of the Egyptian calendar in 4241 B.C. This calendar provided for 12
months of 30 days each, plus 5 feast days.[2] Archaeologists have recovered
Babylonian tablets involving squares and cubes of numbers dated about
2000 B.C. The first treatise on arithmetic is attributed to Ahmes, an Egyptian priest. Various authors date this manuscript as being written prior to
1000 B.C. and possibly as early as 1825 B.C.[3]

The lack of sophistication of early number systems contributed to the
introduction of a tool for calculation, the abacus. The abacus, one type of
counting frame, is still in use today and has been revived as an aid to the
understanding of mathematical operations in the modern elementary school.

Greek mathematicians, represented by Thales, Pythagoras, Plato, Hip-
pocrates of Chios, and Euclid, are associated with the development of
mathematical theory. Thales founded the first Greek school of mathematics and philosophy. The Pythagoras school placed emphasis upon the
science of numbers rather than the art of computation. Interestingly, Pythagoras is usually remembered for the theorem bearing his name, but it
was known in earlier civilizations, notably the Egyptian. Plato advocated
that boys be taught as much arithmetic as would be practically useful, or
essential, for the life of a citizen. He suggested that arithmetic should be
taught as a game far more than as a science, as is advocated by many modern educators. By about 300 B.C., the Greek mathematicians, notably
Euclid, were geometricians. The Alexandrian School dominated the history of mathematics for almost 1,000 years.[4] The science of numbers was
stressed through the study of mathematics, arithmetic, music, and as-
tronomy.

By contrast the Romans were primarily concerned with application.

---

[1]David Eugene Smith, *History of Mathematics* (Boston: Ginn & Co., 1923),
Vol. I, p. 4.

[2]Ibid., p. 42.

[3]W. W. Rouse Ball, *Short History of Mathematics* (London: Macmillan and Co.
Ltd., 1919), pp. 3–6.

[4]Ibid., p. 50.

They contributed the notation system of Roman numerals, the Christian calendar, and a textbook by Boethius which was the standard text of church schools into the 17th century.

Because Hindu astronomers needed to make calculations to support their studies and found existing number systems too cumbersome, they devised the antecedents of our modern Hindu-Arabic number system prior to 300 B.C. The distinguishing characteristics of the Hindu number system were its use of place value and, later, the introduction of the zero. The Arabs are credited with further development of this system; as early as 651 A.D. they had elementary schools in which arithmetic utilizing it was taught. The term "algorism" was obtained from the name of a Persian mathematician, Mohammed ibn Musa al-Khowanizmi.

The Arabs spread the Hindu number system in Europe by introducing it into the Saracen schools of Spain about the 11th century. About 1100 A.D. an Italian, Leonard Fibonacci, wrote a treatise known as *Liber Abaci* in which the advantages of the Hindu system over the Roman system of numeration were listed.

With the invention of printing, many publications on arithmetic made their appearance. Most of these were concerned with compilations of arithmetic into a set of rules by which calculations could be rapidly and correctly made. The general procedure was to introduce a subject by a definition, followed by an appropriate rule and applications. No need for proofs was recognized.[5]

Rule arithmetic of the sixteenth century set the pattern for the following three centuries. Negative numbers, decimal fractions, the decimal point, plus and minus symbols, Napier's bones, and the slide rule were developed about this time.

One aspect of arithmetic has been constantly in flux—the number of so-called fundamental operations. In the medieval period nine processes were recognized in Europe, and the Hindus recognized eight. During the early 16th century the number varied from four to nine, but by the latter part of that century it had been reduced to the four commonly recognized at the present. Even at this early date subtraction was recognized by some as the inverse operation of addition. This foresaw the present-day trend of reducing the number of fundamental operations to two, addition and multiplication.[6]

---

[5]L. L. Jackson, *The Educational Significance of Sixteenth Century Arithmetic* (New York: Teachers College, Columbia University, 1906), p. 168.

[6]Randall C. Hicks, "A Program of Study in Mathematics for Elementary School Teachers based upon Exhibited or Derived Needs" (Ed. D. diss., University of Georgia, 1966), p. 35.

Early instruction in arithmetic in America was influenced by what had been taught in England. Rule arithmetic continued to be in vogue in England in the 17th and 18th centuries, due largely to a textbook published by Edward Cocker in 1694. This popular text lasted through over 100 editions and was the first textbook used in the United States.

Arithmetic was not required by law in Massachusetts and New Hampshire, for example, until 1789. By 1800 it was generally taught in American schools, utilizing the ciphering book procedure. Children did not have textbooks, but the teacher used a ciphering book which he himself had had as a student. The teacher gave the pupils a definition and then a rule. He explained the rule, usually with an example, and then gave the pupils an assignment to be worked out and brought to the teacher to be checked. No attempt was made to help students understand their work or think through their problems.

The 19th century was a golden age for the refinement of the number system. Joseph Liouville proved the existence of transcendental numbers. Sir George Peacock and Herman Hankel paved the way for Richard Dedekind to create in 1879 his theory of the real-number system. Karl Friedrich Gauss presented arithmetic in its proper place as the foundation of mathematics and science. George Cantor introduced the infinite numbers into arithmetic, and Charles Babbage devised the ancestors of the digital computer. The 19th century saw the justification of irrational numbers for our number system, as the 16th century had justified rational numbers.[7]

The lack of any logical considerations in rule arithmetic could not go unrecognized in the light of such mathematical achievements. Johann Heinrich Pestalozzi, a Swiss educator, became the leader in a movement which held that learning should proceed from the concrete to the abstract rather than vice versa. Pestalozzi's work was based upon perception. Number was taught as the perception of concrete objects of many different types, and the fundamental operations were studied in the same manner before abstraction was encouraged. Pestalozzi's aim was to develop the mind to see common elements and to discriminate differences.

These ideas were not accepted in England, where rule arithmetic continued to be popular until about 1880. The chief early disciple of Pestalozzi in America was Warren Colburn.[8] Colburn, who was one of the first advocates of pupil discovery, introduced the inductive method of teach-

---

[7]Ibid., p. 45.
[8]Warren Colburn, *First Lessons in Arithmetic on the Plan of Pestalozzi* (Boston: Houghton Mifflin Co., 1821).

ing arithmetic. Pupils were presented with a new topic with a practical application, not a rule, for motivational purposes, and the development of facility with symbols was delayed until the concept was fully understood. Colburn advocated the use of oral arithmetic, repeating decimals and equivalent fractions, and the modern sense of "borrowing" and "carrying."

About the middle of the 19th century, when public schools were expanding and qualified teachers were few in number, textbooks began to return to the deductive method of presentation. Rules were once again emphasized, and pupil discovery was neglected. The textbooks became more like those of a century earlier and abandoned most of the principles advocated by Pestalozzi, especially in the return to written rather than oral work.

The mental-discipline theory of teaching began to decline in the early 20th century with the growth of the Herbartian movement, which was based on the work of Johann Herbart in Germany. Nineteenth-century arithmetic textbooks were arranged on the *topical plan*, which carried a student completely through one topic before proceeding to the next. About 1898 the *spiral plan* was devised to provide for a study of simple ideas first. As more complex topics were undertaken, a review of basic ideas was provided. About 1910, the spiral approach was recommended for the first four grades and a topical approach for the next four.

The emphasis in the arithmetic of the early 1900s changed from the memorization of long, tedious procedures to social utility. Arithmetic had previously generally been viewed as a practical study. The change at this time was toward what was practical for the child at his present age, not for the adult he was to become.

John Dewey is credited with contributing a different emphasis to the teaching of arithmetic in the late 19th and early 20th centuries. Dewey differed with Pestalozzi in that he viewed number not as a property of objects but as the product of the way the mind makes sense of the objects it perceives. He advocated that number be taught through measurement and that the child become involved in physical activity, doing the actual measuring and relating of quantities. Dewey was probably indebted to Friedrich Froebel, who noted that learning can be a resultant of play.

Dewey's philosophy developed into the activity curriculum, in which the material was arranged around a central theme from which all problems were derived. Colonel F. W. Parker further developed this procedure, which later became the unit-of-instruction approach, a procedure still advocated by a number of educators. Parker wrote in 1879, "I am simply trying to apply well established principles of teaching, principles derived directly from the laws of the mind. The methods springing from them are found in the development of every child. They are used everywhere except in school." [9]

During the 1930s an attempt was made to delay the more difficult topics in arithmetic until understanding was more likely to be present. This was based on the research of such groups as the Committee of Seven of the National Society for the Study of Education, which studied children in over 225 communities for over a decade.[10] Some writers advocated the omission of formal arithmetic study until about the fourth grade.

Changes in arithmetic were few between 1930 and 1945. With the rapid scientific developments since World War II, however, teaching procedures and content of elementary school mathematics have been under considerable scrutiny.

Contemporary Experimental Mathematics Programs

During the late 1950s and early 1960s a revolution in content and teaching procedures for elementary school mathematics resulted from the joint efforts of mathematicians and teachers. This was the period of national projects devoted to the development of particular mathematical concepts and methods. A number of these programs are discussed in this section.

School Mathematics Study Group (SMSG)

The curriculum and materials developed by the School Mathematics Study Group may have had the greatest single impact upon thinking and practice with regard to the teaching of mathematics in the elementary school. Over a period of several years, beginning in 1959, this national project with headquarters at Stanford University developed textbooks for the elementary grades, kindergarten through grade six. Each book has an accompanying Teacher's Commentary which provides relevant mathematics background and specific directions for use of the pupil text.

In contrast to earlier mathematics curricula, this series was one of the first (if not the first) to include a rather comprehensive treatment of geometry, sets, numeration systems, number theory, operations on whole and

---

[9]Lawrence A. Cremin, *The Transformation of the School* (New York: Vintage Books; Random House, Inc., 1961), p. 130.

[10]With Carleton Washburne as chairman, the committee's report was published in *Child Development and the Curriculum*, 38th Yearbook of the National Society for the Study of Education, Part I (Bloomington, Ill., 1939), pp. 299–324.

rational numbers, the integral domain, measurement, graphing (including coordinates), and exponential notation. Most commercial texts developed in the late 1960s reflect the developments of the School Mathematics Study Group.

Madison Project

The Madison Project derived its name from the Madison Junior High School in Syracuse, N.Y., where experimental work was done under the guidance of Robert B. Davis of Syracuse University. A second experimental center was later developed at Webster College, Missouri. From its beginning the Madison Project stressed intuitive algebraic and geometric ideas and was intended for enrichment.

Some of the topics treated are (1) variables, open sentences, and truth sets; (2) arithmetic of signed numbers; (3) functions, including functions obtained empirically; (4) the number line and Cartesian coordinates; (5) implication and contradiction; (6) identities; (7) deriving theorems; (8) matrices; (9) complex numbers; (10) graphing functions of truth sets, including linear functions and conic sections; (11) trigonometric functions; and (12) computer programming.

A commercial series of pupil and teacher textbooks evolving from the Madison Project has been published by Addison-Wesley Publishing Company, Inc.

Greater Cleveland Mathematics Program

The Greater Cleveland Mathematics Program resulted from the efforts of the Educational Research Council of Greater Cleveland, beginning in 1959. The project made extensive use of the discovery approach to learning and drew heavily upon the principles of mathematics to help children learn the underlying structure of the material presented. In addition to the topics covered in the usual elementary school mathematics program, the GCMP contained units or exercises on number sequences; factors and multiples; prime and composite numbers; other numeration systems; an introduction to powers, roots, and negative numbers; physical geometry; and linear, area, and volume measurement. The concepts of language of sets were carried through the topics at all grade levels.

Science Research Associates, Chicago, has published some of the GCMP materials. Texts are available for kindergarten through grade six, and a variety of learning devices designed for use with these texts and films for the preservice and in-service education of teachers have also been produced.

Minnesota Math and Science Teaching Project

The name "Minnemath" is derived from the Minnesota Math and Science Teaching Project, a series of units for use in early grades, including kindergarten, developed by Dr. Paul Rosenbloom and his colleagues. The main mathematical goal was to provide children as early as possible with a geometric model of the real-number system. Examples of topics treated are intuitive geometry, sets, numeration, and measurement. The project aimed at close coordination with the natural and social sciences.

Stanford Projects (Suppes)

Professor Patrick Suppes of Stanford University developed curriculum materials based upon the belief that most mathematical learnings can be developed from notions of sets and operations on sets. The nomenclature and symbolism of sets were stressed, and set operations were extended through the grades. The results of experimental work begun in 1959–60 indicated that children experienced very little difficulty with either the notation or the vocabulary.

With Newton S. Hawley of Stanford, Suppes developed materials in geometry for the primary grades beginning in the spring of 1958. Terms such as bisect, line segment, perpendicular, pentagon, and quadrilateral were included in both oral and reading vocabulary from the time that these ideas are first introduced.

Dr. Suppes has also been project director for the computer-based mathematics instruction activities at the Stanford-Based Laboratory for Learning and Teaching. A large body of curriculum material, encoded for use in computer systems, has been produced for the instruction of children at all ability levels in grades 1–6.

Some of Suppes's materials have been published commercially by Blaisdell Publishing Co., a division of Random House.

University of Illinois Arithmetic Project

David Page of the University of Illinois Arithmetic Project prepared a variety of materials with special stress on the number line and maneuvers on lattices. By exposure to interesting and different ways of approaching familiar tasks, children were encouraged to make their own mathematics discoveries, to develop mathematical insight, and to acquire an intuitive understanding of many mathematical ideas which have usually been initiated much later in the child's school life.

Nuffield (England) Mathematics Teaching Project

This project, which gets its name from the Nuffield Foundation, was begun in 1964. Its purpose was to develop a contemporary course in mathematics for young children, based largely upon Piaget's theories of how children conceptualize. Nuffield Project classrooms organize children into groups of three or four to perform tasks utilizing physical materials. The project seeks to provide the teacher with a set of books or guides to help in lesson planning rather than to provide pupil textbooks. The curriculum is one which individualizes learning experiences for each child rather than moving children along together as a grade-level group. Davis considers this one of the finest and most carefully devised of all the "modern mathematics" projects.[11]

Computer-Assisted Learning

Numerous researchers are attempting to individualize mathematics instruction through the use of the computer. These projects, which are referred to as computer-assisted instruction (CAI) or computer-assisted learning (CAL), are underway in various places in the United States. The Pittsburgh Learning Research and Development Center has been engaged for the past several years in developing and operating an elementary school curriculum allowing individualization of progress (IPI). Many of the manual tasks of test scoring, diagnosis of test results, prescription of instructional tasks, and record keeping have been automated via the computer. The computer provides such data as: (1) a unit summary for each student reporting his scores on the pretest along with a suggested task prescription; (2) a homeroom report listing for each pupil the unit of instruction, the skill, and the number of days spent on the unit; and (3) an instructional report listing the names of the pupils working on a given unit and the specific objectives each pupil is attempting to master.

The Stanford CAI Project emphasized computer-based drill and practice in elementary arithmetic using both the "block" and "strand" approaches. Under the block approach, the arithmetic content of a particular grade level was divided into 24 blocks, each containing a pretest, five days' work, and a posttest. Under the strand approach, a given topic in arithmetic was followed across grade levels to whatever level the pupil was capable of handling. For the block system the computer provided a daily

---

[11]Robert B. Davis, *The Changing Curriculum: Mathematics* (Washington, D.C.: Association for Supervision and Curriculum Development, 1967), p. 26.

report and an end-of-block report.   For the strand approach, the computer daily report listed each pupil, his grade equivalent on the 11 strands, and his average grade placement.

The Individualized Mathematics Curriculum Project (IMCP) has been under development at the University of Wisconsin since 1964.   Its aim is to teach children how to plan their own learning objectives in mathematics and how to become increasingly responsible for the organization of the available human and material resources necessary to attain these objectives.   The elementary school mathematics curriculum was divided into eight major strands, each of which was divided into levels and then into units.   Multiple-choice tests have been prepared for each unit.   Test data are machine scored, and results are entered into the data base via teletype.   The program is a computer-based inquiry system called the Computer Managed System (CMS).   Rather than diagnosing and prescribing, it lists pupils according to the units mastered or attempted.

Other Mathematics-Related Curriculum Projects

The programs described above have been widely publicized and have already made an impact upon the content of commercially published arithmetic textbooks for the elementary school.   In addition, hundreds of curriculum projects are currently in progress in the United States and foreign countries.   The University of Maryland prepares an annual summary of reports dealing with curriculum developments in science and mathematics.[12]   An examination of selected science curriculum experimental programs indicates the current concern for interrelating the teaching of mathematics with the teaching of science in the elementary school.

Science Curriculum Improvement Study

The Science Curriculum Improvement Study at the University of California, Berkeley, has units on Material Objects, Variation, and Measurement which have a strong mathematics orientation.   They provide suggested activities for primary grades dealing with such topics as histograms, ordering by length, measurement of surfaces, sorting, grouping, coordinates, and symmetrical systems.

---

[12]*The Seventh Report of the International Clearinghouse on Science and Mathematics Curriculum Developments* (College Park, Md.: Science Teaching Center, University of Maryland, 1970).

Science—A Process Approach

The American Association for the Advancement of Science has developed materials under the title *Science—A Process Approach* for kindergarten through grade six in which basic ideas of number are arrived at through a scientific approach. The Xerox Corporation has the current responsibility for publishing these materials commercially.

Elementary Science Study

The Elementary Science Study (ESS) sponsored by Educational Services Incorporated has prepared science units for various elementary school grades. Some of these draw heavily upon mathematical principles and contribute to development of basic number skills through challenging the pupil to record data, observe closely, and generalize from his findings. Especially significant are the units entitled: Mirror Cards, Attribute Games and Problems, Ice Cubes, Pendulums, Balancing, Geo Blocks, Heating and Cooling, Pattern Blocks, Tangram, Matrix Blocks, Measuring, Checkerboard, Thermometry, and Time and Clocks. Webster Division of McGraw Hill and Company now publishes most of the ESS units.

National Curriculum Recommendations

Traditionally, development of the mathematics curriculum, like the school curriculum in general, has been a local responsibility in the United States. Undoubtedly the contemporary experimental programs described, most of which received generous financial support from the federal government, have had and will continue to have considerable influence on what mathematics is taught in the elementary schools of this country. Some bases for the development of mathematics curricula have been prepared by certain national groups. One of these, The National Council of Teachers of Mathematics, has listed 32 ideas as basic to elementary school instruction in mathematics.

Idea 1. New numbers are invented by men and defined in terms of old numbers to do new jobs. Some of these jobs are to make the operations of division, subtraction, and extraction of roots always possible, to make linear and quadratic equations always solvable, or to represent geometric, physical, or other quantities such as diagonals of squares, temperatures "below zero," and losses.

Idea 2. Each time a new number is invented the rules of operations with it must be defined. This is usually done to preserve the commutative, associative, and distributive principles of operation which applied to the natural numbers.

Idea 3. Standard units of measurement are arbitrarily chosen, although the units may have arisen historically. Students should understand the nature and variety of standard units of measurement as well as the relation between units of the same measure. Pupils must have many experiences with physical examples of standard units to understand and appreciate them.

Idea 4. Estimates of results and computations are used as a check on computations and as a practical tool for everyday living. Such estimates may be done prior to the paper-pencil work or after it. The main purpose of estimates of results of computations is to help pupils deal with numbers sensibly.

Idea 5. The ability to estimate is refined where pupils are able to locate two numbers such that the result is between them. Some pupils will be able to locate a small interval while other pupils will be able to give a large one.

Idea 6. Number is an abstraction.

Idea 7. Mathematics is a kind of "if . . . then" reasoning in which the "then's' are supported essentially by definitions, assumptions, and theorems which have been proved previously.

Idea 8. Addition and multiplication are the basic operations in terms of which the inverse operations, subtraction and division, are defined.

Idea 9. Numbers and their properties are the same, irrespective of the system of numeration; but our system of numeration with the base 10 and place value together with the associative, commutative and distributive principles dictates the operation algorithms in arithmetic.

Idea 10. As new numbers are invented, we must each time define what is meant by equality as well as by addition and multiplication. This leads to the fact that the same number may have many different names or representations.

Idea 11. Numbers obtained by applying to quantities measuring instruments, such as rulers, scales, and protractors, represent approximations of the quantity. The numbers themselves are not approximate.

Idea 12. Computation with numbers which represent approximations should be done with due consideration for that fact. The same computation procedures are followed for numbers arising for measurement, rounded numbers, and rational approximations for rational and irrational numbers.

Idea 13. In algebra a variable is a symbol for which one substitutes the names of numbers.

Idea 14. Variables in mathematics play a role similar to the role of pronouns in the English language.

Idea 15. A name of a thing is different from the thing.

Idea 16. We may represent numbers geometrically showing some as lengths, some as points, and some as areas.

Idea 17. The language of mathematics has a grammar of its own just as the English language does.

Idea 18.   A mathematical definition is a statement which gives us a set of symbols as a replacement for another set of symbols.

Idea 19.   To indicate that two expressions name the same thing, we use the symbol "=."

Idea 20.   You can see a numeral but you cannot see a number.

Idea 21.   Recognition of the order relations for numbers is fundamental to estimates of computations.

Idea 22.   In operating with new numbers, the former laws of addition, multiplication, order, and commutativity are usually preserved; but some of them may be changed in order to achieve some other desired advantages.

Idea 23.   Sets of ordered pairs of numbers are an important concept in mathematics, and this concept is frequently used on all grade levels.

Idea 24.   A conclusion is established by logical deductions from one or more statements called reasons.

Idea 25.   Induction doesn't "prove," it makes conclusions probable.

Idea 26.   We often seek to establish the truth of a statement called a conclusion by arguing that it follows from one or more other statements called reasons that are only partial evidence of the truth of the conclusion.

Idea 27.   To establish a conclusion, necessary inference may be used in the argument.

Idea 28.   To establish a conclusion, probable inference may be used in the argument.

Idea 29.   The inferences of statistics are inductions which are not certainties and must be given in terms of probability.

Idea 30.   Data from samples should be organized and summarized if they are to be analyzed for inferential purposes.

Idea 31.   Decisions about a whole population can be obtained most efficiently and economically by examining only a small part selected by a process based on the principles of probability.

Idea 32.   Unless the sampling process makes it possible for each sample to have an equal chance of being drawn, inferences based on the sample may not be statistically valid.[13]

The National Council of Teachers of Mathematics,[14] through its national and regional conferences and its publications (including the periodical "The Arithmetic Teacher") has also had other influences on curriculum

---

[13]*The Growth of Mathematical Ideas, Grades K–12,* 24th Yearbook, National Council of Teachers of Mathematics (Washington, D.C., 1959), pp. 480–89.

[14]For brochure, send to: National Council of Teachers of Mathematics, 1201 Sixteenth Street, N.W., Washington, D.C., 20036.

development. For example, one series of publications entitled Topics in Mathematics for Elementary School Teachers consists of eighteen booklets with titles such as *Sets, The Whole Numbers,* and *Numeration Systems* which retail for less than one dollar each. Another publication, *Experiences in Mathematical Ideas,* is actually a package of basic materials necessary to enable slow learners to achieve success in learning important representative segments of mathematics.

In 1963 a national meeting of about 30 leading mathematicians and scientists developed a long-range view of what mathematics might be taught in the schools. This conference, titled Goals for School Mathematics, prepared a report commonly referred to as the Cambridge Report. The report outlines a program for the first 13 years of schooling. The following is the list of topics for grades K-6.

TOPICS FOR GRADES K-2

The Real Number System

1. Experiences with "grouping" that will establish the idea of place-value numerals to various bases, including 10.
2. Extensive use of zero as a number, not merely as a symbol.
3. The idea of inequalities, and the symbols $<$ and $>$.
4. The idea of transitivity of $<$. (This can be built into game situations where the child is asked to guess a "secret" number from a set of carefully devised clues, and so on.)
5. The number line, including negatives from the beginning.
6. Use of rulers with 0 at the center.
7. Use of the number line in the "transitivity" games mentioned above.
8. Use of fractions with small denominators to name additional points on the number line.
9. Use of the idea of "the neighborhood of a point" on the number line; relation to inequalities.
10. Use of the number line to introduce decimals by change of scale.
11. The use of "crossed" number lines to form Cartesian coordinates; various games of strategy using Cartesian coordinates.
12. Use of an additive slide rule, including both positive and negative numbers.
13. Physical interpretations of addition and multiplication, including original interpretations made up by the children themselves (such as 2×4 represented by 4 washers on each of 2 pegs, or 2 stacks of 4 washers each, or a 2×4 rectangular array of washers or dots, or pebbles, etc., of 2 washers of each of 4 different colors, and so on.)
14. Questions that lead the children to "discover" the commutative nature of addition and multiplication.
15. Multiplication of a number "a little bit more than three" by a number "a little bit less than five."
16. Division with remainder using, for example, the pattern: "20 ÷ 8" means

"If we have 20 dots, how many rows of 8 will there be?"

. . . .

. . . .

. . . .

Answer: "2 whole rows and 4 left over."

17. Division with fractional answers. $20 \div 8 = 2\frac{1}{2}$.
18. Recognition of inverse operations.
19. Use of $\square$ as a variable in simple algebraic problems.
20. Experience with Cartesian coordinates, including both discrete and continuous cases, graphs of linear functions, graphs of functions obtained empirically, simple extrapolation ("When will the plant be seven inches tall?") and so on.   Various games of strategy played on Cartesian coordinates, etc.   Graph of $\square + \triangle = 10$, in connection with learning "addition facts," etc.

Geometry

1. Identifying and naming various geometric configurations.
2. Visualization, such as cutting out cardboard to construct 3-dimensional figures, where the child is shown the 3-dimensional figure and asked to find his own way to cut the 2-dimensional paper or cardboard.
3. The additive property of area, closely integrated with the operation of multiplication.
4. Symmetry and other transformations leaving geometrical figures invariant. The fact that a line or circle can be slid into itself.   The symmetries of squares and rectangles, circles, ellipses, etc. and solid figures like spheres, cubes, tetrahedra, etc.   This study could be facilitated with mirrors, paper folding etc.
5. Possibly the explicit recognition of the group property in the preceding.
6. Use of straightedge and compass to do the standard geometric construction such as comparing segments or angles, bisecting a segment or angle, etc.
7. Similar figures, both plane and solid, starting from small and enlarged photographs, etc.

Logic and Set Theory: Function

1. Number as a property of finite sets.
2. The comparison of cardinals of finite sets with emphasis on the fact that the result is independent of which mapping function is used.
3. Numerical functions determined by very simple formulas.
4. The use of logical statements to determine certain sets.   For example, games like *Twenty Questions* in which the set of possibilities is successively narrowed through the answers to yes-no questions.
5. Familiarity with both true and false statements as a source of information.

Applications

1. Measurement and units, in cases of length, area, volume, weight, time, money, temperature, etc.
2. Use of various measuring instruments, such as rulers, calipers, scales, etc.
3. Physical interpretations of $1/2, 1/3, 1/4, 2/3$.

4. Physical interpretations of negative numbers in relation to an arbitrary reference point (as 0° Centigrade, or altitude at sea level, or the lobby floor for an elevator, etc.)
5. Physical embodiments of inequalities in length, weight, etc., again using games where the child must use the transitive property, or the fact that a $> c$ implies $a + b > c + b$.
6. Estimating order of magnitude, with applications related to physics, economics, history, sociology, etc.
7. Visual display of data on Cartesian coordinates, such as recording growth of seedlings by daily measurement of height or graph of temperature vs. time for hourly readings of a thermometer.

TOPICS FOR GRADES 3-6

The Real Number System

1. Commutative, associative, and distributive laws. The multiplicative property of 1. The additive and multiplicative properties of 0.
2. Arithmetic of signed numbers.
3. For comparison purposes
   a. Modular arithmetic, based on primes and non-primes
   b. Finite fields
   c. Study of 2×2 matrices: comparison with real numbers; isomorphism of a subset of 2×2 matrices with real numbers; divisors of zero; identities for matrices, simple matrix inverses (particularly in relation to the idea of inverse operations and the nonexistence of a multiplicative inverse for zero). Possible use of matrices to introduce complex numbers.
4. Prime numbers and factoring. Euclidean algorithm, greatest common divisor.
5. Elementary Diophantine problems.
6. Integral exponents, both positive and negative.
7. The arithmetic of inequalities.
8. Absolute value.
9. Explicit study of the decimal system of notation including comparison with other bases and mixed bases (e.g. miles, yards, feet, inches).
10. Study of algorithms for adding, subtracting, multiplying, and dividing both integers and rational numbers, including "original" algorithms made up by the children themselves.
11. Methods for checking and verifying correctness of answers without recourse to the teacher.
12. Familiarity with certain "short cut" calculations that serve to illustrate basic properties of numbers or of numerals.
13. The use of desk calculators, slide rules, and tables.
14. Interpolation.
15. Considerable experience in approximations, estimates, "scientific notation," and orders of magnitude.
16. Effect of "round-off" and significant figures.
17. Knowledge of the distinction between rational and irrational numbers.
18. Study of decimals, for rational and irrational numbers.
19. Square roots, inequalities such as $1.41 < \sqrt{2} < 1.42$.

20. The Archimedean property and the density of the rational numbers including terminating decimals.
21. Nested intervals.
22. Computation with numbers given approximately (e.g. find π^2 given π).
23. Simple algebraic equations and inequalities.

Geometry

1. Mensuration formulas for familiar figures.
2. Approximate determination of π by measuring circles.
3. Conic sections.
4. Equation determining a straight line.
5. Cartesian coordinates in 3 dimensions.
6. Polar coordinates.
7. Latitude and longitude.
8. Symmetry of more sophisticated figures (e.g. wallpaper).
9. Similar figures interpreted as scale models and problems of indirect measurement.
10. Vectors, possibly including some statics and linear kinematics.
11. Symmetry argument for the congruence of the base angles of an isosceles triangle.

Logic and Foundations

1. The vocabulary of elementary logic: true, false, implication, double implication, contradiction.
2. Truth tables for simplest connectives.
3. The common schemes of inference:
$$\frac{P \to Q \text{ and } P}{Q} \qquad \frac{P \to Q \text{ and } \sim Q}{\sim P}$$
4. Simple uses of mathematical induction.
5. Preliminary recognition of the roles of axioms and theorems in relation to the real number system.
6. Simple uses of logical implication or "derivations" in study-in algorithms, more complicated identities, etc.
7. Elements of flow charting.
8. Simple uses of indirect proof, in studying inequalities, proving $\sqrt{2}$ irrational, and so on.
9. Study of sets, relations, and functions. Graphs of relations and functions, both discrete and continuous; graphs of empirically determined functions.
10. Explicit study of the relation of open sentences and their truth sets.
11. The concepts of isomorphism and transformation.

Theory of Real Functions

1. Intuitive consideration of infinite sequences of real numbers.
2. The logarithm function, built up by interpolation, from approximate equalities like $2^{10} \sim 10^3$.
3. Trigonometric functions.
4. Partial and linear orderings, with applications.
5. Linearity and convexity.

Applications

1. Empirical investigation of many times repeated random events.
2. Arithmetic study of how the ultimate stabilization of observed relative frequency occurs through "swamping." [15]

State and Local Curriculum Recommendations

Larger school systems and some states have prepared curriculum guides outlining suggested mathematics topics for the elementary school. In the state of Georgia, for example, a statewide committee of teachers, state department of education personnel, college and university professors, and national consultants developed a 180-page curriculum guide in 1962[16] which was revised in 1971.

Contributions of Psychologists to Learning Theory in Mathematics

The work of psychologists in developing theories of learner behavior has been consistently reflected in mathematics curriculum development. The rule arithmetic that was popular in the 17th through 19th centuries was largely replaced by the "meaning theory" of the 1930s, which resulted from Gestalt psychology. The textbooks of the 1940s and 1950s were organized to relate the parts of an entire context in order to encourage insight and understanding according to the writer's interpretation of "meaningful" arithmetic. The experimental programs of the 1960s were developed by mathematicians, but some were also greatly influenced by the recent research of psychologists.

Current mathematics textbooks have been influenced by psychologists such as Jean Piaget, Jerome Bruner, and Z. P. Dienes. Piaget, a Swiss psychologist, has made studies of the age-normative basis for intellectual growth. He holds that a child proceeds through three rather distinct periods in developing the ability to conceptualize. The first is a preoperational period extending from birth to about six years of age. During this stage the child relies heavily upon the senses and moves rapidly toward symbolic representations. The second phase, which Piaget calls the period of concrete operations, can extend to about the age of eleven years. During these years objects serve to direct the child's thinking as he interacts with

---

[15]Extracted from *Goals for School Mathematics*, Report of the Cambridge Conference on School Mathematics (Boston: Houghton Mifflin Co. for Educational Services, Inc., 1963), pp. 31–41.

[16]*Mathematics for Georgia Schools*, Vol. I and II (Atlanta, Georgia: State Department of Education, 1971).

his environment in the development of concepts.   The third stage, according to Piaget, is the period of formal operations.   It is at this stage that the individual is capable of formulating ideas without dependence upon concrete objects and can perceive relationships.   It continues through adulthood.   Piaget has not as yet influenced American schools to a great extent, but his theories have been utilized in certain English schools, particularly in the Nuffield Mathematics Teaching Project.[17]

Jerome Bruner of Harvard has had great influence on curriculum changes in the United States.   In his treatment of the use of the structure of discipline as the central force in curriculum design, Bruner contributed a theory that is basic to such projects as the School Mathematics Study Group.   He stresses the inductive approach or the discovery method as the basis of curriculum design.   His assertion, "We begin with the hypothesis that any subject can be taught effectively in some intellectually honest form to any child at any stage of development," [18] is widely quoted in support of modern mathematics programs.

Z. P. Dienes, of Sherbrooke University, Canada, has only recently influenced the teaching of mathematics in the United States, although his contributions have been widely felt in Australia and England.   Dienes is best known for his teaching materials, which are related to Piaget's theory of the three stages of a child's conceptual development.   His materials stress the development of ordering, classifying, determining relationships, and recognizing structural patterns at three levels.   At all levels, Dienes views interactions between children and materials as crucial to concept development.[19] His attribute blocks have recently been produced in various forms by U.S. publishers of mathematics materials and textbooks.

Lloyd Scott summarizes the contributions to mathematics curricula and teaching methods from recent developments in the study of human learning as follows:

1. The structure of mathematics should be stressed at all levels.   Topics and relationships of endurance should be given concentrated attention.
2. Children are capable of learning more abstract and more complex concepts when the relationship between concepts is stressed.
3. Existing elementary arithmetic programs may be severely condensed because children are capable of learning concepts at much earlier ages than formerly thought.
4. Any concept may be taught a child of any age in some intellectually honest manner, if one is able to find the proper language for stressing the concept.

---

[17]Robert B. Davis, *The Changing Curriculum: Mathematics* (Washington, D.C.: Association for Supervision and Curriculum Development, 1967), p. 33.

[18]Jerome Bruner, *The Process of Education* (Cambridge, Mass.: Harvard University Press, 1960).

[19]Z. P. Dienes and E. W. Golding, *Learning Logic, Logic Games* (New York: Herder and Herder, 1966).

5. The inductive approach or the discovery method is logically productive and should enhance learning and retention.
6. The major objective of a program is the development of independent and creative thinking processes.
7. Human learning seems to pass through the stages of preoperations, concrete operations, and formal operations.
8. Growth of understanding is dependent upon concept exploration through challenging apparatus and concrete materials and cannot be restricted to mere symbolic manipulations.
9. Teaching mathematical skills is regarded as a tidying-up of concepts developed through discovery rather than as a step by step process for memorization.
10. Practical application of isolated concepts or systems of concepts, particularly those applications drawn from the natural sciences, are valuable to reinforcement and retention.[20]

Summary

The elementary school teacher makes decisions which determine the mathematics curriculum for the particular group of learners for whom he is responsible. Ideally, the decision as to what to teach and how to teach mathematics in the elementary school results from the teacher's careful study and acquired understanding of the unique needs, interests, and capabilities of the learners in his school situation. The textbook is probably the teacher's major source of curriculum ideas and activities and typically provides the needed structure and sequence for the mathematics program.

The teacher will be successful in choosing appropriate mathematics experiences for a group of learners and ultimately for each individual learner to the extent that he is aware of factors which determine a modern mathematics program. He should, therefore, continue to expand his knowledge of the historical developments in mathematics and mathematics teaching and his knowledge of contemporary mathematics programs and research projects. He must also attempt to keep informed as to the recommendations and significant publications of national, state, and local professional groups.

---

[20]Lloyd Scott, *Trends in Elementary School Mathematics* (Chicago: Rand McNally & Co., 1966), pp. 15–16.

PART III

Teaching–Learning Aids

Chapter 9

MAKING AND USING SELECTED
TEACHING–LEARNING AIDS

In classroom practice the teacher must have available a variety of devices to lend concreteness to the teaching-learning process. Much of this requires little or no additional cash outlay because it is standard classroom equipment. The teacher's ingenuity and imagination can set the only limits to his utilization of a multitude of aids in making the development of mathematical concepts come alive for the student.

This chapter gives detailed suggestions for the use of bulletin boards; flannelboards and feltboards; overhead projectors; number lines; posters, charts, and cards; separate and semifixed objects; abaci and bead frames; place-value aids; pegboards; one-hundred boards; aids for geometry; and geoboards.

Bulletin Boards

The elementary school teacher has customarily utilized bulletin boards to make the classroom more attractive. Seasonal designs and pictures related to social studies or science units are often displayed, and exhibits of pupils' papers and drawings provide recognition for outstanding work. The bulletin board can also be used effectively as a resource in mathematics teaching to:

1. Build or review vocabulary.
2. Provide a simple, visual presentation of a concept.

3. Challenge pupils' thinking.
4. Drill or review basic operations or basic facts.
5. Summarize teaching of a specific topic.

Building or Reviewing Vocabulary

Bulletin boards listing vocabulary words can be used to reemphasize new words or symbols which have been introduced during the teaching of any new concept or process in mathematics. For example, if the teacher is presenting or reviewing set vocabulary or terms and symbols such as equals, less than, greater than, and not equal to, a bulletin board such as that shown in Figure 1 can be a reminder to the pupils of the correct procedure for making the symbols as well as the vocabulary to be associated with them.

Developing Concepts

The bulletin board can be an aid in teaching a specific concept such as numeration, measurement, operations, rational numbers, geometry, and so forth. The teacher might present the new concept first with a social situa-

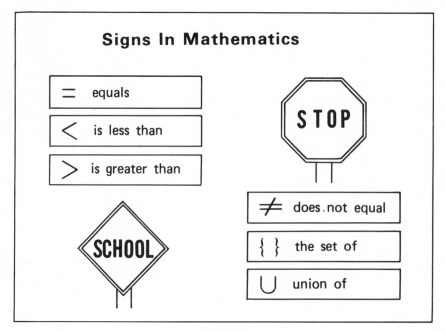

FIGURE 1

tion, then with concrete objects, and finally refer pupils to the bulletin board to reinforce the learning. (Figure 2.)

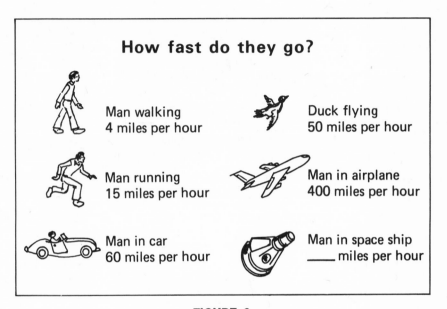

FIGURE 2

Bulletin Board to Develop Concepts

Challenging Pupils' Thinking

At times the bulletin board can stimulate pupils to seek solutions to a specific problem. The teacher might display a collection of pictures of familiar objects with circle shapes with the caption: "How many circle shapes can you find?" Or pictures of items children could purchase at a store, with their prices, can be arranged with a caption "What can you buy for $10.00?" (See Figure 3.)

Reviewing and Summarizing

When a process or concept has been developed through a social situation, use of concrete objects, the chalkboard, or overhead projector, a bulletin board display can help pupils to see in another way the procedure or information that has been "discovered." (See Figure 4.)

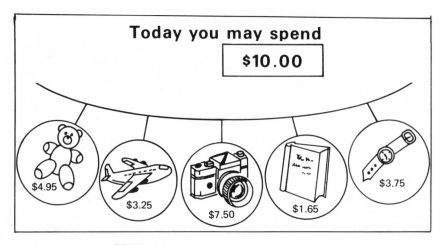

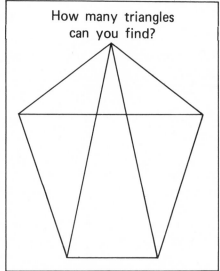

FIGURE 3

Bulletin Boards to Challenge Thinking

Guides to Effective Use of Mathematics Bulletin Boards

1. Have a clear purpose other than to decorate the room.
2. Be ingenious in selecting background materials—colored burlap, corrugated paper, a paper tablecloth, large sheets of wrapping paper. Many materials are superior to crepe paper.
3. Mount all pictures carefully. Mounting paper does not always have to be 9″ × 12″, or square, or black. Pins are less noticeable than thumbtacks.

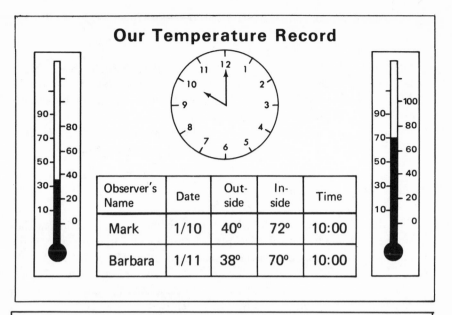

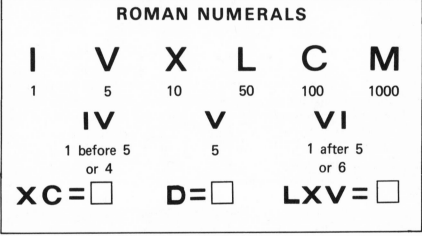

FIGURE 4

Bulletin Boards to Review and Summarize

4. Lettering should be legible to the viewer wherever he is located in the room. It is usually better to have lettering that is too large rather than too small. The teacher who is not confident about correct forms for upper and lower case letters can purchase sets of block letters from a school supply store to use as patterns. Study the arrangement and spacing of letters and words.

5. Avoid stereotyped arrangements. Two pictures at the left do not always

have to be balanced with two pictures at the right. Sometimes an object can extend beyond the fixed border of the bulletin board. A third-dimension effect can be obtained by use of actual objects or by setting the letters out from the background with long pins.

6. Use ample color to enhance eye appeal. Avoid color combinations that may be distracting, such as red letters on a green background.

Flannelboards and Feltboards

The flannelboard is an invaluable aid for teacher demonstration in the development of mathematical concepts. Commercial feltboards are available in a wide variety of sizes ranging from as small as 18″ × 18″ to 36″ × 72″. The 36″ × 48″ folding feltboard with black or light green flannel mounted on a telescoping metal easel is recommended for purchase. The board should be large enough to be easily seen by the entire class.

Construction

Free and inexpensive materials can be used in the construction of a flannelboard. For example, a cardboard refrigerator carton can be dismantled and one side approximately 3′ × 6′ used for the flannelboard. Stretch heavy cotton flannel over one side of the board, and on the reverse side lace the overlap with a wet cotton string. As the string dries it will cause the flannel to be stretched tightly over the surface of the board. Plywood can also be used as a base for a flannelboard but has the disadvantage of being quite heavy.

On smaller size boards flannel can be doubled and a seam sewn on two sides, as in a pillowslip. Insert a piece of cardboard or masonite in the open end of the slipcover·and fasten securely with a stapler or masking tape. The advantage of this simple type of flannelboard is that it can be disposed of as it becomes soiled from use. Some teachers utilize old picture frames with a piece of wallboard or ¼″ plyboard as a backing for the flannel.

At times it is desirable for pupils to have individual flannelboards to use at their desks. A 12″ × 18″ piece of cardboard can easily be covered with flannel. If the lid of a cigar box or a flat cardboard box is covered with flannel, sets of flannel or paper objects can be stored inside the box.

School supply houses offer numerous sets of felt cutouts at a cost of less than $2 per set. Among those which can be purchased are primary cutouts of apples, ducks, rabbits, circle shapes, square shapes; holiday cutouts of pumpkins, hearts, turkeys, flags, shamrocks; numeral assortments;

modern math symbol assortments; vocabulary terms; clocks; fractional parts of circles and squares; coins; geometric shapes; and number lines.

The teacher may prefer to prepare sets of simple objects for use on the flannelboard from scraps of felt, flannel, suede, blotters, sandpaper, foam rubber, styrofoam, or construction paper (Figure 5). If paper objects are used (candles from Christmas cards, numerals from calendars, vegetables or flowers from seed catalogs, magazine pictures of foods, or objects

FIGURE 5

Shapes for Flannelboard

traced on construction paper), a small piece of sandpaper or felt glued on the back of the picture provides a satisfactory method for gripping the paper object to the flannel surface. School supply houses stock a special paper with one smooth side and the other a suedelike finish which is intended for the making of objects for a flannelboard.

Uses of Flannelboards

The flannelboard has many uses similar to the chalkboard, the overhead projector, and the bulletin board. Its advantages are the ease with which representations of colorful objects can be rearranged and displayed. The ingenious teacher will determine the appropriate time and most effective uses for the flannelboard. Pupils and teachers can work together to develop many concepts, such as the following:

1. *Arithmetic Readiness.* As the teacher tells a familiar story such as "The Old Woman Who Lived in a Shoe," objects from the story are placed on the flannelboard such as a large shoe, the old woman, and sets of children. Pupils are guided through teacher questions to develop understanding of concepts of few, more, less, big, and little, and to count the objects.

2. *Counting.* The teacher arranges the flannelboard with a length of colored yarn on which she places 10 felt bluebirds. Then she repeats the following poem, removing the birds as the appropriate lines are said:

> Ten little bluebirds, swinging on the line.
> One flew away and then there were nine.
> Nine little bluebirds that were always late,
> One hurried off and left only eight.
> Eight little bluebirds, blue as the heaven.
> One went bug-hunting, now there were seven
> Seven little bluebirds, doing birdie tricks.
> One tumbled down and left only six.
> Six little bluebirds, please don't go away.
> Stay on the line and let us watch you play.

A recommended source for rhymes is: Louise Binder Scott and J. J. Thompson, *Rhymes for Fingers and Flannel Boards* (Manchester, Mo.: Webster Publishing Company, 1960).

3. *Developing Cardinal Number Concepts.* Arrange sets of one, two, three, four, and five elements (ducks, apples, birds, chickens) on a background of a contrasting color of felt or outline each set as introduced with a length of yarn to make a simple closed curve. Help children count the number of objects in the set, and use spoken number words to identify each set. As appropriate, introduce the felt numeral to identify the cardinal number of each set. Then hand the pupil the felt numeral and have him place it under or over the appropriate set.

Similar procedures should be used for introducing cardinal numbers up to 10. At first use like objects as set elements. Later prepare sets of unlike elements.

4. *Developing the Concept of Empty Set.* Place a set of one, two, three, or four objects on the flannelboard. Use a piece of yarn or a contrasting piece of background felt to outline the set. Ask "What is the number of this set?" Then ask, "How would we picture a set of objects in my pocket?" (An apron with a large empty pocket is useful here.) "How would we picture a set of chickens in an empty chicken coop? A set of children in an empty car? A set of birds in an empty nest? The cookies in an empty cookie box?" Introduce the symbol for zero as appropriate as the cardinal number of a set with no members.

5. *Developing the Concept of One-to-One Correspondence.* Place a set of two, three, or four objects on the flannelboard. Have pupils take felt objects from a box and place a set with the same cardinal number on the flannelboard. Have them show with pieces of yarn or strips of felt that the sets have the same number of elements by connecting each element in the first set with an element in the second set. Introduce term "equivalent sets" as appropriate.

Place a set of smiling egg-shaped faces made from felt and a magic marker on the flannelboard. Then have pupils place a felt hat on each head. Help them see that there is one hat for each head.

6. *Developing the Concept of Ordinal Numbers.* Place four long pieces of yarn horizontally on the flannelboard to make "shelves." Place six pieces of yarn vertically on the flannelboard to divide the shelves into "boxes." Place a felt or flannel object in each box. Direct a child to point to the third object on the top shelf, the fourth object on the bottom shelf, and so forth. Ask questions such as: "What object comes after the second object on the middle shelf? What object comes before the fifth object on the bottom shelf?" A child could be directed to place a felt apple in the fourth box on the top shelf, and so forth.

7. *Developing Addition and Subtraction Facts.* Place five felt objects on the flannelboard and have the pupils count them. Then regroup the felt objects into subsets such as two and three, three and two, four and one, one and four, five and none, none and five. At an appropriate time, after using the terms orally, introduce the mathematical symbols of plus, minus, equals, not equal to, greater than, and less than.

After considerable experience with addition and subtraction facts on the flannelboard, help the children to see the relationship between addition and subtraction—subtraction is the inverse of addition. The concept of the commutative property of addition of whole numbers can be developed as the addition facts are discovered, but the introduction of the spoken and written term "commutative property" should be at the teacher's discretion in the early grades.

8. *Associating Numerals and Number Names.* Use the flannelboard to develop a chart showing the numeral 1, the number name "one," and one object. Continue with other numerals, number names, and objects placed in rows.

9. *Fractional Parts.* Prepare four large felt circles about 7 or 8″ in diameter. Cut one in halves, one in thirds, one in fourths. Help children discover relationships by comparison, such as two halves are the same as one whole, one half is larger than one fourth, two fourths are equal to one half, and one third is less than one half.

Repeat using four large felt rectangles and then sets of two, four, and six objects.

10. *Developing Ability to Tell Time.* Prepare a large clock face from felt about 18″ in diameter with the hours marked with a felt pen. Make movable hands from felt. Place on flannelboard and use to tell time in hours, half hours, quarter hours, and so forth. On another part of the flannelboard place the time of day in numerals, such as 9:30 A.M. and have the pupils arrange felt hands on the clock face to show this time. Terms such as half-past and 20 minutes after can be printed on felt and placed in appropriate positions adjacent to the clock face.

11. *Developing Understanding of Multiplication.* Arrange four rows with three felt objects in each row. Help the children to see that 4 threes are twelve. Rearrange the same objects as three rows with four objects in each row and help them see that 3 fours are 12.

Repeat as each new basic fact in multiplication is introduced. At an appropriate time, help the children to generalize the commutative property for multiplication of whole numbers. Introduce the multiplication symbol, ×, and the algorism form as children appear to be ready.

The concept of multiplication as Cartesian products or as a pairing of elements can also be demonstrated on the flannelboard. Place five long pieces of yarn to represent lines and six pieces of yarn vertically to complete a 4″ × 5″ grid.

In the top row, omitting the first space, place a flannel representation of red pants, blue pants, yellow pants, green pants. In the first column, omitting the top space, place a flannel representation for a white shirt, green shirt, orange shirt. Using duplicate flannel objects show how each of the pants can be paired with each of the shirts, resulting in 12 different pairings.

12. *Developing Understanding of Base Ten and Other Number Bases.* Place 12 objects at random on the flannelboard and have pupils count them. Then rearrange the objects to show one set of ten plus two objects

left over (or two sets of one). Outline the set of ten with a piece of yarn. Repeat with '13 objects, 15 objects, and so forth. Place numerals on the flannelboard to stress the idea that a numeral in the tens position tells the number of sets of ten. The numeral in the ones position tells the number of ones.

Then place six objects on the board. Ask, "How can these be re-arranged to show the number of sets of five represented?" Regroup as a set of five and one left over, using yarn to outline the set of five. Have the word "five" printed with a felt pen on a piece of flannel to show that six means one set of five and one one. Repeat using seven, nine, ten, or eleven objects.

13. *Developing Understanding of Addition and Subtraction of Like Fractions.* Use the flannelboard and objects to review the concept that two halves when joined make one whole; three thirds when rearranged make one whole; and four fourths when rearranged make one whole. Then place three halves, four halves, five halves, and so forth on the flannelboard and have children regroup them. Repeat using fourths and thirds. Use flannel fractional numerals and mathematical symbols (or use the chalk-board) to present examples of addition of like fractions, as:

$$\boxed{1/4 + 2/4 =} \quad \boxed{1/3 + 2/3 =} \quad \boxed{1\ 1/2 + 1\ 1/2 =} \quad \boxed{2\ 1/4 + 1\ 3/4 =}$$

Have pupils show on the flannelboard with circle or square shapes how they would solve these problems.

14. *Developing Understanding of Addition and Subtraction of Unlike Fractions.* Help children to see that to add one-half and one-sixth, the one-half can be renamed or replaced by three-sixths. Then the three-sixths and the one-sixth can be regrouped to make four-sixths. Help them to see that four-sixths is another way of naming or showing two-thirds. Repeat several times with flannel shapes of circles, squares, or rectangles before developing the algorism form for adding or subtracting unlike fractions.

The flannelboard is especially helpful in developing an understanding of how to find a simpler form or another name for what is called an "im-proper" fraction. For example, show that 10/3 is 10 one-thirds on the flannelboard. When regrouped into wholes, this is the same as 3 1/3 or three wholes and one-third more.

15. *Flannelboard Card Strips to Develop Understanding of Fractional Values.* Place the numeral 1 on one strip of tagboard to represent one whole. Cut apart and label similar size strips in halves, fourths, eighths, thirds, sixths, twelfths, and tenths (Figure 6). Place small pieces of flannel or sandpaper on the backs of the cards so they will adhere to the flannel-

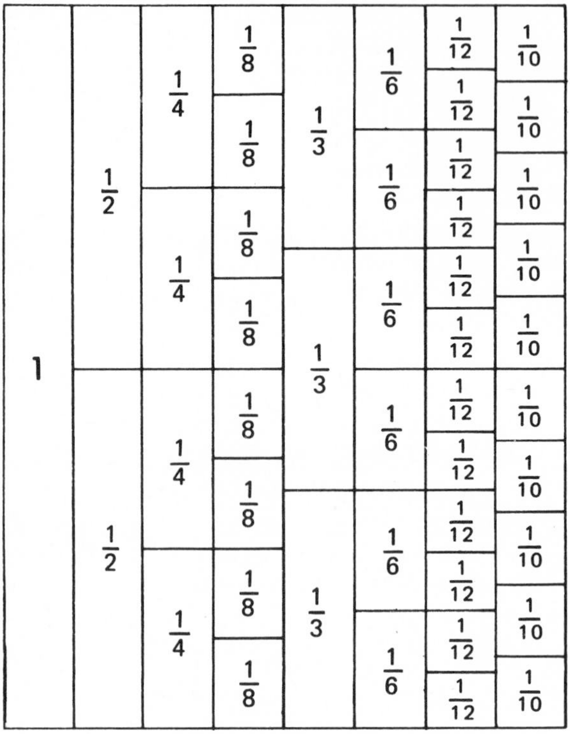

Fraction Card Strips for Flannelboard

FIGURE 6

board. Have the children place the various strips to develop understanding of fractional values and equivalent fractions and to observe that the larger the denominator the smaller the size of the part.

16. *Developing Understanding of Set Vocabulary.* Obtain colored pictures of about 15 boys and 15 girls from a catalog, coloring book, or magazine. Mount these on construction paper and attach triangular pieces of sandpaper or flannel to the back of each picture. Then place pictures of four boys and two girls on the flannelboard and outline the set with a piece of yarn. The teacher could describe this as the set of children in Jane's reading group. She might then say, "Show me the set of boys in Jane's reading group." Rearrange the pictures of boys within the set, outline this set with a piece of yarn, and describe as "the set of boys in Jane's reading group." Introduce the term "subset" as appropriate. Repeat asking for the set of girls in Jane's reading group, the set of children with brown hair,

or the set of children wearing something blue. Repeat using a question which would result in all the members of the subset being members of the original set. Repeat asking a question where there would be no members in the subset, as "the set of children wearing coats."

17. *Union of Disjoint Sets.* Arrange the pictures of boys on the flannelboard and describe as the set of boys in fourth grade. Outline the set with a piece of yarn. Do the same with the girls' pictures and describe as the set of girls in the fourth grade. Outline the set with a piece of yarn. To present the idea of union of disjoint sets, ask a child to indicate how we could show the set of all the children in the fourth grade. The two sets may be joined by removing the pieces of yarn and outlining the new set with one long piece.

18. *Intersection of Sets.* Obtain small pictures of 8 to 10 automobiles and affix pieces of sandpaper or flannel on the back of each. Arrange two pieces of yarn horizontally on flannelboard to represent the outline of a city street. Then arrange two pieces of yarn vertically on the flannelboard to represent the outline of a street which intersects the first one. Give the streets local names such as "Broad Street" and "Main Street." Place pictures of cars on both streets with one or two at the space where the two streets cross. The teacher then might ask: "What is the set of cars on Broad Street? What is the set of cars on Main Street? Which cars are members of both sets?" Use the term "intersection" of streets as related to intersection of sets.

Another illustration might utilize pictures of children. Place on the flannelboard a set of children with names printed on the pictures. Indicate that these children, Jane, John, Bill, Sue, and Mary, are members of Jane's reading group, and outline the set with a piece of yarn. Add another set described as the set of children who are absent today (Louise, Art, Bill, and Mary). Show that Bill and Mary are members of both of these sets by overlapping the colored yarn outlining the two sets. Then move on to using sets of flannel numerals on the flannelboard, such as the set of even numbers from 1 through 10 and the set of even numbers from 6 through 14. Show with yarn that the numerals 6, 8, and 10 are members of both sets.

Overhead Projectors

The overhead projector combines the utility of the chalkboard, the bulletin board, and the printed page while offering the teacher the advantage of facing the students and thus maintaining constant visual contact with the entire class. It takes only a little imagination to utilize the overhead projector to accomplish what can be done with the above-mentioned aids, and in most cases, with far better results.

By using a clear sheet of plastic, also referred to as acetate, and a felt-tip pen, the teacher can write anything to be projected. The plastic can be easily wiped clean and used again and again. With planning, several sheets can be prepared ahead of time to be presented in sequence and then preserved so they can be reused. Colored pens and pencils that project in color are readily available, thus avoiding the problems encountered when colored chalk is used on chalkboards.

Uses of the Overhead Projector

The following are some suggested uses for the overhead projector in the elementary classroom:

1. The projector can present any concept which can also be shown with a two-dimensional aid such as the chalkboard, bulletin board, posters, charts, or textbook.
2. Actual objects such as paper clips, coins, or keys, can be placed on the projector so that their silhouettes appear on the screen. In this way the projector can be used like a flannelboard to arrange and rearrange sets of objects.
3. A grid can be prepared and used repeatedly for developing such aids as an addition and subtraction chart, graphs, or geometric shapes. Several number lines can be prepared.
4. A clock face on a transparency can have opaque paper hands which can be moved rapidly for practice in telling time.
5. Transparent rulers or protractors can be placed on the overhead projector so their use can be effectively demonstrated by the teacher.
6. If chalkboard space is limited, seatwork and homework can be placed on the overhead projector. Some teachers make transparencies of word problems for those who need special challenges.
7. The teacher can make transparencies of pupils' work to help the class note particular difficulties.

Whatever can be written, printed, or drawn can also be projected with the overhead projector. It is even possible to purchase equipment that adds simulated motion to a transparency projection.

Securing Transparencies

There are basically four sources of transparencies:

1. Purchase in sets from commercial sources (see list of publishers in Chapter 10).

2. Purchase of printed paper masters from commercial sources. These are useful in preparing permanent transparencies on a "Thermofax" type copying machine.
3. Teacher-made masters from which permanent copies can be made on the Thermofax machine.
4. Teacher's drawings on transparent material (usually temporary).

Commercially published transparencies have the advantage of vivid color, clear text, and sturdy mountings. Disadvantages of commercial transparencies are their cost and the fact that a set may contain certain transparencies which are not considered useful by the teacher. The cost factor can often be offset by making the sets centrally available in a materials center so that many teachers have access to them.

Number Lines

The number line is one of the most versatile aids available to the teacher. Basically it consists of a series of numbers represented by points designated at equal intervals along a line. Although typically used as a horizontal continuum, it can also be used to provide experiences with a vertical arrangement, as in reading a thermometer or measuring children's heights. A circular arrangement is needed for demonstrating the telling of time or reading of meters.

Construction

Although number lines can be obtained inexpensively from commercial sources, it may be desirable for the teacher or pupils to prepare them for specific uses. On a strip of adding machine tape or a 3″ wide strip of paper or tagboard print the numerals according to the intended use. For primary grades prepare a number line with the numerals from 0–100 with a dot or vertical mark to indicate the position of the numeral. For intermediate grades, prepare number lines with fractional numerals, decimal numerals, or numerals for other number bases. Place the number line across the top of the chalkboard for teacher demonstrations or at a lower level if children are going to use it. Individual number lines can be prepared on masking tape and placed on the pupils' desks. After initial use in these forms, number line transparencies can easily be prepared for use with the overhead projector.

Using Number Lines

Of the many ways creative teachers use the number line, the following are suggested for consideration:

1. *Counting.*   Use the number line for reference in counting from 1 to 100; in counting by twos, threes, or fours, or in counting backwards. Clothespins placed on a cord stretched below the number line can be used to show correspondence (Figure 7).   In first grade, a number line can be

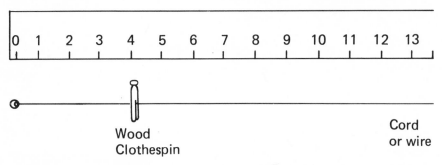

Number Line Used for Counting or One-to-One Correspondence

FIGURE 7

painted on the floor about a foot away from a wall, with numerals spaced about 1′ apart.   Have children stand on the line and move to the left or to the right a designated number of steps.

2. *Understanding the Operation of Addition and Subtraction.*   In conjunction with the chalkboard, use the number line to show that 3 and 3 more are 6; 9 and 4 more are 13; 3 less than 12 are 9, and so forth (Figure 8).

3. *Understanding Operations of Multiplication and Division.*   To show that 3 fours are 12, locate 3 sets of fours, using arcs on the chalkboard beneath the number line (Figure 9).   To show that 15 divided by 3 equals

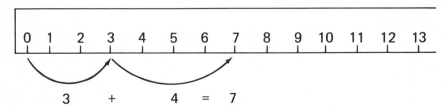

Number Line Used to Show Addition

FIGURE 8

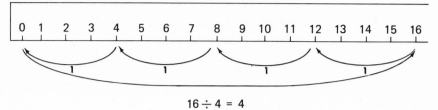

$$16 \div 4 = 4$$

Number Line Used to Show Division

FIGURE 9

5, draw an arc on the chalkboard below the number line to indicate 15, then move back to the left with arcs of 3 and count the 5 sets of threes.

4. *Developing Understanding of Equivalent Fractions.* Place a number line consisting of $\frac{1}{2}$, $\frac{2}{2}$, $\frac{3}{2}$, $\frac{4}{2}$, etc. slightly above a number line marked in fourths, as $\frac{1}{4}$, $\frac{2}{4}$, $\frac{3}{4}$, $\frac{4}{4}$, $\frac{5}{4}$, etc. Help pupils see that $\frac{2}{4}$ is another name for $\frac{1}{2}$, and so forth. Prepare similar number lines for sixths, eighths, etc. Place one above the other to help the children discover equivalent fraction values (Figure 10).

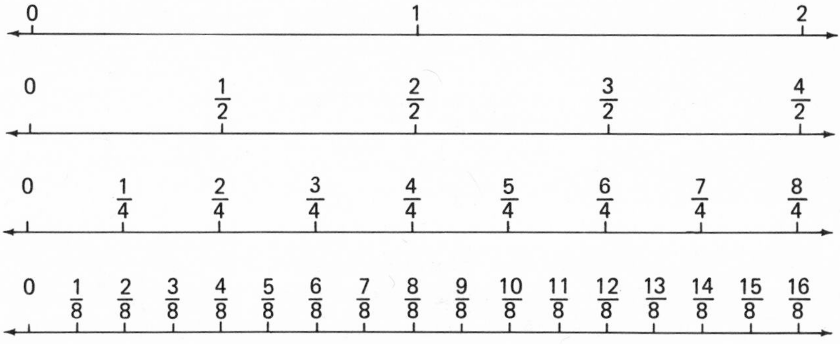

Number Line Used to Show Fractional Numbers

FIGURE 10

5. *Adding and Subtracting Fractional Numbers.* On a number line marked off in fourths, help children see that three-fourths plus one-fourth are four-fourths, or the whole number *1*. Use the number line to count backwards in subtracting fractional values.

6. *Counting and Performing Operations with Other Number Bases.* Use a number line showing base five, base eight, or base two numerals. Use as with base ten numerals to develop skills in counting, adding, or subtracting.

7. *Understanding Decimal Numerals.* Prepare a number line marked with decimal numerals. Use as suggested previously to develop skills in counting, adding, and subtracting.

8. *Understanding Values of Large Numbers.* Use a number line marked off in equal units. Affix to the line small cards with numerals such as 10,000, 20,000, or 30,000. Help children locate the approximate position on the number line of such values as 14,900, 20,500, and 39,995.

Posters, Charts, Cards

The same purposes that bulletin boards serve can in many cases be equally well served by smaller posters, charts, and cards. The advantages of these types of aids are:

1. Ease of preparation.
2. Convenience for storage when no longer needed.
3. Can be kept concealed until most appropriate time for use.
4. Can be displayed on walls other than limited bulletin board space.

In general, charts and posters are not used to introduce a topic but are utilized when ideas are being organized, summarized, or reviewed. Charts are especially helpful in recording vocabulary terms following some other visual representation of the ideas expressed.

Teachers do not always prepare mathematics charts themselves; there are occasions when the ideas for a chart are developed through class participation. These are usually arranged first on the chalkboard, and a chart is then prepared by a pupil committee or the teacher. Sometimes a teacher-made chart can be presented and pupil committees asked to devise another way of presenting the same information. When pupils are asked to explain a teacher- or pupil-prepared chart, the teacher can observe how clearly they understand the concept or process illustrated.

Guides to Chart Preparation

1. Use good quality chart paper or tagboard. Make them durable to stand repeated use.
2. Use correct manuscript lettering. Avoid incorrect combinations of upper and lower case letters.

3. Make charts large enough to be easily seen by all pupils, yet keep in mind the arrangements for storage.
4. Limit ideas to one concept or purpose.
5. Use color for emphasis and eye appeal.

Examples of Useful Charts, Posters, and Cards

1. *One-Hundred Chart.* Divide a piece of tagboard about 30″ square into 100 squares. Using numerals of the same style to which children are accustomed, place the numerals from 0–99 on the chart. One chart should show the numerals from left to right as usually taught (Figure 11), and another should show the numerals in vertical columns. Pocket charts used in the basic reading program can be utilized to build one-hundred charts if strips of numerals are prepared for insertion in the pockets, or the numerals can be printed on 3″ × 5″ rectangles.

The one-hundred chart can be used to teach counting to 100 by ones, twos, threes, fives, and tens. If selected numerals on the chart are covered,

0	1	2	3	4	5	6	7	8	9
10	11	12	13	14	15	16	17	18	19
20	21	22	23	24	25	26	27	28	29
30	31	32	33	34	35	36	37	38	39
40	41	42	43	44	45	46	47	48	49
50	51	52	53	54	55	56	57	58	59
60	61	62	63	64	65	66	67	68	69
70	71	72	73	74	75	76	77	78	79
80	81	82	83	84	85	86	87	88	89
90	91	92	93	94	95	96	97	98	99

One-Hundred Chart

FIGURE 11

children can be provided practice in supplying the numerals in sequence. They can also be helped to count backwards by referring to the chart. A creative use is to study the chart to discover number patterns.

2. *Addition and Subtraction Chart.* Prepare a matrix of 3″ squares as shown in Figure 12. With a felt-tip pen place a plus symbol in the top left square, followed by the numerals from 0 through 9. In the first column on the left also insert the numerals from 0 through 9. As the basic facts of addition are developed, insert them with a felt-tip pen in the appropriate squares. Use the same procedure to develop addition-subtraction matrices for other number bases.

Use the chart as basic sums are discovered or presented and again as a review reference after all 100 basic facts have been introduced. Help children to see the relationship between addition and subtraction by lo-

+	0	1	2	3	4	5	6	7	8	9
0	1	2	3	4	5	6	6	7	8	9
1	1	2	3	4	5	6	7	8	9	
2	2	3	4	5	6	7	8	9		
3	3	4	5	6	7	8	9			
4	4	5	6	7	8	9				
5	5	6	7	8	9					
6	6	7	8	9						
7	7	8	9							
8	8	9								
9	9									

Basic Addition Facts

FIGURE 12

cating the sum, a known addend, and then the missing addend.   Ditto
sheets can be used by children to prepare their own charts for the review
of concepts previously introduced by the teacher.

3. *Multiplication and Division Charts*.   Prepare a matrix of 3" squares
as shown in Figure 13.   With a felt-tip pen place a multiplication symbol
in the top left square, followed by the numerals from 1 through 9.   In the
first column at the left insert the numerals 1 through 9.   As the basic facts
of multiplication are developed, insert them in the appropriate squares.
Use the same procedure with appropriate size matrices for multiplication-
division charts for other number bases.

Use the table as basic multiplication facts are discovered or presented
and as a review when all the facts have been introduced.   Help children to
see the relationship between multiplication and division by locating the product, the known factor, and then the missing factor.

The table can also be used as a challenge to advanced pupils.   Ask

X	1	2	3	4	5	6	7	8	9
1	1	2	3	4	5	6	7	8	9
2	2	4	6	8	10	12	14	16	18
3	3	6	9	12	15	18	21	24	27
4	4	8	12	16	20	24	28	32	36
5	5	10	15	20	25	30	35	40	45
6	6	12	18	24	30	36	42	48	54
7	7	14	21	28	35	42	49	56	63
8	8	16	24	32	40	48	56	64	72
9	9	18	27	36	45	54	63	72	81

Multiplication-Division Chart

FIGURE 13

them what interesting discoveries they can make from the table, such as that a diagonal line forms two triangles which are mirror images of each other; numerals on the diagonal are squared numbers; in each column the sum of the top number plus the bottom number is a multiple of 10; and other pairs vertically and horizontally are multiples of 10.

4. *Primary Number Charts.* Prepare a chart to show the meaning of 1–10 using correct manuscript numerals, pictures of objects, and the number word in correct manuscript lettering (Figure 14). For later use prepare a similar chart replacing the pictures of objects with symbols such as squares or circles.

Use the chart to help children associate the correct numeral with the

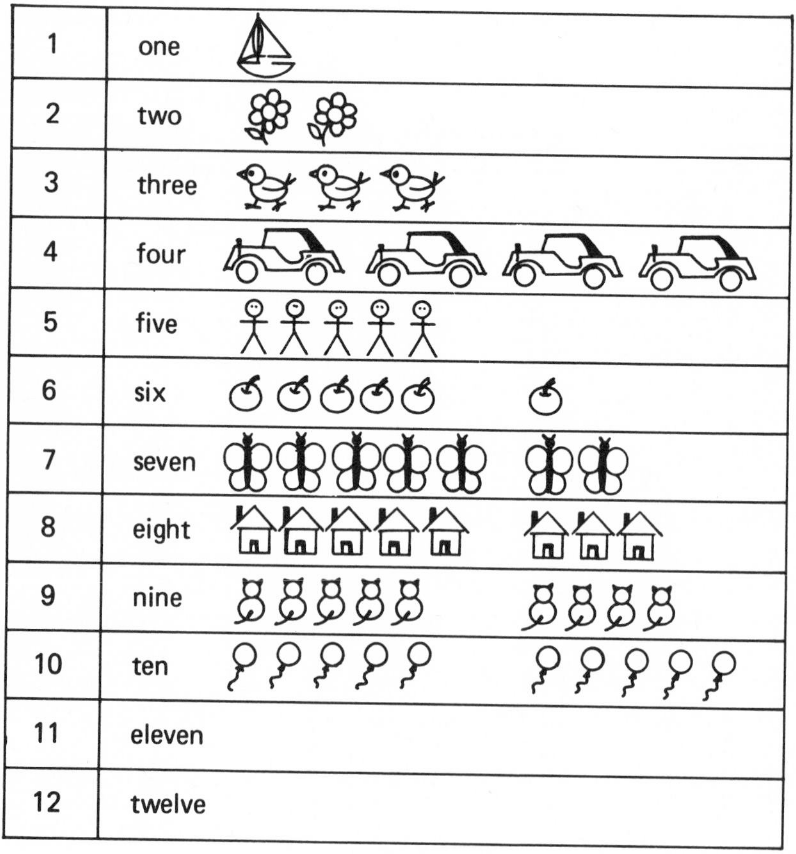

1	one
2	two
3	three
4	four
5	five
6	six
7	seven
8	eight
9	nine
10	ten
11	eleven
12	twelve

Our Numbers

FIGURE 14

quantity it represents and to teach the spelling of the number word. The chart can be developed as the number ideas are presented and then displayed for continued pupil reference.

5. *Primary Number Display Cards.* For each number from 0 through 10 prepare a 9″ × 12″ card with the appropriate number of objects such as animals, birds, insects, cars, vegetables, or whatever the teacher's ingenuity can produce (Figure 15). If possible, prepare one set with actual objects children can touch, such as toothbrushes, miniature automobiles, parchment cake cups, stuffed candy-bar wrappers, wrapped candies, lollipops, or umbrella party favors. Sets can be arranged on cards in a variety of patterns, although there is an advantage to using groupings children can recognize at a glance. One set should be prepared without the number word and numeral. Sets of cards appropriate to the season or unit being taught, such as turkeys at Thanksgiving, bells and candles at Christmas, characters from the basal reading series, or pictures of community helpers, are also useful.

Use these display cards to help children recognize numerals, number words, and the quantities represented by the numeral and to learn to write

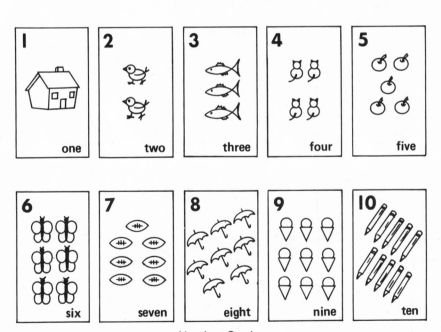

Number Cards

FIGURE 15

the numerals correctly. For the set of cards without numerals and number words, have the children match a number-word card with the corresponding picture card. Use several arrangements of the same numerical value to help children see that "four" is not always four cats but could also be four apples in a row, four boys in two groups of two, or four umbrellas in a diagonal arrangement (Figure 16).

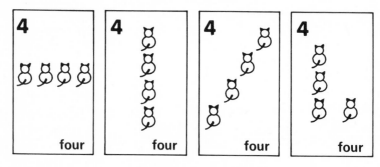

Number Cards—Variations

FIGURE 16

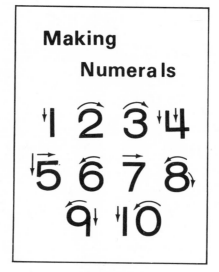

FIGURE 17

6. *Correct Numeral Formation Chart.* Most elementary school class-rooms are provided with alphabet and numeral models on card strips arranged across the top of a chalkboard. If such are not available to the teacher, a chart should be prepared to assist pupils in remembering the correct procedure to follow in forming each numeral (Figure 17).

7. *Perception Cards.* On nine cards (9″ × 9″ or 12″ × 12″), use a felt-tip pen to draw shapes representing number quantities of 1 through 9 (Figure 18). Gummed circles, squares, or triangles can be used in place of the pen.

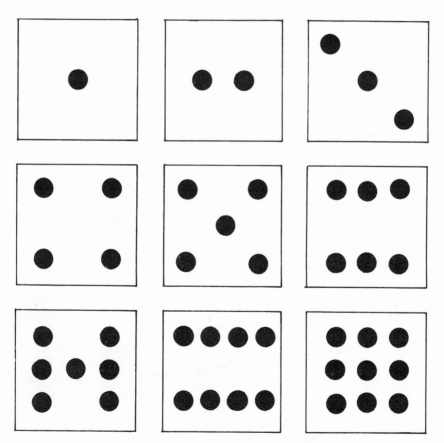

Number Grouping or Perception Cards

FIGURE 18

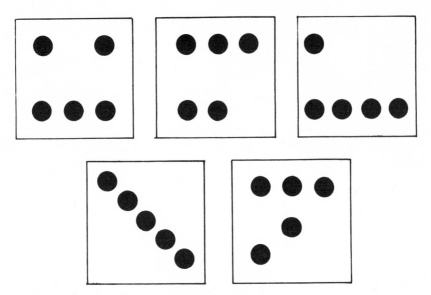

Number Grouping Cards—Variations

FIGURE 19

Use perception cards to help children recognize at sight quantities up to 9. For further practice they can be asked to match numeral cards or number-word cards with the perception cards. When children attain skill with traditional card groupings, vary some of the card arrangements. See Figure 19 as an example of various ways to portray the idea of five.

8. *Folding Perception Cards.* Prepare about 12 pieces of tagboard or heavy cardboard, each about 6″ × 12″ in size. Fold from bottom to top and on each half represent sums to 10, using shapes of circles, squares, or triangles. For example, place six triangles on one half and four triangles on the other (Figure 20).

Use these cards to help children understand and learn the basic addition and subtraction facts. Expose one half of a perception card, then expose the second half, and ask children to provide the sum. Of course, these cards would be used after basic facts have been developed with other concrete materials.

9. *Easy-to-Draw Shapes.* In preparing charts, cards, bulletin boards or illustrations on the chalkboard, the teacher should be able to use a variety of simple shapes to express number ideas (Figures 21). Avoid using the same shapes repeatedly.

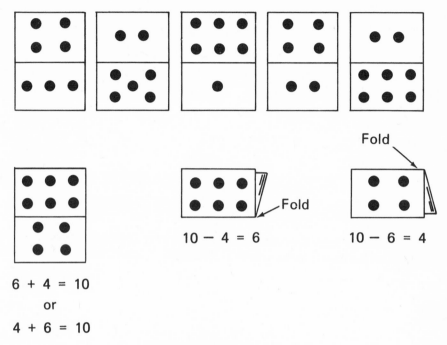

Folding Perception Cards

FIGURE 20

10. *Charts for Teaching and Reviewing Measurement.* In addition to obtaining commercially prepared charts to show tables of measurement, such as time and length, and geometric shapes to display as appropriate, the teacher can prepare charts using data collected in the classroom. For example, the children's birthdays can be the subject of a chart or bulletin board (Figure 22). The children can assist in preparing the birthday chart and can be given the opportunity to develop their own questions or "stories" from the data, for example, "How many boys have birthdays in December? In which months were no class members born?"

11. *Fractional-Value Cards.* Label one side of a 9″ × 9″ card with the numeral 1 to indicate that the card corresponds to one whole. Divide the reverse side of each card into parts and label them. One card might be divided to show ½, ¼, ⅛, ⅛; another might be divided to show ⅓, ⅓, ⅓; another might show, ¼, ¼, ¼, ¼; another might indicate ½, ½ (Figure 23).

Easy-to-Draw Shapes for Numeral Cards or Chalkboard

FIGURE 21

Use these cards to help children see relationships between values of rational numbers. They can also demonstrate that there are many names for 1, that the smaller the denominator, the larger the size of the part, and so forth.

12. *Interlocking Circles to Develop Understanding of Fractional Numbers.* Cut circles about 12″ in diameter from heavy tagboard. Divide

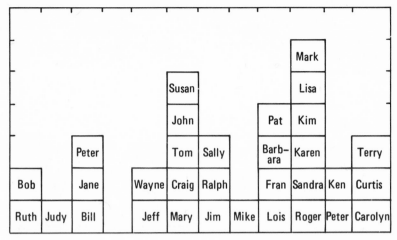

Jan. Feb. Mar. Apr. May Jun. Jul. Aug. Sep. Oct. Nov. Dec.

Our Birthdays

FIGURE 22

circle shapes into fractional parts with one to show fourths, another eighths, and so forth. This can be a pupil activity. Make one cut on each circle shape from the perimeter to the center along a radius. Then one circle can be slipped over another by use of the slots.

Students use circle shapes to see that ¼ is the same as 2/8; that 1/6 is smaller than ⅓, and so forth (Figure 24).

13. *Cards and Strips to Develop Understanding of Decimal Values.* Have each pupil prepare six 10″ squares from contrasting colors of construction paper or tagboard. Cut two of the squares into 10 strips each (tenths). Cut one of the squares into 100 1″ squares. Leave the other three squares whole for comparison purposes (Figure 25).

Use the squares and strips to show that the value of 1/10 means one-tenth of a whole or .1; that .38 is three-tenths and eight hundredths; that .19 can be rounded off to approximately .2 and so forth. When this aid is not in use, pupils can keep the materials in a large manila envelope.

14. *Calendar Reusable for Each Month.* Sand, stain, and varnish or shellac a 2′ square piece of ½″ plywood. Mark off spaces for month, year, picture, and weeks and days (Figure 26). Attach removable cards

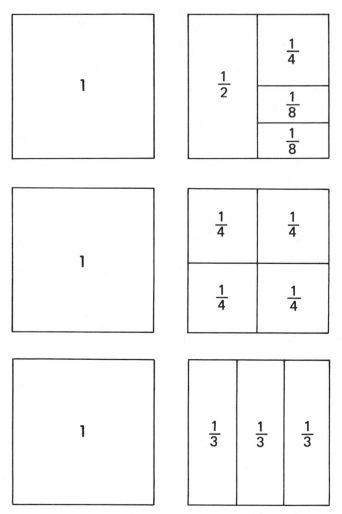

Fraction Cards

FIGURE 23

with the year and month and an appropriate picture in the designated spaces.   Label the columns with abbreviations for days and insert a cuphook at the top of each calendar-day space.   Prepare numerals on 3″ square cards to hang in appropriate spaces.   Hang the completed calendar at children's eye level.

Have pupils assume the responsibility for arranging the calendar each

month. Numerals can be added daily or removed at the end of each day.
In higher grades numerals can be in base five or another number base.

15. *Individual Pocket Card Holders for Practice with Roman Numerals.*
Have pupils make individual pocket charts by folding the long edge of a

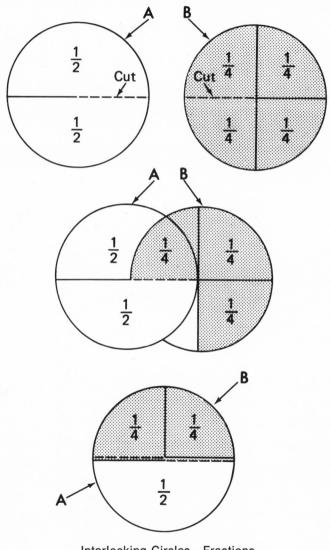

Interlocking Circles—Fractions

FIGURE 24

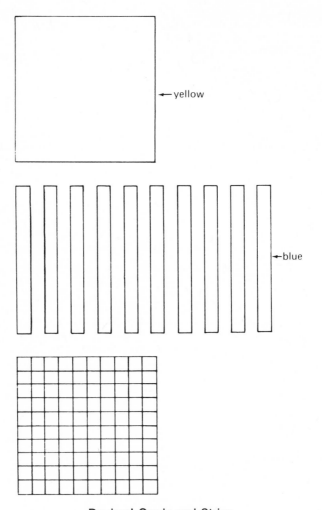

Decimal Cards and Strips

FIGURE 25

5″ × 12″ piece of tagboard to make a 1½″ pocket. Staple at each end. Label 2″ × 3″ pieces of tagboard with the Roman numerals I, V, X, L, C, D, and M, and provide duplicates of the letters used most frequently (Figure 27).

For one use of the pocket card holder, write a Hindu-Arabic numeral such as 36 on the chalkboard. Pupils then assemble the equivalent Roman

Reusable Calendar

FIGURE 26

numeral in their pocket charts and, when completed, hold the chart at chin level so the teacher can check accuracy quickly.

16. *Clock Dial.* On a tagboard circle 18″ in diameter print numerals to make a clock face. Make movable minute and hour hands from tagboard and fasten them with a paper fastener and metal washers. Make concealed tabs from tagboard strips 1″ × 4″ with terms such as "half-past," "quarter to," "twenty-five minutes to," and fasten to the back of the clock face with paper fasteners (Figure 28).

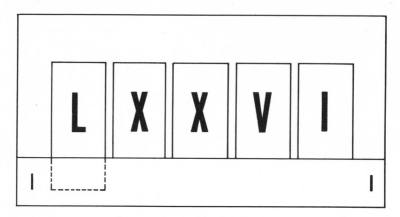

Roman Numeral Builder

FIGURE 27

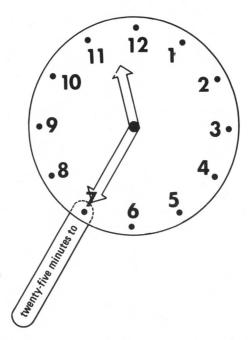

Clock Face

FIGURE 28

The primary-grade teacher has many uses for this aid. For example, he can say specific times and write them on the chalkboard and then have pupils come up to rearrange the clock hands appropriately. Pupils can also make individual clock faces from paper plates and move their clock hands according to teacher directions. In primary grades the large clock face can be mounted on the bulletin board or on a chart and the hands changed to correspond to cards indicating reading time, music time, or lunch time. These uses can also be adapted to a teacher-prepared transparency for use with an overhead projector.

17. *Cards for Developing Understanding of Area Measurement.* Arrange nine 1' squares of tagboard on a table top or the floor to illustrate a square yard (Figure 29). Allow the children to arrange these in various ways.

Use cards to measure the area of the table top, floor, door, bulletin board, and so forth. Have an ample supply of cards on hand and cut

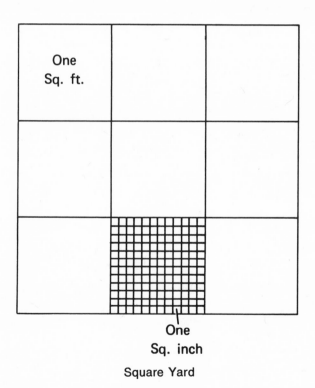

One
Sq. ft.

One
Sq. inch

Square Yard

FIGURE 29

some apart for irregular-shaped surfaces.   Use these to help pupils arrive at a formula for finding an area.   One card can be marked with 144 square inches to help them see that 144 square inches is equal to one square foot.

18. *Cards for Developing Understanding of the Thermometer.*   Draw a representation of a thermometer on a 9″ × 24″ piece of poster board (Figure 30).   Make slots at the top and bottom of the thermometer column and insert red and white ribbon to simulate liquid.   Sew ends together to make a continuous ribbon which can be moved up and down the column.

In primary grades this aid can be used in reading designated "temperatures" or pupils can read actual outdoor and indoor thermometers and move the tape to represent the daily temperature reading.   It can also be used to introduce pupils to signed numbers.

19. *Sandpaper Numerals to Develop Ability to Write Numerals.*

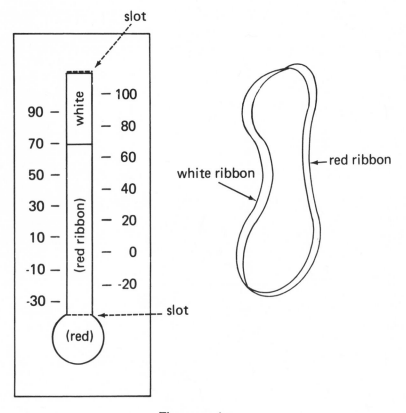

Thermometer

FIGURE 30

From coarse sandpaper cut sets of the numerals 0 through 9 about 3″ to 4″ in height. Mount these on squares of heavy cardboard with rubber cement.

A child who is having difficulty in recognizing numerals visually or reversal problems in writing them can be helped if the teacher holds the child's hand and assists him to trace the sandpaper numerals with his finger. Individual sessions with the pupil should be alternated with experiences in copying numerals from a ditto sheet.

20. *Cards for Individual Practice on Basic Facts.* Make individual pocket card holders from pieces of tagboard about 4½″ × 8″ in size. Fold the 8″ side up about 1″ and staple at each end and at the center to make two pockets (Figure 31). Label one pocket "I Know" and the other "I Need to Study." On 3″ × 5″ cards print the basic facts (addition, subtraction, multiplication, or division) that are to be practiced. Place the correct response on the back of each card.

Individually or in pairs the students test themselves on their ability to provide correct responses, placing cards in the appropriate pockets of

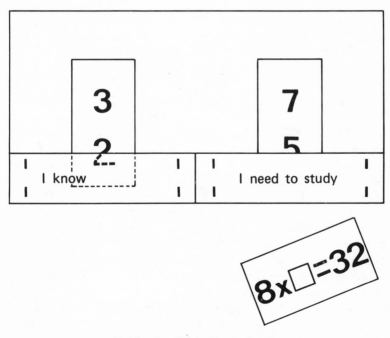

Holder for Basic Facts Cards

FIGURE 31

the card holder. With appropriate guidance and discussions with parents these can be taken home for practice.

21. *Cards for Individual Practice with Basic Addition Facts.*   Prepare 11 9″ × 12″ or smaller cards of tagboard. On one card print a large numeral 8. At the bottom of the same side of the card place the numeral 7 in a circle or box to indicate the number of basic facts that have that sum (omitting zero combinations). On the reverse side of the card place the basic facts that have the sum of 8 (Figure 32). Make similar cards for the sums of 9 through 18.

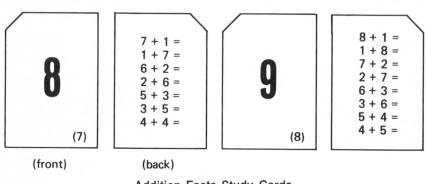

(front)   (back)

Addition Facts Study Cards

FIGURE 32

In one example of the usefulness of these cards, the child places the card with the large numeral side up. On a separate sheet of paper he writes all the basic facts with that sum, using the smaller numeral as a guide to the number of pairs of numerals he must write. He checks his own work by reversing the card. Similar sets of cards can be prepared for subtraction, multiplication, and division.

22. *Reusable Practice Sheets of Basic Addition Facts.*   On several pieces of 9″ × 12″ tagboard write the basic facts to be practiced in four rows of five examples each. Leave about 1″ of space below each row and staple 10 or more ¾″ strips of paper below each one (Figure 33).

The pupil writes his answer on the paper below each row of examples and brings the completed card to the teacher or teacher aide to be checked. The cards can be numbered in sequence of difficulty and an individual record maintained of pupil progress. If the pupil needs more practice, he is helped to develop an understanding of the facts with which he has had difficulty. The answers can be torn off the card and the card reused as needed. Similar cards can be prepared for review of the basic facts in subtraction, multiplication, or division.

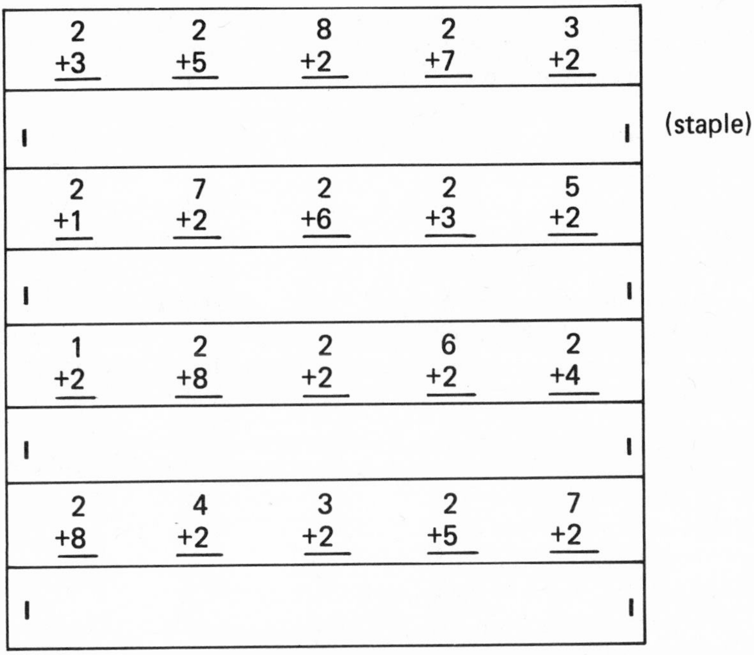

2 +3	2 +5	8 +2	2 +7	3 +2
I				I
2 +1	7 +2	2 +6	2 +3	5 +2
I				I
1 +2	2 +8	2 +2	6 +2	2 +4
I				I
2 +8	4 +2	3 +2	2 +5	7 +2
I				I

(staple)

Reusable Practice Card

FIGURE 33

Separate and Semifixed Objects

To develop rational counting and an understanding of quantity and numeration, a variety of objects is needed. Some objects for the teacher and pupils to collect include thread spools, popsicle sticks or tongue depressors, clothespins, wood or plastic blocks, plastic pop beads, ceramic tiles, cardboard disks, styrofoam squares, muffin tins, egg cartons, plastic bleach bottles, tin cans, cancelled postage stamps, toy animals or toy cars, and artificial flowers.

In addition to a teacher supply for demonstration purposes, primary children should be provided with individual collections in plastic bags or shoe boxes.

Uses of Separate Objects

Although objects are useful in introducing most number concepts, a few specific examples of their application are given below:

Provide each child with a collection of 10 objects and say: "Show me six objects." When the child places six objects on the desk top, ask: "How many ways can you show me 'six'?" The teacher helps children to discover with real objects that six can be arranged as five and one, four and two, three and three, two and four, one and five, six and none, none and six, three and two and one, or two and two and two. Or he could ask the children to show one more than six or two less than six or pose such questions as "How many sets of two objects can you make from six? How can you arrange six objects in two equal sets or groups?" Similar procedures can be used for each of the quantities 1 through 10.

As children become ready for the teen numbers, ask them to show 12 as 1 set of 10 objects plus 2 more objects. At this stage begin to use popsicle sticks or drinking straws so that children can bundle the set of 10 objects and make one set of tens. Continue with the other teen numbers.

At times the teacher can demonstrate with objects using the overhead projector. Paper clips, pennies, jacks, or paper squares can easily be rearranged and grouped on the glass plate of the projector.

Objects are useful in presenting the operation of multiplication to children. Ask the pupils to show three sets of two, three sets of three, three sets of four, and so forth. Help them to see that the total quantity can be found by adding two and two and two, and then say "Three twos are six; three threes are nine; three fours are twelve." Review the procedure for regrouping 12 as 1 set of tens, and 2 more, using the objects. By combining the use of objects with the chalkboard or the overhead projector, the tables of threes, etc., can be developed in algorism form.

As the basic multiplication facts are developed with objects, help children discover the commutative property for multiplication of whole numbers—three sets of five are the same as five sets of three, and so forth.

When children have difficulty in reviewing basic facts in addition, subtraction, multiplication or division, provide objects to illustrate each fact. For example, if a child has difficulty with 7 times 6, have him arrange seven sets of six objects on the desk top. Then help him to regroup them as 4 tens and 2 ones.

The teacher might use objects as other number bases are introduced. First, review grouping by tens with 14, 18, 20, or 22 objects, etc. Then use five as the base group to show that 11 is 2 sets of 5 and 1 more, or 21 five. Help pupils chart the equivalents of base-ten quantities in base five, and so forth, by actual regrouping of base-ten numbers using five as a base.

The teacher can also use objects to develop concepts involving rational numbers as children find parts of a group of objects after finding parts of a whole. For example, use 12 objects. Say, "Show me one half of twelve, one fourth of twelve, one third of twelve," and so forth.

Semifixed Objects

In addition to quantities of separate objects, there are several aids involving use of a fixed number of movable objects on a special apparatus.

1. *Number Chains.* On pieces of plastic clothesline or lengths of coathanger wire place empty thread spools to represent quantities of 1 through 10 (Figure 34). Suspend these chains from cup hooks on the chalk rail or from a chart rack. The chains are referred to as children count, arrange in order, compare lengths, and so forth.

2. *Coat-Hanger Counters.* Hang 10 spring-type clothespins on the horizontal bar of a metal coat hanger (see Figure 1, Chapter 2). Children

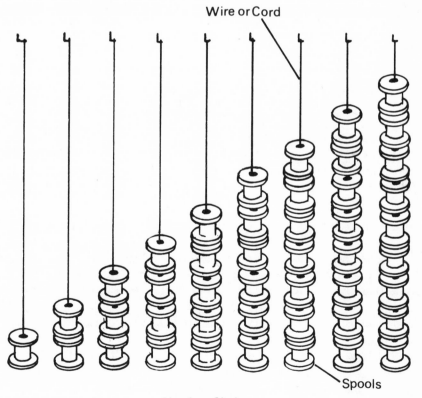

Wire or Cord

Spools

Number Chains

FIGURE 34

can use this device to discover or review basic number facts, cardinal and ordinal numbers, various names for six, and so forth.

When the teen numbers are introduced, additional clothespins are added. Clothespins can be dyed with food color in order to show the base set of ten.

3. *Number-Grouping Frame.* If commercial-type bead rods are not available, the teacher and children can easily improvise a number-grouping frame from a board 3″ × 18″ × 1″, 2 large wooden spools, 10 large wooden beads, and a length of wire from a coat hanger (Figure 35).

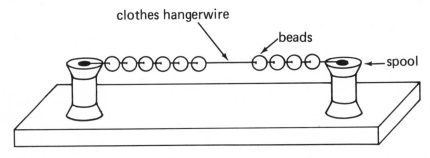

clothes hangerwire

beads

spool

Number-Grouping Frame

FIGURE 35

Glue a spool at each end of the board and then fasten wire with 10 beads on it between the spools. This type of frame is used for discovering and reviewing basic addition facts with sums up to 10 and the related subtraction facts.

Abaci and Bead Frames

Use of the abacus encourages the development of an understanding of number concepts. Various types of abaci or bead frames are available from commercial sources (see Chapter 10). If necessary an abacus or bead frame can be constructed from local material by constructing a wooden frame and using a coat-hanger wire for rods and wooden beads or thread spools.

The bead frame (Figure 36), with 100 beads in 10 rows of 10, can be used for:

1. Showing groupings that represent numbers from 1 to 100.
2. Illustrating operations of addition, subtraction, multiplication, or division.
3. Solving number problems without use of printed words or symbols.

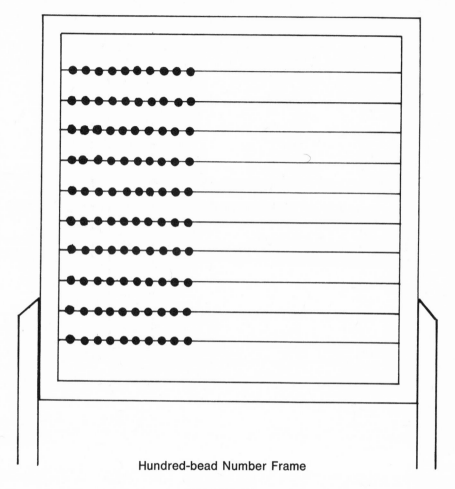

Hundred-bead Number Frame

FIGURE 36

The abacus (Figure 37), with four or more columns of nine beads each, can be used for:

1. Developing recognition of place value or positional values as a property of the Hindu-Arabic system of notation.
2. Developing understanding of regrouping in addition, subtraction, multiplication, and division.
3. Developing appreciation of historical development of our number system.
4. Developing understanding of other number bases (on abaci where some beads can be removed or concealed).
5. Developing understanding of use of zero as a place holder.

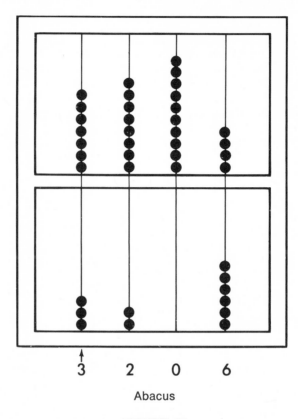

Abacus

FIGURE 37

Decimal Dowel Abacus

If a child or a class is having difficulty in reading decimals, the decimal dowel abacus might prove helpful. Obtain a block of wood 2″ × 2″ × 24″ and drill 13 ½″ diameter holes the length of the block. Cut ½″ diameter dowels into 4″ lengths and glue in the holes. With paint or a felt-tip pen identify the ones space, and place a decimal point in the space between the ones and tens (Figure 38). Carrom rings, washers, or slices of plastic garden hose are placed over the dowels to represent various numerical values.

This aid provides practice in reading decimal numbers, stresses the idea of zero as a place holder, and helps children understand how to round numbers off to the nearest tenth or hundred. It also has many other uses.

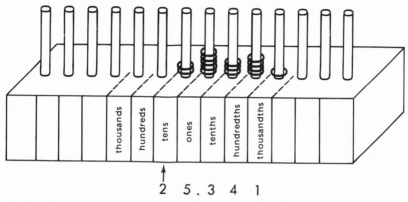

Dowel Abacus: Decimals

FIGURE 38

Place-Value Aids

A variety of objects or commercially produced aids is useful in helping children understand place value. The least expensive aid but probably as appropriate a one as can be obtained might consist of a collection of containers (wooden boxes, tin cans, plastic cups); objects which can be bundled (popsicle sticks, tongue depressors, drinking straws, wooden or plastic spoons); and a supply of rubber bands. In the primary grades three containers could be labeled "ones," "tens," and "hundreds" (Figure 39).

In using to develop an understanding of place value, for example, 12 can be easily represented as one ten (a bundle of 10 popsicle sticks) and two ones. Place the one ten in the "tens" container and two ones in the "ones" container. Repeat with other numerical values from 1 to 100 to reinforce the idea of use of a base group. The same procedure can be followed in upper grades as other number bases are being utilized by relabeling the containers as "ones," "fives," "twenty-fives"; or "ones," "eights," "sixty-fours," etc.

Another use of place-value containers is to develop understanding of regrouping in addition and subtraction of whole numbers. To add 26 and 38, for example, first place two bundles of 10 sticks in the tens container and 6 sticks in the ones container. Then put three bundles of 10 sticks in the tens container and 8 sticks in the ones container. There are now 14 sticks in the ones container, which when regrouped yield 1 bundle of tens and 4 ones. Place the bundle of 10 in the tens container. Count the bundles

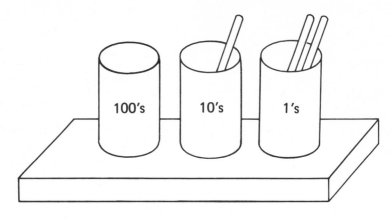

12 = 1 ten and 2 ones

Place-Value Cans

FIGURE 39

of tens in the tens container. There are now six. So the sum of 26 and 38 is 64, or 6 tens and 4 ones.

A similar procedure is used in developing understanding of the regrouping necessary in subtraction. To subtract 27 from 43, first represent the 43 with four bundles of 10 sticks and three ones placed in the place-value containers. To subtract the quantity 27 it is necessary to regroup one bundle of 10 from the tens container as 10 ones and place the 10 sticks in the ones container. Now the teacher can demonstrate removing 7 ones from the ones container and 2 tens from the tens container. The place-value containers now have 1 bundle of tens and 6 ones, showing that 43 − 27 = 16.

Individual Place-Value Pocket Charts

Children need some type of arithmetic aids to use individually in developing an understanding of place value. A desk-top place-value pocket chart can be prepared from a tagboard strip about 5″ × 12″ in size. Fold the long edge of the tagboard up to make a pocket about 1½″ deep. Staple each end and at intervals along the length to make two or three pockets as desired. Label the pockets as "ones," "tens," and "hundreds." Prepare quantities of 1″ × 3″ pieces of construction paper which can be bundled in packs of 10.

Pocket charts were introduced in Figure 21, Chapter 1, and their application has been illustrated at various points in the text above. They can be used by pupils in ways similar to those described for place-value containers.

Pegboards

Pegboards are readily available from commercial sources. They are also easily made from squares of acoustical ceiling tile or squares of masonite pegboard mounted on wood bases. Pegs can be purchased from

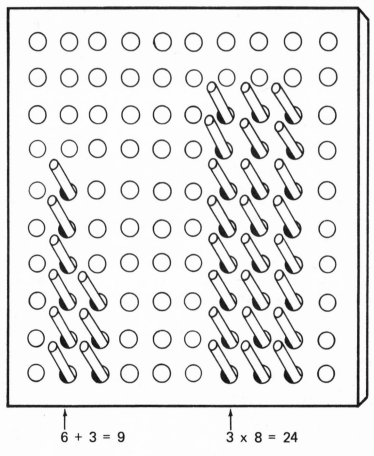

6 + 3 = 9   3 x 8 = 24

Pegboard

FIGURE 40

school supply houses or can be made from tinker-toy sets, dowels, plastic drinking straws, match sticks, or golf tees.

In primary grades, the pegboard with 10 rows of 10 holes each is used for counting and for discovery of simple addition, subtraction or multiplication and division facts (Figure 40).

The pegboard can also be used for discovery of relationships of rational numbers. Plastic straws can be cut into halves, fourths, thirds, etc., as needed. To add rational numbers such as 1½ and 2½, plastic straws corresponding to these numbers are placed in the pegboard. The two ½″ straws can be exchanged for a whole straw, and the pupil sees that the sum is four. To add rational numbers such as ⅜ and ¼, the pupil exchanges ¼ straw for two ⅛ straws, places them on the board, and can see that the sum is ⅝.

Ten pegboards can be grouped to show the number 1000. One peg placed on one of the 10 pegboards would represent 1/1000th of the whole, a decimal value of .001, or a percent value of .1.

One-Hundred Boards

There are many occasions when a teacher needs to be able to construct a 10 × 10 or smaller array. Charts can be used for this purpose, as described previously, but a one-hundred board with removable numerals has many uses with elementary school age children. To make one, obtain a piece of ½″ plywood 24″ or 36″ square. Mark the plywood to make a 10 × 10 array, then varnish or shellac. Insert a cup hook or nail near the top center of each square and prepare appropriate-size numeral tags from tagboard to hang on the hooks (Figure 41).

The one-hundred board can be used to help children develop an understanding of the cardinal and ordinal aspects of numbers; counting by tens; the meaning of teen numbers; counting by twos, threes, or fours; counting backwards; basic addition, subtraction, multiplication and division facts, and so forth.

In teaching the numbers from 1 to 100, add the numeral cards to the board as the number idea is introduced to the class. The board can then be used for counting by removing numerals at random and asking the child to name the missing numerals. The numerals can also be placed on the board in mixed order and the child asked to arrange them in the correct sequence. To provide practice in counting by twos, remove all the odd numbers. Some teachers prepare all the even numbers in a color different from the odd numbers. Similar procedures can be used to teach counting by three, fours, etc. To illustrate the concept of ten as basic to our number system, 28 is represented as 2 rows of 10 tags and 1 row of 8 tags. In

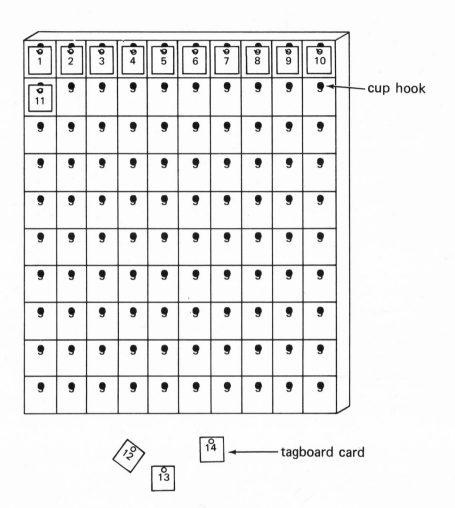

cup hook

tagboard card

One-Hundred Board

FIGURE 41

upper grades unnumbered tags may be used to show fractions, decimals, and percent. Ten cards in one row are one-tenth of all the cards; 50 cards are five-tenths or one half of all the cards; two cards are two-hundredths or 2 percent of all the cards.

Geometric Shapes

Commercial sources now offer a wide variety of geometric shapes for use in elementary schools (see Chapter 10). For the teacher who prefers to prepare his own aids, two suggestions are given below.

One interesting way to develop recognition of geometric shapes is by means of a pegboard, 2′ × 3′ or larger. The pegboard may be left unpainted, but it is preferable to paint or spray it with a light enamel. When dry, lines are drawn through the holes to make a grid. Golf tees or pegs are inserted in the holes to form the angles of the geometric shapes to be represented. Stretch-type yarn is then extended around the pegs to suggest a geometric shape. This device can also be used to help develop understanding of the perimeter of a geometric shape and the area of the surface enclosed by the yarn.

Geometric shapes can also be cut from ¼″ or ½″ plywood. A spool or drawer pull, sprayed with bright-colored enamel, is attached to the center of each as a handle. These are used to help children recognize by sight and touch the various geometric shapes. Teachers and pupils also find them helpful as patterns for blackboard drawings.

Geoboards

One of the most fascinating arithmetic aids is the "geoboard" or nailboard, which is available commercially (see Chapter 10) but is relatively simple and inexpensive to make in classroom quantities. Obtain scraps of plywood ⅜″ or ½″ in thickness and have it cut into 10″ or 12″ squares. Mark the surface to make a grid of 25 squares and pound a nail firmly in the center of each square (Figure 42). Children can be given the opportunity to construct these, since much learning can result from the questions arising during the construction process. The geoboard is then ready for use with an assortment of different-sized rubber bands.

The list of uses of the geoboard in exploring mathematical ideas is practically endless. For detailed descriptions see: *Notes on Mathematics in Primary Schools,* Cambridge University Press (American Branch: 32 East 57th Street, New York, N.Y. 10022), pp. 161–196; *The Geo-Board: A Manual for Teachers,* by Irving Kreitzberg; and *Inquiry in Mathematics*

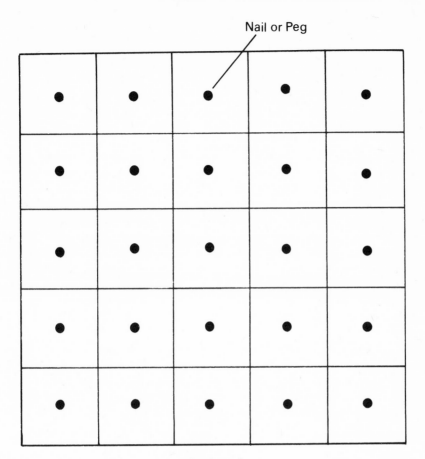

Geoboard

FIGURE 42

via the Geo-Board, by Donald Cohen, and the Geo-Card Math Lab, from Walker Educational Book Corp. (see Chapter 10).

Children should be allowed to satisfy their own curiosities with the geoboard. However, some suggestions the teacher might make include the following directions to the pupil:

Geometry

(1) Use rubber bands to make all the recognizable shapes you can. Name the shapes. Can you make some shapes you don't recognize? Try to make up names for them.
(2) How many ways can you put bands on the board?
(3) Put a rubber band around four nails to make a square shape. How many small squares are inside the band?

(4) Make a rectangle on the board. What is its area?

(5) What is the largest triangle you can make?

(6) Make as many shapes as you can which are six times as big as one square.

(7) How many rectangles can you make?

(8) How many shapes can be made using four nails only?

Fractions

(1) Make a square and show quarters of it. How many ways can it be done?

Graphs

(1) Show the number of days of school four boys missed last month.

Chapter **10**

LOCATING COMMERCIALLY
PREPARED TEACHING–LEARNING
AIDS AND RESOURCES

Throughout this text many suggestions have been made of aids for the teaching and learning of mathematics, many of which can be prepared by the teacher or pupils. In recent years commercial sources have also made available to schools, teachers, and parents a wide variety of items related to mathematics. This chapter provides an extensive listing of such items from commercial sources, arranged according to their suggested uses. A list of addresses of the manufacturers or distributors is provided at the end, but inasmuch as prices are subject to change they are not included.

The authors do not endorse the items listed. The brief annotations are intended to identify the nature, possible uses, and typical grade level for each item.

Items are listed alphabetically according to major category of possible uses, as follows:

1. Number readiness, whole numbers.
2. Basic operations, whole numbers.
3. Rational numbers, decimal notation.
4. Geometry.
5. Measurement.
6. Enrichment, games, puzzles, devices.
7. Individualizing instruction, drill.

8. Transparencies, films, film loops, filmstrips, slides.
9. Recordings and tapes.
10. Textbooks, teaching-learning systems.
11. Resource materials for the teacher.

Aids for Developing Number Readiness and for Teaching Whole Numbers

The Abacus. Frame with 10 rods and beads used for demonstrating left-to-right relationships, place value, and whole-number operations. Developmental Learning Materials.

Algeblocks. Intended to help students discover functional number concepts and mathematical relationships. (1–6) Silver Burdett Co.

Arithmecubes. 16 blocks to help children develop the idea of sets, review basic facts, form equations for problem-solving. Blocks show numerals 0–9 and mathematical signs. (K–6) Scott, Foresman & Co.

Arithmetic Sticks. Different-colored sticks of the same size for conservation, one-to-one correspondence, and counting. Ginn & Co.

Arithmetictube. Visual and manipulative aid for demonstrating basic concrete number groups 1–9, addition facts through $6 + 6$, and inverse operations. Students work problems by placing beads and separators in tube. Reinforcement provided with flash cards. Manual. (Presch.–1) Ideal School Supply Co.

Attribute Blocks Materials. Wooden blocks and cubes, plastic squares with pictures of people, colored loops and label cards, problem cards suggesting activities, "creature" cards, and a teacher's guide. Activities allow children to deal with problems involving classification and the relationships between classes and gain experience in distinguishing attributes and a better understanding of the properties of sets. (K–9) Webster Div.

Attribute Games. 60 plastic manipulables of different colors and thicknesses used to develop basic number concepts, concepts for sets, logical reasoning, problem-solving skills. (K–8) Teaching Resources Corp.

Charts for Developing Mathematics. 32 plasticized charts on 16 boards with stand and teachers manual to stimulate discussion of mathematical ideas such as classification, function, and number. (K–1) Macmillan Co.

Colored Plastic Washers. Plastic washers in six colors (white, yellow, pink, blue, red, and gray) with a hole in the center to be used for "chip-trading" and other counting activities. (K–6) SEE.

Counting Picture Cards. Visual aids for progress in counting. Five sets, each with one to six items, on many topics. (1–3) Developmental Learning Materials.

Cubacus. Plastic tray sectioned into six columns, wooden rod to establish a number base, and 81 wooden cubes. Useful in developing mathematics concepts and operations. (5–12) Holt, Rinehart & Winston.

Cuisenaire Rods. Wooden rods of 10 different colors and sizes, the smallest a white cube 1 cm. on a side. Each larger rod is 1 cm. longer. Used to teach numeration, operations with numbers, computation, and fractions. Cuisenaire Co. of America.

Developing Number Experiences Kit A. Manipulative materials and game cards to provide experiences in classifying, structuring, and ordering sets of objects. (K–2) Holt, Rinehart & Winston.

Development of Number Readiness. 60-plus learning situations emphasize number groups, number recognition, one-to-one experiences. Student manipulatives, number cards, counters, blocks, detailed lesson plans. (Presch.–K) Milton Bradley Co.

Dienes Logical Blocks. Set of blocks with games designed to give experience in distinguishing attributes and carrying out logical operations such as conjunction, disjunction, union, and intersection. (K–9) Herder & Herder.

Direct Reading Abacus. Vertical-form Chinese abacus with numerals placed on bars to represent the numbers of beads displaced. Scientific Educational Products.

Discovery with Blocks. Set of blocks and activity cards. Teacher's manual. (1–3) Scott Education Div.

Dot-O-Grouper. For student and teacher use in demonstrating place value, grouping principles, inequalities, addition, subtraction, multiplication, division, and most elementary mathematics concepts. (4–6) Mead Educational Services.

Dot-to-Dot Pattern Sheets. Used to teach number and set progression. Consists of 20 sheets, each of a different design. (1–4) Developmental Learning Materials.

Equation Balance. Uses weights and balance to illustrate numerical equality and inequality. Also applicable to addition, subtraction, multiplication, division, theory of sets, and other basic number relationships. Study guide and accessories. (1–8) Mead Educational Services.

First Step Program, A, B, C,— 1, 2, 3. 20 primary books, 2 records, 25 activity books, game cards, and teacher's guide, for number and reading readiness. (K–1) Children's Press.

Geometric Shape Spotting. Game consisting of 4 boards and 32 cards. For the very young, it can be used purely to help develop sensory powers. Encourages awareness of shape and form and stimulates interest in mathematical properties. (K–4) SEE.

How Many Apples Counting Blocks. Teacher's guide and 21 to-be-assembled fiberboard blocks which show a number of apples with the appropriate numeral and word on each side. *How Many Apples Counting Capes.* 26 plastic capes, each printed with a numeral and a corresponding set of apples. Both sets for use in instructing children in basic mathematics procedures. (Pre–K–2) Union Camp Corp. Educational Systems.

Hundred Chart. Develops basic understanding of our number system. Can be used for counting by 1's, 2's, 3's, 5's, 10's, etc. Leads to discovery of number patterns. Chart separates into strips for presentation of sets of 10's. (1–6) Instructo Corp.

Inch Blocks. 1″ hardwood cubes with 35 sequenced activity cards designed to help children discover math concepts and improve computational skills. (3–6) Walker Educational Book Corp.

Lowenfeld Poleidoblocs. 54 wooden blocks of various shapes and sizes, red, blue, green, and yellow, packed in a wooden box with a slide-in lid. In observing, handling, and constructing with these blocks, children gain an intuitive understanding of a large number of mathematical relationships. (K–4) SEE.

Mathematics Filmstrips: Using Sets and Numbers and Discovering the Number Line. Filmstrips intended to help children visualize basic ideas of modern mathematics. Sets include 10 color filmstrips with manual. Ginn and Co.

Mathkit. 18 multipurpose items

including clocks, number lines, abacus, and property blocks to supplement primary programs. (K–3) Silver Burdett Co.

Math Matrix Games. A teaching game for mathematics readiness that develops ability to verbalize and follow complex directions. Covers numerals, counting (0–10), ordering, and sequence. 20 matrix boards, 4 magnetic rings, magnetic opaque square, set of magnetic numerals, teacher's manual. (Presch.–1) New Century.

Mirror Cards. Box of cards, several sets of colorful pictures, four unbreakable plastic mirrors, and teacher's guide. Activity involves matching picture on one card to picture on another by using a combination of some part of that picture and its reflection in a mirror. Some cards are easy to match; some only seem easy, and many cannot be matched at all. Four children can use one box at a time. (K–9) Webster Div.

Number-Blox. Physical models of our base-ten system which present the properties of place value in concrete form. (K–3) Creative Publications.

Number Line. 1" transparent high-quality, plastic ruler on which number line is marked off in 25 1 cm. intervals. No numerals are embossed on the line, so pupils may write on it with a grease pencil or No. 1 pencil and erase easily by rubbing. (1–9) Houghton Mifflin Co.

Number Line Desk Tape. Perforated rolls provide 40 individual number lines for pupil use. Available in 0–20 or as fractional number lines for 1/8, 1/6, 1/4, 1/3, 1/2. (K–6) Instructo Corp.

Numbers. Foot-high number cards containing removable numeral, removable letters spelling the number, and removable objects in quantities corresponding to the numeral.

(Presch.–1 and enrichment) Educational Games.

Numero-cubes Set 1. 10 sets of die marked with numerals and dots for use in teaching values and recognition. (1–4) Development Learning Materials.

Open-end Abacus Kit. High-quality base-ten abacus designed to form a lightweight compact unit. The abacus base is itself a part of the semi-rigid plastic container in which all of the kit materials (5 rods of uniform size and 45 beads in three colors) are stored when not in use. "Open-ended" rods fit securely into one of three receptacles in the abacus base and accept at most nine beads. Identical second rod can be fitted onto the base rod to allow for temporary situations arising in renaming. Can be adapted for bases 2, 5, and 8. (1–6) Houghton Mifflin Co.

Papy Minicomputer. Manipulative device for teaching addition, subtraction, multiplication, and division of whole and decimal numbers. (Primary) Macmillan Co.

Pegboard. Plastic pegboard, washable and unbreakable, with 100 holes, and 25 each of 8 colors of pegs. (K–9) SEE.

Readiness in Mathematics. Programmed "tour" of the numbers 1–9 and the concept of zero. Consists of a "giant" book with classroom easel and two teacher's manuals. Teacher-administered, requires no reading by students. (Preschool–Primary) Behavioral Research Laboratories.

Sensanumber Track. Yellow plastic runner for counting, linear measurement, addition, subtraction, and fractional concepts. (1–6) Developmental Learning Materials.

Sets and Numbers for the Very Young. Book explaining sets in terms a kindergartner or first-grader can understand. Many illustrations and diagrams. (K–3) John Day Co.

Setsplay. 12 word cards, 24 games and activities of progressive difficulty, 2 sets of colored shapes. A new method of introducing the concept of sets, the language of sets, and basic elements of logical thought. Two groups can work on one set. (4–6) SEE.

Shape Dominoes. 28 thick wooden dominoes useful for shape and color-matching exercises. (K–3) SEE.

Shape Matching Cubes. Set of six 2″ cubes designed to help students develop an understanding of size order in a series. Different geometrical patterns embossed on each face and repeated on each cube but in a dif-ferent size, so that there are six patterns in six sizes for the child to choose and arrange. (K–3) SEE.

Spot the Set. 4 boards and 32 cards from which players discover qualities of collections through the classification and comparisons of shapes and sets. Intended to follow "Geometric Shape Spotting." (K–4) SEE.

Unifix Mathematics Materials. Interlocking plastic cubes in a variety of colors together with number indicators, pattern boards for affixing cubes, tens and unit trays, stairs and number trays. For place value and numeration. Philip and Tacey Ltd.

Aids for Teaching Basic Operations with Whole Numbers

Abacus Board. Allows children to handle and see the processes of addition, subtraction, multiplication, and division for themselves. Can be used for three lines of addition and has a wide variety of basic uses. (K–6) SEE.

Add-A-Square. Manipulables designed to teach the child how to add and subtract various combinations of numbers which equal 10. (Presch.–2) Connor Toy Co.

Addo Calculator. Designed for primary use showing addition, subtraction, and division up to 249. In tough plastic, with instructions. (K–4) SEE.

Colorfax Addition and Subtraction Kit. Plastic tiles, plasticized work cards, teacher's guide for teaching addition and subtraction facts. (1–3) Macmillan Co.

Easy Adder. Equipment made of colorful plastics aids in the teaching of addition and subtraction. (1–6) SEE.

Flip-Flop^{TM} Multiplication Facts, Flip-Flop^{TM} Division Facts. (3–6) *Flip-Flop^{TM} Subtraction Facts, Flip-Flop^{TM} Addition Facts.* (1–4) Motivational, individualized, self-corrective puzzle programs. Can be used for basic instruction or remedial work. Instructional Media Associates, Inc.

Fundamath. Device to demonstrate written math processes in addition, subtraction, and transfer. Manual. (1–2) Ideal School Supply Co.

Hear and Do Number Line. Sliding number line with operating instructions. 1 record, 18 manipulative number lines, teacher's guide. (1–4) Weber Costello.

Mathfacts Games. Five games for drill in addition and subtraction facts, 0 to 18. Two games of addition, two of subtraction, one combining the two. Game trays, self-checking equation cards, spinners. (1–2) Milton Bradley Co.

Musical Multiplication Records. Five double-faced, 33 1/3 rpm records provide drill and quizzes for helping children master multiplication. Tables from 2 to 12 are covered. (3–5) Bremer Multiplication Records.

Napier's Rods. Makes it possible

to do (or check) multiplication by addition. Set contains 10 rods and can be used as a sample for students to make their own. (4–6) SEE.

Number Activity Program. Introduces concepts and provides practice in addition and subtraction of numerals 0–9. Write-on, wipe-off charts, records, and guide. (K–3) Weber Costello.

Number Facts. Four boxed sets (eight cards each) of plastic-laminated motor activity cards (for use with wax crayon) for practice in number facts. 27 problems on each card, plus drills. Sets cover basic operations. (1–3) Singer/SVE.

Numero. Number game. Purpose is to "cover up" all the numbers by throwing two die, adding the addends together, and covering up the sum or other addends of the sum. (3–6) SEE.

Pickett Slide Rules. Elementary Rule. Simple student's rule contains six scales for basic operations in addition, subtraction, multiplication, and division, plus negative and positive numbers and exponential notations. Plastic, with sheath-type case and instruction manual. Also available are: *7-foot Demonstration Rule, Pickett Projection Rule.* Pickett.

Picture Addition. Children are helped to answer the printed sums by arranging small picture counters against a background. Set contains 4 background cards, 12 picture counters, and a supplementary set of sum cards using numbers up to 12. (K–2) SEE.

Quinto. "A Mathematical Scrabble" game intended to be played using multiples of 5, but can be used to strengthen all of the multiplication and addition facts. Approximate playing time: 40 minutes. (3–9) Minnesota Mining & Manufacturing Co. (3M Co.)

The Real Numbers Games. Children roll five die with numerals and operation signs to obtain as many numbers as possible from the set of naturals, integers, rationals, or reals. Good for practice in computation. (4–9) Wff'n Proof.

SEE "Calculator." Aids in making addition and subtraction understandable processes. Primary-school children learn basic relationships of numbers. Some can follow the workings to gain an understanding of simple calculators. Entire case is transparent; from front, student can see numerals moving into place, while back shows how mechanism works. Stylus provided to facilitate dialing. (K–6) SEE.

Sensorithmetic Program. Three sets of visual-tactile aids for solving whole-number operations. Three wooden troughs: add or subtract box, join or separate box, multiply or divide box. (1–6) Developmental Learning Materials.

Tabletamer. Simple-to-operate desk-top machine for use in study of multiplication, addition, and subtraction. Individualized approach allows for self drill and immediate correction at student's own pace. (2–5) AIM Industries.

Ten-inch Math Rule. Simple slide rule designed for use in elementary schools. Student can add, subtract, multiply, and divide on one rule, which has both a linear and a logarithmic scale. Slide is reversible and blank back provides an excellent writing surface so student can create his own scales. Made of sturdy styrene plastic. (2–9) SEE.

Twin Choice. Hearts-like game played by solving mathematical problems given on cards. Eight separate decks give pupils practice on progressively harder problems in addition, subtraction, multiplication, and division. (1–6) Holt, Rinehart & Winston.

Aids for Teaching Positive Rational Numbers and Decimal Notation

Action Fractions Games. Three mathematics games with circles, squares, and triangles to develop concepts and skills with fractional numbers. Each has gameboards for eight children, 72 fractional parts, 2 sets of fraction-marked cubes, and teaching guide. (1–6) Instructo Corp.

Come Out Even. Game of mathematical rummy helps students add simple fractions and find common denominators. Shadings and markings on cards help in recognizing equivalent fractions. Two decks: Deck A: 1/2, 1/4, 1/8, 1/16; Deck B: 1/2, 1/3, 1/6, 1/9. (4–7) Holt, Rinehart & Winston.

Competitive Fractions Board. Apparatus consisting of 3 16″ × 16″ baseboards, 2 sets of fractions, and 24 cards to aid the teaching of fractions. Object of the game is for three players to cover their boards with fractions drawn from the banker board according to instructions on the cards. (1–5) SEE.

Decimal Beads. Single beads, "rods" of 10 beads, "flats" of 10 rods, and cubes of 10 flats to teach decimal numeration system. Beads made of glass and strung together by wire. Montessori Leermiddelenhuis.

Edmund Graph Stamps. (*a*) 100 blocks per square inch. Full pattern measures 3″ square. Stamp prints 100 1/10″ blocks per square inch. (*b*) 16 blocks per square inch. For plotting in large scale, full pattern measures 3″ square. Stamp prints 16 ¼″ blocks per square inch. (*c*) *Polar Coordinate Graph Stamp.* Edmund Scientific Co.

Elementary Arithmetic: Decimal Numbers. Programmed instruction course covering basic operations with decimals, relation of decimals to fractions, percent, etc. Includes course, tests, and manual. Grolier Educational Corp.

Elementary Arithmetic: Fractions. Programmed instruction covering all aspects of fractions—adding, subtracting, multiplying, dividing, equivalent fractions, etc. Grolier Educational Corp.

Fraction Board. Hardboard, 22″ × 22″ holds 3″ die-cut rubber squares with various fractional cuttings (fractional equivalents, operations in fractions). Creative Playthings.

Fraction Finder. Small desk-top machine for use in studying fractions, decimals, and percentages. Individual, self-drill approach. (4–6) AIM Industries.

Fractions; Percents, Decimals and Ratios; Basic Geometry. Each subject covered by 16 individual audio-visual-response programs for use with the Dorsett Audiovisual Teaching Machine M86. Programs also available on number systems, measurements and work problems. Dorsett Educational Systems.

Multiplication of Fractions by Fractions; Equivalent Fractions. Three sets of sequenced overhead transparencies. Eye Gate House.

Understanding Fractions and Time. Kit of five "pupil packs" for learning how to tell time and developing the concept of fractions through manipulating parts. Five miniature flannelboards, more than 35 pieces, including fractional parts and movable clock hands. (1–3) Instructo Corp.

Aids for the Teaching of Geometry

Basic Shapes Set. Young children can learn about the shapes of things by handling and building with the 192 colorful pieces, about 1″ each in size, in hard-wearing plastic. (K–6) SEE.

Block Mosaic Tiles. 7″ square

containing 40 shaped, polished wooden tiles with colored sheet of designs. (K–6) SEE.

Centimeter Grid Paper. Available in pads of 100 sheets—each 5″ × 8″ printed on one side only. Ruled with grid lines 1 cm. apart for an area 10 cm. by 10 cm. An area of approximately 3″ × 5″ is left blank to provide space for computation or other writing. Paper is useful in the early grades for coloring, cutting, and paper folding. (1–9) Houghton Mifflin Co.

Chalkboard Sets. Complete set with magnetized components containing T-square, straightedge, protractor, right triangle, and compass, all of sturdy hardwood, with holding knobs and hanger holes. Teacher use. (1–9) Frederick Post Co.

Color Math. Printed, original geometric designs for pupils to color according to computations and a color legend. Increasing in difficulty, exercises provide opportunity for individual work and reinforce computing skills. Includes 20 separate printed designs for levels 1–2, 30 designs for levels 3–4. All suitable for making masters. (1–4) Paul S. Amidon and Associates.

Compasses. Senior compasses with a highly polished brass finish. Unique feature is a screw fastener to secure the pencil. (2–9) SEE.

Construct-A-Cube Puzzle. Set 1 consists of 27 1″ cubes in natural-color wood. Some of the faces are painted so that they can be put together to form (*a*) a painted 3″ cube, (*b*) an unpainted 3″ cube, (*c*) a painted 2″ cube or (*d*) an unpainted 2″ cube. (K–3) Set 2 consists of 27 1″ cubes in wood made up into seven different shapes. It has been calculated that it is possible to build a 3″ cube in about a quarter of a million different ways with these shapes. (4–9) SEE.

Contack Game. Game has 36 triangular pieces—the three sides in contrasting colors, with different numbers. Pieces are divided equally between 2 to 7 players, and the first to get rid of all of his triangles is the winner. (2–9) Miles Kimball Co.

Directions and Angles. Book introducing the concepts of direction, angle, up and down, measurement of angles, compass direction, etc. (3–6) John Day Co.

The Dot and Line. Animated film exploring two-plane geometric relationships. Films Inc.

Elementary Geometry: Forms We See. Five film loops with manipulative materials to help children identify basic geometric forms. (4–6) Hester and Associates.

Geo-Blocks Materials. Various geometric shapes cut out of wood. Suggested activities provide opportunities to gain awareness of the properties of each solid figure and the inter-relationships between various shapes. (K–9) Webster Div.

Geo-Boards. Strong, bake-finished pressed masonite, equipped with multicolored rubber bands and ring point markers to be used on the brass pins. (K–8) Walker Educational Book Corp.

Geo-D-Stix. Color-coded, sturdy, vinyl sticks in various lengths fit into flexible plastic connectors to build all sorts of structures, including the three basic polyhedra. 350 sticks and instructions. (2–9) Childcraft Equipment Co.

Geoboard Kit. Pegboard with geometry activity cards, teacher's notes, and problem answers. (K–8) Houghton Mifflin Co.

The Geometer. Template that can be used to draw or copy with speed and accuracy geometric diagrams found in any standard geometry textbook. Fits standard-size looseleaf binder. Also has number line; 8″ ruler; full 360° protractor that can be used in conjunction with coordinate grid; and centimeter scale. (5–9) Academic Industries.

Geometric Dominoes. Game with 24 domino cards for one or two players, designed to teach quick recognition and identification of geometric shapes, and shape and pattern correspondence. (K–4) SEE.

Geometric Matching. Card game for the child who has been introduced to geometrical terms. Half of the 56 cards are printed with diagrams illustrating the geometrical properties, and the remainder with descriptions of each property. (4–9) SEE.

Geometric Shapes. Kit contains transparent models of sphere, cube, rectangular solid, cylinder, cone, and pyramid which enable pupils to visualize the "hidden" lines and surfaces. All models are of equal volume (1 cubic inch). Compactly packaged in a durable, semirigid plastic case. (K–9) Houghton Mifflin Co.

Geometric Solids. 19-piece set of transparent plastic on which teacher can use china-marking pencil to put formulas, dimensions, letters, etc. on each shape. Edges outlined in red. Height of largest piece is 4 11/16"; other solids are in exact proportion. Packed in sturdy hardwood box. (5–9) Edmund Scientific Co.

Geo-Shapes. Dominolike tiles to help children recognize basic geometric shapes. (K–3) Scott, Foresman & Co.

Geosquare. Round and square patterns. Consists of 30 10" × 10" boards, escutcheon pins, rubber bands, teacher's manual and dot paper. (1–9) Scott Scientific Inc.

Geo Strips. Made of strong, pliable polythene in four bright colors. Each strip is drilled and can be joined quickly by brass paper fasteners. By using the special protractor, students can construct accurately angled geometric figures and random designs. Set, housed in strong storage box, includes 68 strips and 144 fasteners. 11 work cards pose simple and advanced problems. (4–7) SEE.

Inquiry in Mathematics via the Geoboard. (Donald Cohen, manual, and masters, Geo-Card Math Lab.) Manual suggests games and puzzles for exploring such topics as counting; even, odd, triangular and square numbers; addition and multiplication of whole numbers and fractions; variables; coordinate geometry; perimeter; area of polygons; congruence; similarity; symmetry, rotations, and reflections. Card lab introduces 150 problems and experiments students can select to work on individually or in small groups. (K–9) Walker Educational Book Corp.

Invicta Plastics Technical Drawing Models. Plastic three-dimensional models allow a wide range of possibilities. More advanced drawings are possible by placing two or more models together. (4–9) SEE.

Jigged Geometric Shapes. Kit of 16 plywood plaques in jigsaw format to help children learn to identify geometric shapes. Weber Costello.

Knupperli. Popular easy-assembly construction toy providing flexible plastic components for chains, boards, shapes, baskets, and geometric forms. (K–2) Creative Playthings.

LaPine Sage Kit. Clear plastic, hollow shapes fit bases to form geometrical models. Colored plastic sections fit supporting grooves in bases to illustrate geometrical relationships of right sections, slant height, etc. 7 basic shapes—cone, cylinder, hemisphere, cube, square, pyramid, triangular prism; 3 multipurpose bases—square, triangular, circular; and 15 sections to form intersecting planes. (5–9) LaPine Scientific Co.

Linjo. Design medium, developed in Europe, of 108 colorful cards that can be combined in an endless number of geometrical patterns. Vigorous colors and harmonious curved lines provide creative opportunities. (K–3) Childcraft Equipment Co.

Matchmaker. Small individualized machine for desk-top use in various math operations. Provides experience in geometric shape recognition, size, groupings. (K–1) AIM Industries.

Mathematics Using String. Set of independent exploration cards dealing with distances, thickness, equal lengths, rectangles, index of rotundity, graphing, and open sentences. (3–6) Math Media Div.

Mirror Magic. Helps children recognize both symmetric and asymmetric shapes as they cut and fold paper, draw figures, use the mirror provided, and graph points on a plane. (3–5) Franklin Publications.

Moby Linx Construction Kits. Set of 536 pieces, includes specially formed plastic tubes, precision-grooved chips, pliable rubber-band connectors, accessory wires, and simple instructions to be used to make multidimensional geometric models and decorative mobile objects. (3–6) Kindrey Manufacturing Co.

New Math 4-in-1 Ruler. Unbreakable four-scale ruler with 1/16, 1/10, metric and number-line scales; and *New Math Protractor*, with 6″ rule in 10ths and 16ths, centimeter and millimeter scales, parts of a circle in measured degrees, and a 180° protractor reading both left and right. (4–6) Sterling Plastics Co.

Oxford Maths. Comprehensive set housed in a strong metal box consists of brass nickel-plated compass and divider, 6″ clear plastic ruler, transparent set squares, 45° and 60° graduated compass pencil, eraser, transparent protractor, chemistry stencil, 7″ pencil, pencil sharpener, blotter, and useful tables. (2–9) SEE.

Paper and Pencil Geometry. Informal approach with correct usage of terms and definitions. Both two- and three-dimensional topics are explored. (4–6) Franklin Publications.

Paper Folding for the Mathematics Class. Donovan A. Johnson. Directions for folding paper to illustrate basic constructions, geometric concepts, circle relationships, products and factors, polygons, knots, polyhedra, and symmetry. (6–9 NCTM.

Pic-A-Puzzle. Book of geometric patterns to be used for making ditto and mimeograph masters, student worksheets and overhead transparencies. (K–12) Creative Publications.

Plastic Mosaic. Box of 24 large plastic triangles and squares. (K–6) SEE.

Plastic Mosaic Shapes. Set of 148 thin plastic mosaic shapes has many uses, including mosaic patterns, picture building, geometric figures, fraction work, and simple algebra. (K–6) SEE.

Plastic Shapes Board. Manufactured in unbreakable plastic, hygienic and washable. Pins are at ½″ centers, and a 1″ grid line is incorporated on the board. 19 by 19 pins on 9″ × 9″ grid size. Very versatile. (K–9) SEE.

Polyhedron Construction Kit. 60 sheets of precut card stock in six pastel colors to make 24 multicolored polyhedra. (6–9) Math-Master Labs.

Polyhedron Models for the Classroom. Magnus J. Wenninger. Directions for constructing various models, with notes on the history and mathematics of polyhedra. Over 40 illustrations and a bibliography. (6–9) NCTM.

Polyshapes. For the construction of geometric models, set consists of 8 plastic templates, 36 sheets of construction cards (20″ × 25″), elastic bands, and 28 work cards. (2–9) SEE.

Prisms and Cubes. Collection of precision-cut squares, cubes, and other prisms painted in 10 colors and boxed in drawers. Uses range from arithmetic computation and multibase work to algebraic topics and solid geometry. (K–9) SEE.

Pythagoras. Voo-Doo, Euclid, Kwazy Quilt, Hexed, Tormentor. Various "take-apart" and "put-to-gether" puzzles, on the idea of Tangram, but involving many kinds of shapes. (4–9) Kohner Bros.

Rack of 30 Protractors. Highly accurate (½°), two-scale (L to R, R to L) protractors made of pliable non-crack, clear plastic and housed in a rack which provides a convenient way of checking returns. (4–9) Geyer Instructional Aids Co.

Scope. Using a basic trapezoid shape, colorful pieces can be combined to form hexagons, triangles, and diamonds with a three-dimensional effect. 144 pieces, hexagonal tray, instructions, and starting patterns. (K–6) Childcraft Equipment Co.

Sigma Geosquare. Full 10″ × 10″ size makes patterns easy to make and see. Boards made of ½″ five-ply board with black plastic permaply covering. (K–9) Sigma Enterprises.

Snap Sticks. Unbreakable connectors, wheels, and hardwood dowels snap together and hold firmly to allow children to construct many different structures. 166 brightly colored pieces. (K–3) Childcraft Equipment Co.

Solid Geometry Set. Gray slotted plastic board provides a base on which to build cubical and pyramidal geometrical figures with the 14 plastic shapes. (4–6) SEE.

Space Spider. "String sculpture" kit makes designs in three dimensions. Special elastic string, in brilliant fluorescent colors, can be threaded through perforated black panels to make hundreds of mathematical patterns. (4–9) Childcraft Equipment Co.

String Figures and How to Make Them, Caroline F. Hayne. Book describes how to make over 100 figures by maneuvering a loop of string. (6–9) Creative Playthings.

Tilecraft. Over 220 plastic tiles for making thousands of patterns and colored designs on a strong pegboard. (1–4) SEE.

True Equal-Volume Geometric Solids Set. Set of six basic shapes; cube, pyramid, sphere, cone, rectangle, and cylinder, made of solid, durable plastic. Each solid is a cubic inch and will displace the same liquid volume. (5–9) Edmund Scientific.

Aids for the Teaching of Measurement

Angle Meter. Calibrated angle board is hinged and can be fixed at right angles to the upright. (4–9) SEE.

Balance with Weights. Equal pan scales, 6″; enameled case; metal base; weights ¼ oz. to 4 lbs. (K–9) SEE.

Calipers. Large beechwood calipers with both English and metric scales. (K–4) SEE.

Crowell Young Math Books. Series of illustrated books, each devoted to a single mathematical topic and designed to actively involve the young reader in "doing and learning" math. Recent titles: *Estimation; Straight Lines, Parallel Lines, Perpendicular Lines; What Is Symmetry? Weighing and Balancing.* (K–3) Thomas Y. Crowell Co.

ETA Discovery Blocks. Presents the child with a perceptual program structured so that whatever his capabilities, he can find success as well as a challenge. Set consists of 140 hard maple 3/8″ thick blocks in 17 shapes and 15 activity cards graduated from simple to complex. Intended to lead the child to self-discovery of basic information concerning area, fractions, and spatial relationships. (4–9) ETA School Materials Div.

F. & C. Wide-Range Thermometer. Durable thermometer, filled with red liquid, has stainless steel body etched and filled in black. Marked every 5° from − 20° F. to + 220° F. and every 2° from − 20° C. to + 100° C., with numerical values every 10° on both scales. Glass tube 4″ long, calibrated at 70° F. and 150° F., is mounted with stainless bands and waterproof cement. Size 5¼″ × ⅝″. (2–6) Edmund Scientific Co.

First Balance. Made of hardwood with 7″ diameter pans suitable for first experiments in weighing. Height 18″; overall width 24″. (K–6) SEE.

4-in-1 Ruler. Handy 12″ ruler of plastic features four scales: one side divided into 1/16″ and 1/10″ calibrations; reverse has both a +/− number line and a metric scale (30 cm). Markings are recessed, sharp, clean, and accurate for quick and easy student reference. (K–9) SEE.

Gradient Measure. 20″ base is placed on the ground, and the gradient is measured. (4–9) SEE.

Hear and Do—Telling Time. Basic program for teaching time includes quadrant clock, 18 student clocks, one record. (K–3) Weber Costello.

"Invicta" Clinometer. Device to determine height of buildings by pointing the "gun" at the top of the building and, after looking along the sights, pulling the trigger. Booklet describing use is included. (K–9) SEE.

"Invicta" Plastics Mathematical Balance. Balance has 10 stations at each side on both front and back. Each number peg is capable of taking 10 weights, placed on the pegs to show relationships between numbers, addi-

tion, subtraction, and multiplication. Reverse side of the arm is blank, and white self-adhesive labels can give each peg fraction, money, or length values. Equations may also be solved on this balance. Comprehensive guide provides many illustrations. (K–6) SEE.

Lake and Island Board. For work in linear measurement, area, and volume. Set consists of blue board 15″ square with green "islands," 30 plastic squares, and 50 cubes based on a unit of 1″. Used to demonstrate different lengths and distances, rectangles and squares of different sizes, irregular figures, area, equal perimeter with different area, ratios 2:1 and 3:1. Instruction booklet. (K–6) Math Media Div.

Learning about Measurement. Book introduces fundamental notions of measurement in an intuitive manner. Includes an inch ruler, centimeter ruler, square inch grid, and square centimeter grid. (3–4) Franklin Publications.

Map Measure and Compass. Students can trace along route and obtain distance by multiplying the miles-per-inch factor. Magnetic compass on other side. (4–6) Math Media Div.

Meterstick. Metric and English; one side, both edges to millimeters; other side, upper edge only. Inches to eighths; opposite sides reading from same end. (6–9) Geyer Instructional Aids Co.

Meterstick. Plastic 20 cm. rulers and wooden metersticks, workbook, and metric pamphlet. (1–8) Metric Association.

Metric Trundle Wheel. Circumference of wheel is 1 meter, marked in 5 cm. and 25 cm. divisions. Excellent aid in introduction of the metric system. (3–9) SEE.

Nonmetallic Woven Measuring Tapes. One of the best measuring tapes available in a steel case with folding handle. 33′ length. (K–9) SEE.

Pedometer. Range 0–25 miles, with clip for belt. (1–6) Math Media Div.

Pocket Compass. 35 mm. spun brass case with ring and brass-capped needle. (4–9) Math Media Div.

Pupil Geo-Boards. Demonstrate units of measure for areas and perimeters of polygons. Set includes 6 geoboards, 300 pegs. (3–8) Weber Costello.

Scales with Weights. Oval pan scales to weigh up to 7 lbs.; weights ¼ oz. to 4 lbs. (K–9) SEE.

Sequential Calendar. Provides visual representation of a continuous clockwise progression of time. Includes three-dimensional spiral calender, "today," "yesterday," and "tomorrow" markers, birthday, and month markers. (1–4) Developmental Learning Materials.

Stopwatch. Dial reads in 1/10 second. One revolution of long hand every 60 seconds. Small hand registers up to 30 minutes. Has side reset button. 1 jewel. (1–9) Edmund Scientific Co.

Student Micrometer. Inexpensive beginners' micrometer for students to learn fundamentals of use and technique. Has adjustable anvil. Capacity 0 to 1″. Accuracy of .001″. (6–9) Edmund Scientific Co.

Student Transit. Wooden board with sighting tube, protractor, magnetic compass, circular bubble level on top and straight level on side for elevation work. Mounted on swivel socket attached to 36″ dowel. (3–8) Math Media Div.

Sunwatch. Timepiece without mechanism, needing only the sun to determine the hour. Combination of sundial and compass (with a chart for correcting latitude, longitude, and

time of year) contained in a brass case, pocket size, with full directions. 2″ × 3″. (6–9) Creative Playthings.

Surveyor's Land Chain. Good-quality chain with brass handles fitted with labels. (4–9) SEE.

Ten Seconds Timer. Simple device for measuring time. Steel ball rolls down a series of inclined planes and as it drops from one to the other, "beats" seconds. Timer thus measures 10 seconds for each run of the ball. (1–3) Math Media Div.

Trundle Wheel. Circumference of the wheel is 1 yard, marked in feet and inches. After each complete revolution, a loud "click" can be heard. Pupils hold the wheel and walk along the distance to be measured, counting the "clicks." (1–8) SEE.

Vernier Caliper. Fully enclosed sliding head, inside and outside jaws, depth gauge, sensitive roller adjustment, and locking lever for gauging purposes. Graduated in 1/16″ to 5½″ and in 1 mm. to 140 mm. Vernier reads to 1.128″ and 0.1 mm. Well constructed of special drawn steel. Complete instructions. (6–9) Edmund Scientific Co.

Weight Area Volume Set. Valuable in the discovery of relationships of weight, area, and volume. Set consists of 16 ¼ oz. weights, 8 ½ oz. weights, 4 1 oz. weights, 2 2 oz. weights, 1 4 oz. weight. Contained in a strong box with instruction booklet. (1–6) Math Media Div.

Yard Rule with Four Faces. Can be used for measuring in yards, half-yards, feet, and inches. One measurement can easily be converted to the other by turning the rod. Nontoxic enamel finish. (K–6) SEE.

"Your Foot" Measure. Shoe length to measure distance is made of wood with slide and plastic scale. (4–6) SEE.

Enrichment Materials, Games, Puzzles, and Devices for Pupil Use

Analog Computer Kit. Analog computer to be assembled by students. (6–9) Lano Co.

The Arithmetic Drill Games: A Game of Fractions. (5–9) *A Game of Multiplication and Division.* (4–5) *A Game of Addition and Subtraction.* (2–3). To stimulate interest in drill work and to simplify the teaching of many of the number facts. Rules are similar to Bingo, and, while call cards are faster, there is a spinning device. Entire classroom may participate at the same time (48 cards in each game). Imout Arithmetic Drill Games.

Chinese Friends. Unique oriental game for two. If partners use the same color, four may play. Game is also called Reversi. Hardwood plywood board, 64 men of two-color rubberized cork. (4–9) World Wide Games.

Compendium of Mathematical Games. Lucky Seven, Pick-up Sticks, Triple Chance, Metal Puzzles, Tantalizing 7, The Challenge, The Maestro, Square, Shake-Numbers, and the Enigma Puzzle. (K–9) SEE.

Configurations. Series of intriguing mathematical and geometrical puzzles that will challenge and delight those who enjoy careful reasoning. Based on Dorwart's book, *The Geometry of Incidence*, a copy of which is included. (6–9) Childcraft Equipment Co.

Cross-Number Puzzles Box, Story Problems. 2,000 story problems in a crossword-puzzle format. Section titles are Whole Numbers, Fractions, Mixed Fractions, Decimals and Percents. (5–8) Science Research Associates.

Cuisenaire Geoboard Kit. Classroom set of geoboards and complementary instructional materials for introducing mathematical relationships to children. (K–12) Cuisenaire Co. of America.

Deluxe Back Up Three. Object is to send four marbles all the way around the board by throwing dice. A three sends you back three spaces. Two, three, or four players. Rules can be modified. (3–6) World Wide Games.

Design Posters. Six 18″ × 24″ posters in two colors. Instructive as well as decorative. (1–6) Creative Publications.

Dienes Multi-base Arithmetical Blocks. Provides experience in various number systems. In decimal number system: small cubes represent units; rods of 10 units (longs) represent tens; slabs of 10 longs ("flats") represent hundreds and large cubes of 10 flats ("blocks") represent thousands. Four other number systems (of base numbers 3, 4, 5, and 6 respectively) are represented similarly. Four sets of cards for addition and subtraction, division, multiplication, and problems and a manual are provided with the main set. Each set includes enough material to equip a normal-size class. (1–6) Herder and Herder.

Digi-Comp. Working digital computer that demonstrates the operations usually hidden in electronic circuits. Instructions include simple explanations of computer theory, binary numbers, and programming. (5–9) Childcraft Equipment Co.

Digital Computer Lab. Digital computer to be assembled by students. (6–9) Lano Co.

Dr. Nim. Fascinating, challenging application of computer principles. Children can play Dr. Nim—a working binary computer—or a live opponent in a variety of games. (2–9) Childcraft Equipment Co.

The Elementary Kit. Booklet and preprogrammed activities to be used with the company's 200 series of programmable calculators with "penny round off" decimals. (3–7) Wang Laboratories.

Equations. Five-game kit that provides practice in elementary arithmetic operations in a variety of number bases. (4–9) Wff'n Proof.

Experiences in Discovery. Enrichment materials for more able students. (1–6) Silver Burdett.

Fours. Game of three-dimensional tick-tack-toe; the object is to place four pegs in a straight line either diagonally, horizontally, or vertically, using any single one or all four surfaces. (4–9) SEE.

Function Computer. Designed for both student and teacher use, program introduces basic concepts and language of computer technology. Can be programmed by students for math and most other subjects. Computer, reusable input and rule cards, grease pencil. (1–4) Mead Educational Services.

Heads Up. Fun game in which numerals and symbols are "thrown" on die from which the student has to form true mathematical sentences. (5–9) E. S. Lowe Co.

Hex. Plastic board with hexagonal patterns on which is played a strategy game that utilizes principles similar to Twist. (4–9) SEE.

Hindu Pyramid Puzzle. Known also as the *Tower of Hanoi.* Object is to shift the "tower" of discs from the center peg to an outside peg, moving only one disc at a time and never putting a larger one on a smaller one. Leads to student discovery and formulation of rules in the form of equations. Seven discs. (4–9) World Wide Games.

Hi-Q Brainbuster. Strategy game involving the removal of pegs by jumping schemes in order to try to end with one peg in a particular hole. (4–9) Kohner Bros.

Japanese Tantalizer Puzzle. Each of four wood blocks has blue, white, red, or yellow dots on its face. Object is to line them up so that the same color dots appear on each side. (4–9) Miles Kimball Co.

Jumpin. Strategy game for two players or two teams. Board, pawns, and instructions included. Approximate playing time: 20–40 minutes. (4–9) 3M Co.

Kalah. Stimulating game uses counters placed in hollows in a hardwood board. Develops interest in arithmetic and teaches counting at various levels as rules are made more difficult. Game can be made conveniently out of egg cartons (providing the 12 pits) and beans (as pebbles). (K–9) Childcraft Equipment Co.

Korean Yoot. Object of game is to get four men from start to finish first. Moves are determined by throwing four Yoot sticks. Can be played by two, three, four, or six persons. (4–9) World Wide Games.

Krypto. Game involving students in numerical computation. Krypto Corp.

Learn to Fold—Fold to Learn. Provides opportunity for children to enjoy making paper objects while learning more about mathematics. (3–4) Franklin Publications.

Making and Using Graphs and Nomographs. Develops graphing using the number line, and nomographs stress understanding of whole numbers, fractional numbers, and integers. (5–6) Franklin Publications.

Mathematics Games and Puzzle. Kit consists of five small items in plastic: geoboard, pyramid puzzle, strip puzzle (Chinese shuttle), tangram puzzle, and triangle puzzle. Each puzzle can be bought separately. (2–9) Concept Co.

Math Game Packs. Two series of math games for augmenting individualized work through interactive learning. (1–6) New Approaches to Learning.

Math Games. Classroom kits: Playing Card Number Games, Spinner Number Games, Domino Number Games. Each provides 10 sets for class use. (2–8) D. C. Heath & Co.

Math Puzzles. Two boxed sets of plastic laminated motor activity cards posing problems which can be solved with simple addition, subtraction, multiplication, division. Sets are *Math Path*, levels 1–2, and *Number Puzzlers*, 3–6. Singer/SVE.

More Math Puzzles. Two sets of illustrated puzzles on plastic cards to teach addition, subtraction, number sequence, modern math combinations. Dot drawing, bingo formats. Sets include *Follow the Dots*, (K–1); and *Addition and Subtraction Bingo:* (1–3). Singer/SVE.

Multi-Base Converter with 100 Pegs. 20 each of 5 colors. A multibase converter to illustrate how groups of numbers can be arranged into various bases. Instruction booklet included. (4–9) SEE.

The New Concept of Math. Set of 12 curriculum-related "math concept books" which explore concepts of new math within framework of traditional methods. Titles are: *Zero Is Something; One Is Unique; Primes Are Builders; Sets—What Are They?; Points, Lines and Planes; Polygons—Points in a Plane; Polyhedrons—Intersection Planes; Patterns—What Are They?; Counting Systems—The Familiar and the Unusual; Ten—Why Is It Important?; Measurement—How Much? How Many? How Far?; Infinity—What Is It?* (5–9) Lerner Publications.

Nine Men Morris (or Mill Game). Game is played by two people; object is to capture the opponent's men. Each time a player gets three of his marbles in a row he can take one of his opponent's marbles off the board. (4–9) World Wide Games.

Numo. Game for two to six players to provide drill on addition, subtraction, multiplication, and division. (4–8) Midwest Publications Co.

Oh-Wah-Ree. Game for two to four players, with a history of 3,500 years and many nations. Players make captures by "sowing" pebbles into pits. Approximate playing time: 20 minutes. (1—9) 3M Co.

On-Sets. Game on set theory, containing 18 logic cubes, 15 color cards, 2 playing mats, and an instruction manual of 30 different games. (K–9) Wff'n Proof.

Ornabo. Set of 36 Beechwood cubes, 3 cm. to 5 cm., from which children can make abstract designs, pictures of trains, flowers, people, and letters of the alphabet. Made in Switzerland. (K–3) SEE.

OxBow Solitaire Game. Known also as the *Chinese Shuttle Puzzle.* Good puzzle for one person. Object is to put marbles from the right into holes on the left and vice versa. Leads to student discovery and formulation of rules in the form of equations. (4–9) Miles Kimball Co.

Patterns and Puzzles in Mathematics. Tangrams, Soma Cube activities, the making of line and curve designs and various geometric shapes, fraction games, and topology are presented. (5–7) Franklin Publications.

Polyhedron Rummy. Rummy-like game for helping children learn to recognize and manipulate basic shapes. (3–6) Scott, Foresman & Co.

Puzzle Posters. Five posters 22″ × 35″, each of which is a puzzle, encourage pupils to see difference, compare, and find exceptions. (1–6) Creative Publications.

Qubic. Real "plan-ahead" game —tick-tack-toe in three dimensions, for two to six players. (1–9) Childcraft Equipment Co.

Reversal. Strategy game involving a move of "men" from one side of the board to the other. (3–9) Creative Playthings.

Slide Rule. Individualized audio-programmed set of lessons with slide rule, records or cassette tape, program books and practice problem sheets. (7–12) Acoustifone Corp.

Solar Bases. Game kit for 1–12 players which teaches the concepts of number bases and places. Materials include matrix cards, base and situation cards, playing cards, base converter wheel, transparent chips, score pad, and instruction booklet. (3–9) University Creations.

Soma Wood Block Puzzle. 14 cubes make all sorts of fascinating structures which illustrate the value of analyzing the constructions rather than using trial-and-error methods. (5–9) Edmund Scientific Co.

Squiggle Wood Contour Puzzle. 10 pieces in natural-wood finish and 10 pieces with red finish, all contoured to fit together to form a rectangular solid 6″ long with checkerboard ends. (5–9) Miles Kimball Co.

Stocks and Bonds. Stock market game in which each player buys and sells stocks and bonds as he tries to make $1,000. Approximate playing time: 1 hour. (6–9) 3M Co.

Tangram Cards, Tangram Pieces, Tangram Teacher's Guide. Set includes cardboard borders of various designs into which the pieces can be fit. (2–9) Webster Div.

Tangram Puzzles. Pack of 12 in assorted colors. (3–9) SEE.

Tangram Puzzles. Each tangram is packed with a work card in a polythene bag—the two-piece square; the three-piece square; the square and four

triangles; the square and eight pieces; the hexagon and ten triangles; and the Chinese Tangram Puzzle. (4–6) SEE.

Tangrams: One Hundred and Thirty Puzzles. Excellent book to accompany tangram pieces. Dover Publications.

Think a Dot. Color-pattern game employs a plastic digital computer that changes spot colors when marbles are dropped into three holes on top. Can be played by one or two. Many variations, including the programming of special patterns. (K–7) Childcraft Equipment Co.

Three-D Dominoes. Game has 45 plastic dominoes in triangular shape. Each has three sections to be matched as regular dominoes. Also six domino charts and a solitaire game. (2–9) Miles Kimball Co.

TUF. Series of games progressing from simple number sentences involving only addition and subtraction to more advanced mathematical concepts: multiplication, division, parentheses, fractions, decimals, negative numbers, number systems in other bases, ratio, proportion, percentage, and even exponential powers, fractional roots, logarithms, etc. On signal, two, three, or four players throw their cubes and work simultaneously and individually to build the longest possible equation. Set contains 60 ¾″ colored and impressed cubes, 4 blank cubes as extra replacements, 3 timers, rule book, container. (5–9) Cuisenaire Co.

Twixt. Board game with chess-like strategy of move and counter-move. Each player tries to connect his borders with an uninterrupted chain of linked pegs. Either two or four players. Approximate playing time: 30 minutes. (4–9) World Wide Games.

Two-Piece Pyramid Puzzle. Puzzle to fit together two precision-cut pieces of cherry wood to make a three-sided pyramid (tetrahedron). (4–9) World Wide Games.

Wff'n Proof. 21 games designed to teach student to create well-formed formulas, to use rules of inference, and to construct logical proofs. (4–8) Wff'n Proof.

Wooden Puzzle Assortment. Puzzles are precut, finished-wood blocks in shaded effect. Each can be taken apart and put together again. There are a 2¼" square block, a 2½" ball, and a 3¼" elephant. (3–9) Miles Kimball Co.

What's Your Score Puzzle Assortment. Made of wood. Contains the famous T puzzle, square puzzle, Hindu Pyramid puzzle, magic squares, and star puzzle. (6–9) Miles Kimball Co.

Which Is Longer? Game in which five players calculate the greater of two lengths on each of 36 cards. Instructions. (2–4) SEE.

Yahtzee. Game includes one dice cup, 5 red plastic die, 20 bonus chips, 1 thick score pad and 2 pencils, and complete simple instructions. Object is to get at least three of every number on the die. A good chance to discuss ideas in probability. (5–9) Miles Kimball Co.

Materials for Individualizing Instruction (including Drill Activities)

Action Book-Labs. Packages of self-pacing, individualized materials and activity ideas in such areas as map making, mirrors, mathematical shapes, polyhedral shapes. (4–6) Book-Lab.

Action Mini-Labs. Self-pacing, individualized materials and instructions in bulletin form for study of flat shapes, shapes with tubes, measuring circumference of circles. (4–6) Book-Lab.

Adventures in Computing. Exercises to motivate slow learners with the adventures of Chucko the Computer, who learns computational skills along with them. Two paperbound, write-in texts, 200 illustrations. (5–8) Ginn & Co.

Arithmetic Fact Kit. Sequenced set of cards for helping students develop speed and accuracy in basic operations. (3–up) Science Research Associates.

Arithmetic—Step by Step, Kit A. 10 units, three levels each unit. Pretests determine instructional level for each child. 300 carbon masters of liquid duplicating included. Continental Press.

Computational Skills Development Kit. For discovering and dealing with computational weaknesses. Covers whole numbers, fractions, decimals and percents. (6 and up) Science Research Associates.

Coordinated Cross Number Puzzles. Individualized program to develop competence in and enthusiasm for the operations of mathematics. Includes nine consumable books, teacher's editions. (2–9) McCormick-Mathers Publishing Co.

Cuisenaire Student Activity Cards. Set of 60 cards offering games and other activities for use with Cuisenaire rods. (1–6) Cuisenaire Co. of America.

Descriptive Geometry, Imre Pal. Text explains how to represent spatial objects and forms, use constructive methods for solution of space problems, and develop rich perspective ability. 284 3–D figures (students wear viewers to see them), plus 235 regular illustrations. (9–12) Edmund Scientific Co.

Developmental Mathematics Cards. Series of 12 kits, 2 per grade level, stressing open-ended activities for individual or small-group work.

(1–6) Addison-Wesley Publishing Co.

Discovery Mathematics Workbooks: Weight Book 1; Weight Book 2; Length Book 1; Length Book 2; Time Book 1; Time Book 2. Each book contains approximately 40 pages (9" × 7") of graded practical exercises. (3–7) SEE.

Discovery Programmes. A First Book of Sets, John Clarke. *A Second Book of Sets*, John Clarke. *The Geometry of the Point and Line*, Cyril Harris. *Area and Volume*, Leedham and Packer. *The World of Numbers*, Norman Beard. *A First Book of Fractions*, John Clarke. *A Second Book of Fractions*, John Clarke. *Understanding Number Base*, John Clarke. *Understanding A Contour Map*, Kathleen Brooke. Series of programmed texts designed for pupils with reading age of 10.4 or above assume no previous knowledge of subjects. Tests included to assess pupil's understanding of the material. (5–9) SEE.

Education Instruction Network, (EDINET) Complete package for implementing computerized instruction into the curriculum. (2–6) Honeywell EDINET.

Experiences in Mathematical Discovery. Unit 1: *Formulas, Graphs, and Patterns*, 60 pp. Unit 2: *Properties of Operations with Numbers*, 38 pp. Unit 3: *Mathematical Sentences*, 35 pp. Unit 4: *Geometry*, 98 pp. Unit 5: *Arrangements and Selections*, 50 pp. *Booklet of Answers*, 129 pp. Series of booklets written for students of general mathematics. Also might be used as enrichment for grades 6–9. NCTM.

Experiments in Mathematics, Stage 1 and Stage 2, Pearcy and Lewis. On every page there are experiments which in most cases are graded into a number of parts so that each pupil may pursue a topic to the limit of his ability

and interest. (6–9) Houghton Mifflin Co.

Exploring Mathematics on Your Own, William H. Glenn and Donovan A. Johnson. Series of enrichment booklets to be used by students for individual work or by the class as a whole. Each is complete in itself, with exercise sets and answers. *Sets, Sentences and Operations; The Pythagorean Theorem; Invitation to Mathematics; Understanding Numeration Systems; Fun With Mathematics; Number Patterns; Topology—The Rubber-Sheet Geometry; The World of Statistics; Short Cuts in Computing; The World of Measurement; Adventures in Graphing; Computing Devices.* (6–9) Webster Div.

Geoboard Geometry. Background book for teachers and activity sheets for students provide experiences in making and using a geoboard. (K–8) Scott, Foresman & Co.

HP Mathematics Drill and Practice. Computer-based program provides individualized drill, automatic record-keeping and teacher reports. Described and supported by five manuals: *Introduction, Operating Procedures, Curriculum Guide, Proctor's Handbook, Teacher's Handbook.* (1–6) Hewlett-Packard.

Imperial Intermediate Math Program. Tape-centered approach to individualizing math instruction, developed under the guidance of Dr. Lola J. May. Includes 40 tapes, 30 pupil response books for each tape, 3 copies of teacher's manual. (4–6) Imperial International Learning Corp.

Independent Exploration Material —Madison Project. Shoe Box Kits, developed under the direction of Dr. Robert B. Davis, contain instruction cards and materials to be used independently. Contents: workcards for geoboard, tower puzzle, centimeter blocks, discs, weights, springs, peg game. (5–8) Math Media Div.

Individualized Book-Lab Sets. Books provide individualized activities with materials and instructions in four mathematical areas. (5–8) Book-Lab, Inc.

Individualized Mathematics. Drill and Practice Kits AA–DD. Intended for individualized drill and practice in essential mathematical skills. Each kit includes 500 lessons on five ability levels, student profile cards, tests and posttest answer cards, teacher's guide. (3–8) Random House/Singer School.

Individualized Mathematics Laboratory. Individualized activities, with materials and instruction for 18 individual lab sets in 9 different areas and a set of 15 Picture-Graph Booklets. (4–8) Book-Lab.

Individualized Mathematics Program. Computer-based package for mathematics. Test/drill generator program writes tests and drills according to teacher-specified objectives in addition, subtraction, multiplication, division, fractions, percents, and decimals. Honeywell EDINET.

Individualized Study Units in Arithmetic. Self-diagnostic tests, self-study and self-practice lessons for students, class record sheet for teacher —all on duplicating masters, with answer cards on display boards. (3–9) Holt, Rinehart & Winston.

Individual Mathematics Skill Builders. Self-administered program of paced drill, recorded on tape cassettes. Provides computational practice for basic and supplementary facts, as well as fractions and decimals. 72 cassettes. (2–8) Harcourt Brace Jovanovich, Inc.

Introduction to Modern Math; Modern Mathematics. Seatwork lessons available as workbooks, transparencies, spirit masters, or individually printed lessons. (1–6) Jenn Publications.

An Introduction to Modern Mathematics. Programmed instruction course covering sets, number systems other than base 10, base 10 number system, changing from one system to another, etc. Includes course, tests, and manual. Grolier Educational Corp.

LRA Math Mates. 80 activity cards to use with math balance, attribute blocks, abacus, number board, geo-strips, clinometer, primary shapes and mosaic shapes, teacher's guide. (3–8) Learning Research Associates.

Macmillan Math Activity Cards. Five boxes of 48 plasticized cards to suggest mathematics laboratory activities, teacher's guides. (2–6) Macmillan Co.

Mathematical Topics, Oxford University Press. Series of little booklets full of ideas. First Year: *Number Patterns, The Bus Services, The School Camp.* Second Year: *Number Patterns, Curve Stitching, A Farm Holiday.* Third Year: *Mathematical Patterns, the Aircraft Pilot, The Travel Agency.* (4–7) SEE.

Mathematical Topics Series, Arthur Razzell and K. G. O. Watts. Series of booklets on such topics as *Circles and Curves, Shape of Three, Symmetry, Probability, Question of Accuracy.* (4–9) SEE.

Mathematics in the Making Series, Stuart E. Bell. 12 pamphlets published in England on mathematical topics. Particularly suitable for schools doing group or extension work on individual topics. 1. *Pattern, Area and Perimeter.* 2. *Binary and Other Number Systems.* 3. *Looking at Solids.* 4. *Rotation and Angles.* 5. *Curves.* 6. *Scale Drawing and Surveying.* 7. *Transformations and Symmetry.* 8. *Networks.* 9. *All Sorts of Numbers.* 10. *Graphs.* 11. *Sets and Relations.* 12. *Statistics.* (5–9) SEE.

Mathematics Laboratory. Provides practice for the development of speed and accuracy in math computation. Designed to track down and eliminate major difficulties with arithmetical operations. Three sets of 573 cards, record book, teacher's guide, test. (3–6) McCormick-Mathers Publishing Co.

Mathematics Laboratory Materials. Set of 649 separate worksheets dealing with 26 elementary topics from counting to work problems. Padded with 10 sheets per pad. Arranged according to six levels of difficulty. Written by Lore Rasmussen of the Philadelphia Public Schools. Xerox Educational Division.

Mathematics Workshop Supplementary Activities. Exercises to help children think about and develop facility with basic arithmetic facts. Six levels, 64 exercises in each. (1–6) Encyclopaedia Britannica Educational Corp.

Math Facts Puzzle Kits. Sequenced puzzle series for individualized supplementary instruction in math facts. Book of puzzles, teacher's guide. No reading required. Series 101, 1 up; Series 103, 3 up. New Approaches to Learning.

Mathlab. Child-centered discovery activities in fractions, measurement, geometry, number fun, graphing. Includes 300 cards, teacher's manual. (5–8) Benefic Press.

Math Laboratory. Combines electronic desk-top calculators with a directed-discovery approach teaching package. (5–9) Monroe.

Math Modules. Skill-oriented math program prescribes and provides individualized course of instruction for each student through testing. Skill booklets for each learning area, placement and pretests, teacher's guides, and manuals. (K–6) New Century.

Mathsets. Cards grouped into units, numbered sequentially, and color-coded for level of difficulty provide students with more than 200 purposeful activities in measurement

and geometry. (3–8) Scott, Foresman & Co.

Minisystems. Designed to teach all of the concepts and operations basic to mathematics curricula. Each of the 100 Minisystems consists of a prerecorded nonerasable cassette or reel program, student activity sheets, and teacher's guide. (K–6 and remedial) Electronic Futures, Inc.

Modern Math Concepts. 23 tapes with work sheets for review of basic concepts or use as a classroom unit. Tapes and worksheets on sets, equation solving, perimeter, algebra, etc. (5–9) Tapes Unlimited.

Mollie Clarke Books from Wheaton of Exeter. Series of colorful little books, excellent for very young children. Titles are *Symmetrical Shapes, A Dozen Eggs, Buttons, Shapes, What Is Inside?, Cakes and Candles, Sweets, Square in Inches, A Box of Crayons, The Calendar, Houses, 20 Sticks, What Is Missing?, Dominoes, Number, A Group of Children, Beads, The Piggy Bank.* (K–3) SEE.

Multi-Facts. Two multiplication boards for students to use in correcting their own work. (K–3) Connor Toy Co.

Non-graded Mathematics Topic-Texts. Spirit duplicating workbooks for supplemental use (independent, remedial, or enrichment) with any mathematics series. Consists of eight booklets of 24 spirit duplicating masters. (1–6) Charles E. Merrill Publishing Co.

Noonan-Spradley Diagnostic Program of Computational Skills. Provides work in all arithmetic computational skills needed in grades 1–6. No narration. Can be used as consumable or nonconsumable program. Test book and answer sheet, teacher's manual, and student book. (1–6) Allied Educational Council.

Numbers in Everyday Life. F. I. Sergeant and E. Stockbridge. Little booklets for young children on such topics as *Numbers, Words We Need for Numbers, More Words for Numbers, Understanding Numbers, Telling the Time, Addition Made Easy.* (K–2) SEE.

Picture Graph Booklets. Helps students learn to locate coordinates on a graph by constructing pictures from coordinate information. 15 booklets. (5–8) Book-Lab.

Practice for Modern Mathematics. Three 96-page workbooks provide supplementary exercises and practice in fundamental operations and numbers relationships. Test with answer keys and teacher's edition. (4–6) Steck-Vaughn Co.

Primary Mathematics, Intermediate Mathematics, Math Facts. Three Study Scope Classroom Labs to provide supplementary material for reinforcement of class instruction and individualized remedial and enrichment work. Study Scopes, printed programs, individual Study Scribes, pupil progress reports, teacher's manuals. (1–6) Benefic Press.

Programmed Modern Arithmetic. Logic, J. Franklin Fitzgerald and John Blyth. 40 pp. *Introduction to Sets. S–1; Set Relations, S–2;* and *Set Operations,* J. Franklin Fitzgerald and Raytheon Co.: Jack Starr, 32 pp. each. *Instructor's Guide,* J. Franklin Fitzgerald and John Blyth. 32 pp. (4–6) Raytheon Education Co.

Puzzles and Graphs, John Fujii. Provides a variety of geometric puzzles for recreation and intellectual stimulation. Gives clues to solutions. Over 90 illustrations. (7–12) NCTM.

Scholastic Self-Teaching Arithmetic. Includes five levels of workbooks, magic slates, and teaching guides for individualizing instruction and practice. (1–4 and remedial) Scholastic Book Services.

Self-Instructional Basic Mathematics. Five programmed levels of instruction for use with EFI Audio Flashcard Reader. Designed as a core program around which other materials may be employed. (K–6 or remedial) Electronic Future.

SSS (Self-Study System) Mathematics. Card-type management system to facilitate individualized instruction based on regular tests and materials. Cards, skill inventory, progress checks, tests and answer books, guide. (4–6) Learning Research Associates.

Visual Discrimination Materials. Book 1: *Pictures*; Book 2: *Shapes*; Book 3: *Lines and Shapes.* Graded exercises in discrimination, designed to help reading difficulties. Each page presents five numbered alternatives from which one shape must be selected; answers on the back. 16 card pages per book, wire-bound. (K–1) SEE.

Visual Learning Center. Individual student projection carrel with its own 35 mm. projector and write-on screen desk. Comes with 20 strip projectuals designed for individualized instruction in middle-school mathematics. (4 up) E. H. Sheldon Co.

Walker Geo-Board Program. Lucite geoboards with teacher's guides, set of 150 activity cards. (K–9) Walker Educational Book Co.

Projection Materials: Transparencies, Films, Filmstrips, Film Loops, Slides

Basic Number Concepts Kit. Multimedia kit for teaching basic number concepts. Includes transparencies and taped lessons with spirit master worksheets. (K) Tapes Unlimited.

Chalkboard Transparencies. 30 transparencies for projecting various patterns on the chalkboard. Children may write on the pattern with chalk and erase. Includes mounted transparencies and teacher's manual. (1 up) Scott Scientific Co.

Dienes Arithmetic Films. 19 Super 8-mm. film loops in color. Included are topics such as grouping, addition, multiplication, and division. (1–6) Herder and Herder.

Elementary Mathematics. Set of 139 transparencies. LaPine Scientific Co.

Elementary Mathematics for Teachers and Students. Color films designed to take the mystery out of rational numbers. Includes 30 films for use with students, 12 for training teachers. (3–8) Silver Burdett Co.

Elementary Mathematics Transparencies. Overhead transparency system for use with any elementary program to reinforce concepts and skills. Printed and blank transparencies, paper tracing sheets, manipulative symbols, permanent and erasable markers. (1–8) Holt, Rinehart & Winston, Inc.

Elementary Primary Modern Mathematics. Multicolored transparencies for presenting concepts which relate to sets, one-to-one matching, and equivalent or nonequivalent sets. Program consists of 78 overhead transparencies, several of which are for testing and review. (1–6) United Transparencies, Inc.

Filmstrip Sets. Filmstrip sets for all levels. Subjects include *Mathematics for the Primary Grades, Using Sets and Numbers, Introduction to Fractions,* and *Fundamentals of Modern Mathematics.* (1–6) Scott Education Division.

First Ideas in Mathematics. Set of animated film loops in color to simplify and clarify some of the ideas in elementary school mathematics. Loops cover place value, number lines, the operations, fractions, odd and even, perimeter and area, probability. (2–6) Ealing Corp.

Fractions. Set of 43 multioverlay,

multicolor transparencies. LaPine Scientific Co.

Harbrace Mathematics Instructional Slides. Daylight Blackboard Projection slide program. Contains 700 slides covering addition, subtraction, multiplication and division of whole numbers, geometry, measurement, graphs, rational numbers, problem-solving. (3–6) Harcourt, Brace Jovanovich.

Kenner on Modern Mathematics. 48 captioned filmstrips take an eclectic approach to basic concepts of math. Teacher's guide. (1–7) Filmstrip House, Inc.

Macmillan Elementary Math Filmloops. 40 single-concept, four-minute 8-mm. film loops with teacher's guidesheets, for individualized instruction or group use. (2–6) Macmillan Co.

Mathematics for Children. Four filmstrips covering beginning mathematics (addition and subtraction, ordinal numbers, measurement and fractions) in story form. Teacher's guides. (Pre-K–2) Hudson Photographic Industries.

Mathematics Readiness. 14 overhead transparencies with overlays. (1–2) Projectable abacus. (K–3) Projectable slide rule. Tweedy Transparencies.

Mathematics Transparencies. Set of almost 900 overhead question and teaching transparencies—some with multiple overlays, masks, single-line exposure device. (1–6) Creative Visuals.

MLA Mathematics Transparency Sets. Eight sets of transparencies covering number lines, tables for the basic operations, geometric figures and solids. Each set has 8 to 10 transparencies. (Primary, Middle grades) Modern Learning Aids.

Modern Math 1. For introducing new topics, reinforcing basic concepts and skills, and providing enrichment activities and remedial exercises. Reusable practice workbook, teacher's manual, overhead projection transparency set. (1–2) Kleeco Publishing Co.

More Ideas in Mathematics. Film loops show mathematics manipulation and simplification, developed in such areas as factors and multiples, averages, surface area, maximum and minimum, fractions, counting and computing in bases other than 10, and problem solving. (2–8) Ealing Corp.

Numbers, Names, and Colors. Five filmstrips with word number chart, flashcards, phrase cards. (1–3) Scott Education Div.

Set Theory. Explains sets and set theory, subsets, Venn diagrams, universal sets, disjointed sets, etc. Available as filmstrip with phonodisc, film strip and cassette, or filmstrip and tape. (5–8) Library Filmstrip Center.

Transparencies and Filmstrips. 15 programs on various facets of the new math, for all grade levels. Programs cover sets, operations, computation skills, measure, fractions, geometry, many other areas. Colonial Films.

Transparency Mathematics Program. Almost 1,000 overhead transparencies for teaching and evaluation. (1–6) Math-Master Labs.

Transparency Sets. Overhead transparency sets for all grade levels on such topics as basic addition and subtraction, sets, the slide rule, discovery in geometry and algebra, and mathematics games. (1–6) Scott Education Div.

Using Modern Mathematics. Program of 49 filmstrips correlated to many modern mathematics texts. Includes seven groups of five to eight graded filmstrips. Using a spiral approach, filmstrips cover topics ranging from sets to binary numbers. (1–6) Singer/SVE.

Visonetics. Cardboard manipulatives and overhead transparencies. (K–8) General Learning Corp.

Visualizing Elementary Mathematics. Kits A–D. Overhead transparencies and flannelboard kits to help children visualize mathematical concepts. Teacher's manuals. (K–8) Random House/Singer School Div.

We Discover Equivalent Fractions. 16 mm. color film explains how different fractions can name the same parts of an object or group and how they can be represented on the number line. (Intermediate) Coronet Films.

We Discover Fractions. 16 mm. film shows how fractions are used, how they can be shown on number lines, the meaning of denominator and numerator. (Primary) Coronet Films.

We Use the Number Line. 16 mm. film shows use of number line in representing "how many" and in understanding addition and subtraction. (Primary) Coronet Films.

Recordings and Tapes

Auditory Skills Basic Math Concepts. Self-directed activities to increase computational skills. Each tape presents a series of games on a specific mathematical concept. Five tapes and 50 game cards. (1–3, 4–6) Tapes Unlimited.

Countdown. Self-pacing lessons on tape to give slow learner repetition and practice in fundamental operations of arithmetic. Includes pacer audio tape player, 25 tape cassettes of 50 lessons, and plastic-coated folders for student responses. (1–3) Economy Co.

Directed (or Signed) Numbers. Uses step-by-step procedures to introduce operations with positive and negative integers on the number line. 5 self-correcting teaching-tape kits (cassette or reel), 72 student response worksheets, teacher's guide. (6–10) 3M Co.

Drilltapes.™ Instruction and computational practice in an audio format, with cassette or reel tapes. (1–6) Science Research Associates.

Elementary School Mathematics. Designed to teach basic math curriculum concepts and operations. Correlates with basic textbook series. 100 taped lessons (cassette or reel), 30 activity sheets, teacher's guide. (K–6) Learning Systems Corp.

Imperial Primary Mathematics Program. Tape-centered program containing hundreds of exercises to help reinforce concepts and operations learned previously. 40 tapes, 30 pupil response booklets for each tape, 3 copies of teacher's manual. (1–3) Imperial International Learning Corp.

LP5000—Teaching Children Mathematics Through Games, Rhythms and Stunts. Provides learning situations in which children engage in games, stunts and rhythm activities while practicing mathematical skills. Two record albums and teacher's manual. (1–2) Kimbo Educational Records.

Mathematics Learning Tapes. Audio tapes (cassette or reel) with worksheets where necessary in ditto master form. For use by individuals or small groups with earphones or by entire class. Approximately 300 titles. (K–up) Scott Scientific Co.

Math Master Tapes. Individual tapes presenting mathematics concepts and skills aimed at motivating more intensive student participation and learning. Two sets: *Number and Numeration*, 15 tapes plus work-study guides and teacher's guide, and *Introduction to Fraction Concepts*, 8 tapes plus guides. (3–8) Learning Research Associates.

Merrill Mathematics Skilltapes. 40 cassette tapes color coded with nine student study booklets and a teacher's guide. Program covers 11 major topics of basic computational skills. (1 up) Charles E. Merrill Publishing Co.

Motivation in Mathematics. Four recordings designed to motivate students. Whimsy and fantasy introduce children to the idea of math in the future, the history of math, and the basic nature of fractions. Available on records, tapes, or cassettes. (4–6) H. Wilson Corp.

Programmed Mathematics For Fun. Audio, reel or cassette, lessons with thermal master student work sheets aimed at the fast learner. (6–9) Educational Sensory Programming.

Set Concepts. Introduces set theory through single concepts such as union, difference, intersection, subset, equivalent and equal. 9 self-correcting teaching-tape kits (cassette or reel), 72 student response worksheets, teacher's guide. (1–3) 3M Co.

Textbooks and Teaching-Learning Systems

Continuous Progress Laboratory. Classroom management tool for individualized instruction, multimedia resources, behavioral objectives, continuous progress learning, and the use of multiple texts. Cards containing objectives, resources, and evaluation; tapes; teacher's guides; student progress books; tests; answer books; charts; poster. (1–8) Educational Progress Corp.

Developing Mathematics. Basal series of elementary mathematics materials in Macmillan School Mathematics Program. Textbooks, wall charts (for kindergarten), workbooks and keys, duplicating masters, teacher's edition. (K–8) Macmillan Co.

Distar™ *Arithmetic*. Basic arithmetic for children who have difficulty in learning. Stresses fast-paced presentation to small groups, student participation and immediate feedback. (Presch.–2) Science Research Associates.

Elementary Mathematics: One by One and Two by Two. Blends modern mathematical content with modern teaching methods. Paperback textbooks, duplicating masters, manual aids, teacher's edition, and guides. (1–2) Harcourt, Brace Jovanovich, Inc.

Elementary Mathematics: Patterns and Structure. Presentation of mathematics essentials stresses intuitive development of basic geometry topics. For grades 1–2 texts are in workbook or nonconsumable edition. Duplicating masters, Spanish-language exercise books, filmstrips for use with texts in grades 3–7. (1–8) Holt, Rinehart & Winston.

Elementary School Mathematics. Basal program supplemented by activity cards, duplicator masters, tests and manipulatives. Teachers' editions. (K–6) Addison-Wesley Publishing Co.

Essential Modern Mathematics. For students low in ability or achievement—socially relevant topics in short, highly pictorial units at low reading level. Texts, annotated editions, number strips kit, practice pages, transparencies. (3–6) Ginn & Co.

Exploring Elementary Mathematics. Enables average students to use modern mathematics for grasp of basic arithmetic facts and proficiency in basic computational and problem-solving skills. Texts, teacher's editions, exercises, tests with keys, guide for teachers in nongraded situations. (K–6) Holt, Rinehart & Winston.

Foundations for Mathematics. Program of four units covering concepts for sets, comparison and ordering sets, class building, number concepts, reproduction of figures and numerals, set operations. Flannelboards, geometric forms and numerals, sets of cards, wooden cubes, demonstration charts, student worksheets, guides. (Presch.–2) Teaching Resources Corp.

The Franklin Mathematics Series. Activities, projects, puzzles, and games to put math principles to work. 11 texts, teacher's editions. (1–8) Lyons & Carnahan.

Ginn Elementary Mathematics. Modern mathematics program based on research into learning and cognitive development. Uses concrete references, physical models and applications to develop mathematical thinking. Paperbound write-in texts, teacher's editions. (1–2) Ginn & Co.

Greater Cleveland Mathematics Program. Discovery mathematics program developed by Educational Research Council of America introduces concepts at concrete or visual level. Teacher's guides, tests, and teaching aids. (K–6) Science Research Associates.

Heath Elementary Mathematics. Teacher-controlled learner-oriented program designed for group-paced instruction, with provisions for individual differences. Includes pupil texts, worksheets, tests, overhead projectuals, teacher's editions. (K–6) D. C. Heath & Co.

Let's Explore Mathematics, Vols. 1–4. For enrichment and reinforcement in regular classroom instruction; designed to supplement all basic textbooks and correlate with math lab activities and apparatus currently in use. Teacher's guide and bibliography. (ungraded, suggested for grades 2–6) ARCO Publishing Co.

Mastering Mathematics Series. Supplementary program use⌐ nonverbal techniques to develop computational skills in average and slow learners; nongraded, soft-covered, and cross-referenced to all major textbook series. Worktexts and teachers' annotated editions. (K–8) W. H. Sadlier.

Mathematics for Special Education. Basic audio math program on reel or tape for the slow learner. Thermal master student worksheets. (R–3) Educational Sensory Programming.

Mathematics for Today. Basal program combining traditional approach with modern mathematics. Heavy emphasis on computation, frequent review of previously learned skills, and logical, step-by-step sequence of learnings. Teacher's edition for each grade. (1–3) Economy Co.

Mathematics We Need. Guided discovery program combines modern mathematics with computational skills development and problem solving. Text, manual, workbook with teacher's edition, test. (K–8) Ginn & Co.

Math in Action Series. For students who have difficulty with the standard mathematics program. Slower paced, less dependent on reading level, less emphasis on abstractions. Text, activity book, tests, duplicating masters, teacher's editions, guide, and key. (1–8) American Book Co.

Math Workshop. Nonverbal, problem-solving approach to modern math. Guide, pupil books on seven levels. (K–8) Encyclopaedia Britannica Educational Corp.

MINISYSTEMS Elementary Mathematics Series. Teacher-directed, self-instructional learning systems for use by student in classroom or at home. Cassette or reel tape program, student activity sheets, teacher's guide. (K–6) Electronic Futures.

Modern Mathematics. Presents fundamental concepts and practice exercises to enhance understanding of concepts, reinforce computational skills, and encourage application of mathematics to practical situations. Carbon masters for liquid duplicating. (K–6) Continental Press.

Modern Mathematics, Concepts and Skills. Teaches contemporary concepts of modern math operations while stressing computational skills. "Write and See" text-skill books and corresponding teacher's editions with hardbound text (K–2); skill books and teacher's edition for grade 3; "Write and See" markers. New Century.

Modern Mathematics Series. Emphasis on discovery approach and unified structure of mathematics. Text, tests, laboratory booklets, filmstrips, activity board, activity kits, charts, overhead transparencies, teacher's editions, guides, answer keys. (K–8) American Book Co.

Modern Mathematics through Discovery. Stresses individual differences, easy readability, practice and enrichment. Students' and teacher's texts, workbooks, tests, readiness materials, manipulatives, films. (K–8) Silver Burdett Co.

Modern School Mathematics. Complete program provides a variety of approaches to meet individual pupil needs. Texts, teacher's annotated editions, many supplementary materials. (K–6) Houghton Mifflin Co.

New Dimensions in Mathematics. Basic, multiple-methods approach program for students of all abilities. Features dual-track story problems, core and noncore activities. Readiness lab and books, texts for levels 1–6, enrichment workbooks 3–6, duplicating masters, teacher's editions. (Readiness–6) Harper & Row.

The New Laidlaw Mathematics Program. Uses the inductive approach to provide concept development and many opportunities for individualization. Emphasis on geometry. (Presch.–8) Laidlaw Bros.

New Ways in Mathematics. Softbound work texts providing drill and practice in fundamentals of mathematics. (1–8) D. C. Heath & Co.

Numbers for Beginners (primer), *Understanding Numbers* (grade one), *Using Numbers* (*grade two*). Consumable text-workbooks with teacher's editions, introducing arithmetical concepts and practice opportunities. (P–2) Laidlaw Bros.

Sadlier Contemporary Mathematics. Program in soft covers stresses computational efficiency and an inductive approach to concepts. Texts and teacher's annotated editions. (K–9) W. H. Sadlier.

Seeing through Arithmetic. Modern mathematics program stressing visuals approach. Student books, teacher's editions, workbooks, practice tablets, tests on duplicating masters, standardized achievement tests. (1–6) Scott, Foresman & Co.

Self-Instructional Basic Mathematics. Individualized system designed to teach fundamental concepts, operations, and skills in mathematics. Audio flashcard sets, workbooks, teacher's manuals. (K–6) Electronic Futures.

Sets and Numbers. Textbooks, workbooks, and teacher's editions stress concepts, structure, and logic of mathematics. (K–6) Random House/Singer School Div.

Skill in Basic Mathematics with Write and See. Remedial mathematics program for learning basic concepts and skills. Five soft-cover "Write and See" text-skill books, teacher's guide, markers. (6 and up) New Century.

Spectrum Mathematics Series. Nongraded, consumable mathematics program for students who need assistance with the basic concepts and skills of computation and reasoning. (3–8) Laidlaw Bros.

SRA Elementary Mathematics Program. Group activities for concept development, using inexpensive and easy to obtain materials. Pupil texts, teacher's guides, multimedia manuals. (K–6) Science Research Associates.

Sullivan Basal Mathematics. Self-instructional, programmed, developmental course incorporating more than 100,000 problems. 37 texts without words (especially helpful for non-English speaking and nonverbal children), tests, student and teacher's manuals. (Nongraded; placement determined by test) Behavioral Research Laboratories.

Sullivan Mathematics Laboratory. Self-teaching, self-pacing programmed course without words for remediation, diagnosis, and review. 12 skill textbooks, test book, record book, placement exam, teacher's manual. (Nongraded; placement via test) Behavioral Research Laboratories.

Resource Materials for the Teacher

Aftermath. Four 128-page booklets of cartoons, humor, designs, puzzles, codes and games about arithmetic. Can be used as ditto and mimeograph masters. (5–9) Creative Publications.

Amusements in Mathematics. British creator of math puzzles provides over 430 mazes, games, and problems involving weighing, packing, age, chess boards, plane figure dissection, etc. Full solutions. Over 450 illustrations. Dover Publications.

The Arithmetic Teacher. $9.00 a year. Subscription price includes membership in the NCTM. Journal published monthly eight times a year, October through May, by the National Council of Teachers of Mathematics.

Beginning Mathematics. Part I: *Learning Logic, Logical Games.* An extended introduction to the study of logic using the Logical Blocks. Part II: *Sets, Numbers and Powers.* Introduces numbers through the properties of sets and continues up to the idea of "powers." Part III: *Exploration of Space and Practical Measuring.* Deals briefly with the practical application of number in situations involving measurement, weight, capacity, time, and area and suggests an early approach to geometry. Herder and Herder.

Balance. Mathematics balance for teacher demonstrations or pupil use. (3 and up) Sargent-Welch Scientific Co.

Beginnings, Mathematics Begins, Computation and Structure, Shape and Size, Desk Calculators, How to Build a Pond, I Do and I Understand. Pictorial Representations. Nuffield Foundation Mathematics Project materials. *I Do and I Understand* is a guide for teachers and deals with the practical problems of classroom management encountered when children are set free to make their own discoveries with concrete materials. *Pictorial Representations* is designed to help teachers develop pupils' ability to use graphs. (K–6) John Wiley & Sons.

Boxes, Squares, and Other Things. Teacher's guide to an informal geometry unit based chiefly on work with construction paper and milk cartons. (4–7) NCTM.

Concept and Skill Cards. Various manipulative aids designed to reinforce Modern School Mathematics program but useful with other basal programs. (K–6) Houghton Mifflin Co.

Contemporary School Mathematics. Series 1: *Matrices,* G. Matthews; *Sets and Logic,* C. A. R. Bailey; *Computers,* F. B. Lovis; *Shape, Size, and Place,* J. A. C. Reynolds. Series 2: *Matrices 2,* G. Matthews; *Sets and Logic 2,* C. A. R. Bailey; *Computers 2,* F. B. Lovis; *An Introduction to Probability and Statistics,* A. J. Sherlock. (7–12) Houghton Mifflin Co.

Discovery, by Robert Wirtz, Morton Botel, and B. G. Nunley. Multipurpose book for elementary school teachers contains explanations and illustrations of the unifying ideas constituting the structure of the "new" math. Multilevel Worksheets (24 units, 6 worksheets per unit) and 27 Multilevel Research Activities. (K–6) Encyclopaedia Britannica Educational Corp.

Discovery in Mathematics, and Explorations in Mathematics. Two Madison Project publications full of ideas for enriching and supplementing regular programs. (K–9) Addison-Wesley Publishing Co.

Enrichment Mathematics for the Grades. 27th yearbook of the National Council of Teachers of Mathematics. (K–6).

First Grade Diary, Robert Hightower and Lore Rasmussen. Ideas for teaching mathematics to primary children. (K–2) Xerox Education Div.

Fun with Numbers, Lines and Angles. Activities for teaching basic math. (4–6) Highlights for Children.

A Game and Activities Approach to Helping Underachievers Learn Mathematics. Teacher sourcebook containing hints for helping underachievers, plus descriptions of games and activities classified according to topic and specific student behavioral objective. (4–8) National Textbook Co.

The Geo-Board: A Manual for Teachers. Provides guides to application of geo-board to concepts of sets, operations, lines, angles, polygons, measurement, and number patterns. (K–8) Walker Educational Book Corp.

Geometry with a Tangram, David Fletcher and Joseph Ibbotson. Some applications of the tangram puzzle. SEE.

Index to Computer Assisted Instruction. Comprehensive compilation of information on 910 CAI programs currently operational and available. Sterling Institute.

Informal Geometry. One of a series of booklets published by NCTM for the elementary teacher. Provides overview of content and self-testing exercises. National Council of Teachers of Mathematics.

Involving the Child in Math. A British infant school headmistress describes how the Nuffield approach to mathematics can be used to individualize instruction, encourage children to see math in the world around them. Five 1-hour tapes. Listener Corp.

Kindermath. Uses an activity approach to develop an understanding of number ideas, mathematical terms and geometric ideas in preparation for grade one. Series of 30 charts with teacher's guide. (K) Ginn & Co.

Let's Play Games in Mathematics. Teacher sourcebooks containing descriptions of games and activities, cross-referenced with specific student behavioral objectives and content topics. Separate paperbound volume for each grade level. (K–8) National Textbook Co.

Mathematics in Primary Schools. Curriculum Bulletin No. 1, The Schools Council. English bulletin aims not only at presenting the philosophy of changes but also at providing material help for teachers, particularly those with large classes in small classrooms. Contains a great deal of helpful material for elementary teachers. (K–6) SEE.

Mobile Utility Lab. A mathematics laboratory in miniature; storage for instructional materials and teaching/working surface. Starter kit of manipulative materials also included. (4–9) E. H. Sheldon Co.

Modern Mathematics for Young Children, Z. P. Dienes. Contains some helpful ideas for teachers at the primary level. Herder and Herder.

Moiré Patterns. Patterns are produced by overlaying precise repetitive figures so that the line elements are nearly superimposed. 16 pieces, the *Science of Moiré Patterns*, halftone and fiberglass screens. (6–9) Edmund Scientific Co.

Notes on Mathematics in Primary Schools, Members of the Association of Teachers of Mathematics. Contains many ideas on mathematics content and methods of teaching. (K–6) Cambridge University Press.

Number Line, Functions and Fundamental Topics, David Page. Ideas for interesting activities for students, written by the director of the University of Illinois Arithmetic Project. (1–6) Macmillan Co.

Peas and Particles. Booklet gives ideas of how to get children involved in such adventures as guessing how many beans it might take to fill a given jar, and how to make reasonable approximations. Webster Div.

Plus. Games, ideas, activities for elementary math teacher. Book covers nine different areas of study. (K–3) Educational Service.

Practice in Mathematics. Duplicating masters for practice on mathematical skills. (K–8) D. C. Heath & Co.

Probability and Statistics Lab Unit. Unit contains various items, such as die, hexostat, inclined planes, etc., for some excellent experiments suggested in the teacher's book. Math-Master Labs.

Short-Cut Math. Uses descriptive instead of technical terms to teach rapid computation. Each shortcut identified by name and number, followed by a rule, example, solution, proof and summary. Text covers addition, subtraction, multiplication, division, fractions, mixed numbers and percentages. (Advanced upper elementary and above.) Sterling Publishing Co.

Super-Line, Build-a-Rule, and *Fractions, Decimals and Per Cents Chart* for classroom demonstration.

Count-A-Ladder, Count-A-Line and *Count-A-Bars* for demonstration and student manipulation. EduKaid of Ridgewood.

System 1-Math and Arithmetic Applications. A generic gaming method, applicable to various subject-matter tasks and instructional uses. Data is input by both student and teacher; procedures of gaming parallel the subject-matter rules. Display boards, timer, data tiles, verification materials, instructor's manual. (K–6) Instructional Simulations.

Teaching Aids for Modern Mathematics. Source book of ideas for elementary school teachers. Contains items that are inexpensive and easy to make, with directions for construction and use and suggestions for possible variations. (K–6) Holt, Rinehart & Winston.

Teaching-Learning Board Kit. Large "A Frame" board with 376 display objects for illustrating many mathematical concepts. Teacher's manual. (K–6) Houghton Mifflin Co.

"U" Film Kit. Materials for making original filmstrips or sections to splice into prepared filmstrips. 25′ roll of film, marking pencils, filmstrip storage cans and labels, filmstrip splicer and splicing tapes, manual. (1–6) Hudson Photographic Industries.

What Is Mathematics? Excellent resource book for teachers who wish to extend their background in math. Oxford University Press.

Sources of Materials Listed

Academic Industries, Inc.
1754 Walton Avenue
Bronx, New York 10453

Acoustifone Corp.
8954 Comanche Ave.
Chatsworth, Calif. 91311

Addison-Wesley Publishing Co. Inc.
2725 Sand Hill Rd.
Menlo Park, Calif. 94053

AIM Industries, Inc.
253 State St.
St. Paul, Minn. 55107

Allied Educational Council
P.O. Box 78
Galien, Michigan 49113

American Book Co.
540 W. 33rd St.
New York, N.Y. 10001

Paul S. Amidon and Associates, Inc.
5408 Chicago Ave. S.
Minneapolis, Minn. 55417

ARCO Publishing Co., Inc.
219 Park Ave. S.
New York, N.Y. 10003

Behavioral Research Laboratories
866 United Nations Plaza
New York, N.Y. 10017

Benefic Press
10300 W. Roosevelt Rd.
Westchester, Ill. 60153

Book-Lab, Inc.
1449 37th St.
Brooklyn, N.Y. 11218

Milton Bradley Co.
Springfield, Mass. 01101

Bremer Multiplication Records, Inc.
161 Green Bay Rd.
Wilmette, Ill. 60091

Cambridge University Press
32 East 57th St.
New York, N.Y. 10022

Childcraft Equipment Company, Inc.
155 East 23rd St.
New York, N.Y. 10010

Children's Press
1224 W. Van Buren St.
Chicago, Ill. 60607

Colonial Films, Inc.
752 Spring St. N.W.
Atlanta, Ga. 30308

Concept Company
P.O. Box 273
Belmont, Mass. 02178

Connor Toy Company
207 N. First Ave.
Wausau, Wis. 54401

The Continental Press, Inc.
520 E. Bainbridge St.
Elizabethtown, Pa. 17022

Coronet Films
65 E. South Water St.
Chicago, Ill. 60601

Creative Playthings, Inc.
Princeton, New Jersey 08540

Creative Publications
P.O. Box 328
Palo Alto, Calif. 94302

Creative Visuals
Box 1911, Big Spring, Texas 79720

Thomas Y. Crowell Co., Publishers
201 Park Avenue S.
New York, N.Y. 10003

Cuisenaire Company of America, Inc.
12 Church Street
New Rochelle, New York 10805

The John Day Co.
257 Park Avenue S.
New York, N.Y. 10003

Developmental Learning Materials
3505 N. Ashland Ave.
Chicago, Ill. 60657

Dorsett Educational Systems, Inc.
Box 1226
Norman, Oklahoma 73069

Dover Publications
1 East 2nd Street
Mineola, New York 11501

The Ealing Corp.
2225 Massachusetts Ave.
Cambridge, Mass. 02140

The Economy Company
1901 N. Walnut
P.O. Box 25308
Oklahoma City, Okla. 73152

Edmund Scientific Company
100 Edscorp Building
Barrington, New Jersey 08007

Educational Games, Inc.
200 Fifth Avenue
New York, N.Y. 10010

Educational Progress Corp.
8538 E. 41st St.
Tulsa, Oklahoma 74145

Educational Sensory Programming
Box 418-A
Jonesboro, Arkansas 72401

Educational Service, Inc.
Box 219
Stevensville, Mich. 49127

EduKaid of Ridgewood
1250 E. Ridgewood Ave.
Ridgewood, N.J. 07450

Electronic Futures, Inc.
57 Dodge Ave.
North Haven, Conn. 06473

Encyclopaedia Britannica Educational
   Corporation
425 North Michigan Ave.
Chicago, Ill. 60611

ETA School Materials Division
159 East Kinzie Street
Chicago, Illinois 60610

Eye Gate House, Inc.
146-01 Archer Avenue
Jamaica, N.Y. 11435

Films, Incorporated
1144 Wilmette Ave.
Wilmette, Ill. 60091

Filmstrip House, Inc.
432 Park Ave. S.
New York, N.Y. 10016

Franklin Publications, Inc.
   c/o Vroman's
367 S. Pasadena Ave.
Pasadena, California 91105

General Learning Corp.
250 James St.
Morristown, N.J. 07960

Geyer Instructional Aids Company
1229 Maxine Drive
Fort Wayne, Indiana 46807

Ginn and Co.
275 Wyman St.
Waltham, Mass. 02154

Grolier Educational Corp.
845 Third Ave.
New York, N.Y. 10022

Harcourt, Brace Jovanovich, Inc.
757 Third Ave.
New York, N.Y. 10017

Harper & Row, Inc.
2500 Crawford Ave.
Evanston, Ill. 60201

D. C. Heath and Company
125 Spring St.
Lexington, Mass. 02173

Herder and Herder, Inc.
232 Madison Avenue
New York, N.Y. 10016

Hester and Associates
11422 Harry Hines
Dallas, Texas 75229

Hewlett-Packard
11000 Wolfe Rd.
Cupertino, Calif. 95014

Highlights for Children, Inc.
2300 W. Fifth Ave.
Columbus, Ohio 43216

Holt, Rinehart and Winston, Inc.
383 Madison Avenue
New York, N.Y. 10017

Honeywell EDINET
2710 4th Ave. S.
Minneapolis, Minn. 55408

Houghton Mifflin Company
110 Tremont St.
Boston, Mass. 02107

Hudson Photographic Industries, Inc.
2 S. Buckout St.
Irvington-on-Hudson, N.Y. 10633

Ideal School Supply Co.
11000 S. Lavergne Ave.
Oaklawn, Ill. 60453

Imout Arithmetic Drill Games
706 Williamson Building
Cleveland, Ohio 44114

Imperial International Learning Corp.
Box 548
Kankakee, Ill. 60901

Instructional Media Associates, Inc.
481 Valley Brook Ave.
Lyndhurst, N.J. 07071

Instructional Simulations, Inc.
2147 University Ave.
St. Paul, Minn. 55114

The Instructo Corporation
Paoli, Pennsylvania 19301

Miles Kimball Company
41 West Eighth Ave.
Oshkosh, Wis. 54901

Kimbo Educational Records
P.O. Box 55
Deal, N.J. 07723

Kindrey Manufacturing Company
P.O. Box 11606
Palo Alto, California 94306

Kleeco Publishing Co.
600 W. Jackson Blvd.
Chicago, Ill. 60606

Kohner Brothers, Inc.
Tryne Game Division
P.O. Box 294
East Paterson, N.J. 07407

Krypto Corporation
2 Pine Street
San Francisco, Calif. 94111

Laidlaw Brothers
Thatcher and Madison
River Forest, Ill. 60305

Lano Company
4741 West Liberty St.
Ann Arbor, Mich. 48120

LaPine Scientific Company
6001 South Knox Ave.
Chicago, Ill. 60629

Learning Research Associates, Inc.
1501 Broadway
New York, N.Y. 10036

Learning Systems Corp.
60 Connolly Pkwy.
Hamden, Conn. 06514

Lerner Publications Co.
241 First Ave. N.
Minneapolis, Minn. 55401

Library Filmstrip Center
3033 Aloma
Wichita, Kan. 67211

Listener Corp.
6777 Hollywood Blvd.
Hollywood, Calif. 90028

E. S. Lowe Company, Inc.
27 West 25th St.
New York, N.Y. 10022

Lyons and Carnahan
407 E. 25th St.
Chicago, Ill. 60616

The Macmillan Company
866 Third Ave.
New York, N.Y. 10022

Math-Master Labs
P.O. Box 1911
Big Spring, Texas 79720

Math Media Division
H. & M. Associates
P.O. Box 1109
Danbury, Connecticut 06801

McCormick Mathers Publishing Co.
450 W. 33rd St.
New York, N.Y. 10001

Mead Educational Services
245 Highland Ave. N.E.
Atlanta, Georgia 30307

Charles E. Merrill Publishing Co.
1300 Alum Creek Drive
Columbus, Ohio 43216

Midwest Publications Co. Inc.
P.O. Box 307
Birmingham, Michigan 48012

Metric Association, Inc.
2004 Ash St.
Waukegan, Illinois 60085

Minnesota Mining and Manufacturing
    Co. (3M Co.)
St. Paul, Minn. 55101

Modern Learning Aids
Box 302
Rochester, N.Y. 14603

Monroe
550 Central Ave.
Orange, N.J. 07051

Montessori Leermiddelenhuis
The Hague, Netherlands

National Council of Teachers of
    Mathematics (NCTM)
1201 Sixteenth St. N.W.
Washington, D.C. 20036

National Textbook Co.
8259 Niles Center Rd.
Skokie, Ill. 60076

New Approaches to Learning, Inc.
63 Leonard Ave.
Plattsburg, N.Y. 12901

New Century
440 Park Ave. S.
New York, N.Y. 10016

Philip and Tacey Ltd.
London, England

Pickett, Inc.
Pickett Square
Santa Barbara, Calif. 93102

Frederick Post Company
Chicago, Illinois 60690

Random House/Singer School
    Division
Random House, Inc.
201 E. 50th St.
New York, N.Y. 10022

Raytheon Education Company
Heath Educational Materials
200 North Richard Ave.
Indianapolis, Inc. 46219

W. H. Sadlier, Inc.
11 Park Place
New York, N.Y. 10007

Sargent-Welch Scientific Co.
7300 N. Kinder Ave.
Skokie, Ill. 60076

Scholastic Book Services
904 Sylvan Avenue
Englewood Cliffs, N.J. 07632

Science Research Associates, Inc.
259 East Erie Street
Chicago, Ill. 60611

Scott Education Division
104 Lower Westerfield Rd.
Holyoke, Mass. 01040

Scott, Foresman and Company
1900 East Lake Avenue
Glenview, Ill. 60025

Scott Scientific, Inc.
Box 2121
Fort Collins, Colo. 80521

Selective Educational Equipment
(SEE)
3 Bridge St.
Newton, Mass. 02195

E. H. Sheldon Co.
716 Nims
Muskegon, Michigan 49443

Silver Burdett Co.
250 James St.
Morristown, N.J.

Singer/SVE
1345 Diversey Parkway
Chicago, Ill. 60614

Steck-Vaughn Co.
P.O. Box 2028
Austin, Texas 78767

Sterling Institute
Suite 3750
Prudential Tower
Boston, Mass. 02199

Sterling Plastics Co.
253 Sheffield St.
Mountainside, N.J. 07092

Sterling Publishing Co., Inc.
419 Park Ave. S.
New York, N.Y. 10016

Tapes Unlimited
13001 Puritan Ave.
Detroit, Mich. 48227

Teaching Resources Corp.
100 Boylston St.
Boston, Mass. 02116

Tweedy Transparencies
208 Hollywood Ave.
East Orange, N.J. 07018

United Transparencies, Inc.
P.O. Box 688
Binghamton, N.Y. 13902

Union Camp Corp.—Educational
Systems
1600 Valley Rd.
Wayne, N.J. 07470

University Creations, Inc.
Box 774
Cherry Hill, N.J. 08034

Walker Educational Book
Corporation
720 Fifth Ave.
New York, N.Y. 10019

Wang Laboratories, Inc.
836 North St.
Tewksbury, Mass. 01876

Weber Costello
1900 N. Narragansett Ave.
Chicago, Ill. 60639

Webster Division
McGraw-Hill Book Company
Manchester Road
Manchester, Mo. 63011

Wff'n Proof
P.O. Box 71
New Haven, Conn. 06501

John Wiley and Sons, Inc.
605 Third Ave.
New York, N.Y. 10016

H. Wilson Corp.
555 W. Taft Dr.
South Holland, Ill. 60473

World Wide Games
Delaware, Ohio 43015

Xerox Educational Division
600 Madison Ave.
New York, N.Y. 10022

GLOSSARY

Abacus. An instrument for performing calculations by sliding counters along rods or in grooves; a counting frame to aid in arithmetic computation.

Addend. A number to be added to another.

Algorism. A rule of procedure for solving a recurrent mathematical problem; some special process of solving a certain type of problem, particularly a method that continually repeats some basic process.

Arithmetic. A branch of mathematics that deals with real numbers and computations with them; the study of the positive integers under the operations of addition, subtraction, multiplication, and division, and the use of the results of these studies in everyday life.

Array. A regular and imposing grouping or arrangement; a number of mathematical elements arranged in rows and columns; arrangement of a series of items according to values of the items, usually from largest to smallest or the reverse.

Associative. Combining elements in such a manner that the result is independent of the grouping. Example: $a + (b + c) = (a + b) + c$ $a(bc) = (ab)c$.

Cardinal number. A number (as 1, 5, 15) that is used in simple counting and that indicates how many elements there are in an assemblage; the property that a mathematical set has in common with all sets that can be put in one-to-one correspondence with it.

Cartesian product. The Cartesian product of two sets A and B is the set $A \times B$ of all pairs (x,y,) such that x is a member of A and y is a member of B.

Closure. If a and b are elements of R, the $a + b$ and ab are also elements of R.

Common fraction. A fraction whose numerator and denominator are both integers.

Commutative. Combining elements in such a manner that the result is independent of the order in which the elements are taken. Example: $a + b = b + a$ $ab = ba$.

Computer. An automatic electronic

machine for performing calculations; any instrument which performs numerical and mathematical operations.

Congruent. Two figures are congruent if one can be made to coincide with the other by a rigid motion in space; two figures are congruent if they differ only in "location."

Cuisenaire. Rods that are a physical model for rational numbers and for a rational field.

Curriculum. A set of courses; the courses offered by an educational institution or one of its branches.

Decimal. A proper fraction in which the denominator is a power of ten, usually not expressed but signified by a point placed at the left of the numerator (as $.2 = 2/10$).

Denominator. The part of a fraction that is below the line signifying division and that in fractions with 1 as the numerator indicates into how many parts the unit is divided.

Difference. The result of subtracting one quantity from another.

Digit. Any of the arabic numerals 1 to 9 and usually the symbol 0.

Disjoint. No element in common; two sets are disjoint if the intersection of the two sets is empty.

Dividend. A quantity which is to be divided by another quantity.

Divisor. The number by which a dividend is divided.

Equivalent. Sets that can be put in one-to-one correspondence; having the same measure.

Equivalent fractions. Two fractions which have the same value.

Factors. Any of the numbers or symbols in mathematics that when multiplied together form a product.

Identity. A statement of equality, usually denoted by $=$, which is true for all values of the variables.

Identity element. That element which when added to a variable or multiplied by the variable will not change the value of the variable. Identity for addition: 0; identity for multiplication: 1.

Improper fraction. A fraction whose numerator is larger than, or equal to, or of higher degree than the denominator.

Intersection. The set of elements common to two sets.

Inverse. That element which when added to or multiplied by another element gives the identity element.

Inverse operation. That operation which, when performed after a given operation, annuls the given operation. Example: addition is the inverse of subtraction.

Like fractions. Two fractions which have the same denominators.

Mathematics. The science of numbers and their operations, interrelations, combinations, generalizations, and abstractions and of space configurations and their structure, measurement, transformations, and generalizations; the logical study of shape, arrangement, quantity, and many related concepts.

Minuend. A number from which the subtrahend is to be subtracted; the quantity from which another quantity is to be subtracted.

Multiple. The product of a quantity by an integer (35 is a multiple of 7).

Natural numbers. The positive integers.

Number. A sum of units; an indefinite total.

Number line. A straight line on which points are identified with real numbers, points identified with successive integers usually being spaced at unit distance apart.

Numeral. A conventional symbol representing a number.

Numeration. The art of reading in words numbers expressed by numerals; the process of numbering; the process of writing or stating numbers in their natural order.

Numerator. The part of a fraction that is above the line and signifies the number of parts of the denominator taken.

One-to-one correspondence. Pairing each element of a class or set uniquely with an element of another class or set.

Operation. Any of various mathematical or logical processes of deriving one expression from others according to a rule.

Ordered pair. A set with two members for which one member is designated as the first and the other as the second.

Overhead projector. A device for transmitting images which have been printed or drawn or placed on a transparent material.

Parallel. Extending in the same direction, everywhere equidistant, and not meeting.

Partition. A finite collection of disjoint sets whose union is the given set.

Partitioning. Separating a set into a finite collection of disjoint subsets.

Perpendicular. Being at right angles to a given line or plane.

Place value. The value given to a digit by virtue of the place it occupies in the number relative to the units place.

Polynomial form. A sum of two or more algebraic expressions; a sum of a finite number of terms each composed of a positive power of a variable multiplied by a constant.

Product. The number or expression resulting from the multiplication together of two or more numbers or expressions.

Proper fraction. A fraction in which the numerator is less or of lower degree than the denominator.

Quotient. The number resulting from the division of one number by another.

Rational number. An integer or the quotient of two integers.

Set. A collection of mathematical elements (as numbers or points) that are actually listed or are identified by a common characteristic or by a rule of formation.

Subtrahend. A number that is to be subtracted from a minuend.

Sum. The result of adding numbers.

Unit fraction. A simple fraction in which the numerator is 1.

Whole numbers. Integers.

INDEX

Teaching Elementary School Mathematics was typeset by Wolf Composition Company, Inc., Watford, England. Printing and binding were by Kingsport Press, Kingsport, Tennessee. The paper is Perkins & Squier Company's Glatfelter Special Book XL. The internal design was by the F. E. Peacock Publishers art department, cover design by Charles Kling & Associates. The type is Times with Univers display.